Prentice Hall
LITERATURE
Timeless Voices, Timeless Themes

Open-Book Tests

THE AMERICAN EXPERIENCE

Prentice
Hall

Upper Saddle River, New Jersey
Glenview, Illinois
Needham, Massachusetts

ISBN 0-13-058395-2

 2 3 4 5 6 7 8 9 10   05 04 03 02

Prentice
Hall

CONTENTS

UNIT 1: BEGINNINGS (TO 1750)

Part 1: Meeting of Cultures

"The Earth on Turtle's Back" by Onondaga
"When Grizzlies Walked Upright" by Modoc
from *The Navajo Origin Legend* by Navajo
from *The Iroquois Constitution* by Iroquois...1

"A Journey Through Texas" by Alvar Núñez Cabeza de Vaca
"Boulders Taller Than the Great Tower of Seville" by García López de Cárdenas.........4

from *The Interesting Narrative of the Life of Olaudah Equiano* by Olaudah Equiano.....7

Part 2: Focus on Literary Forms: Narrative Accounts

from *Journal of the First Voyage to America* by Christopher Columbus......................10

from *The General History of Virginia* by John Smith
from *Of Plymouth Plantation* by William Bradford...13

Part 3: The Emerging American Identity: The Puritan Influence

"To My Dear and Loving Husband" by Anne Bradstreet
"Huswifery" by Edward Taylor...16

from *Sinners in the Hands of an Angry God* by Jonathan Edwards...........................19

UNIT 2: A NATION IS BORN (1750–1800)

Part 1: Voices for Freedom

from *The Autobiography* and from *Poor Richard's Almanack*
by Benjamin Franklin...22

The Declaration of Independence by Thomas Jefferson
from *The Crisis, Number 1* by Thomas Paine...25

"To His Excellency, General Washington" and "An Hymn to the Evening"
by Phillis Wheatley...28

Part 2: Focus on Literary Forms: Speeches

"Speech in the Virginia Convention" by Patrick Henry
"Speech in the Convention" by Benjamin Franklin......................................31

Part 3: The Emerging American Identity: Defining an American

"Letter to Her Daughter From the New White House" by Abigail Adams
from *Letters From an American Farmer* by Michel-Guillaume Jean de Crèvecoeur 34

UNIT 3: A GROWING NATION (1800–1870)

Part 1: Fireside and Campfire

"The Devil and Tom Walker" by Washington Irving......................................37

"A Psalm of Life" and "The Tide Rises, The Tide Falls"
by Henry Wadsworth Longfellow 40

"Thanatopsis" by William Cullen Bryant
"Old Ironsides" by Oliver Wendell Holmes
"The First Snowfall" by James Russell Lowell
from *Snowbound* by John Greenleaf Whittier 43

"Crossing the Great Divide" by Meriwether Lewis
"The Most Sublime Spectacle on Earth" by John Wesley Powell 46

Part 2: Shadows of the Imagination

"The Fall of the House of Usher" and "The Raven" by Edgar Allan Poe 49

"The Minister's Black Veil" by Nathaniel Hawthorne....................................52

from *Moby Dick* by Herman Melville...55

Part 3: The Emerging American Identity: The Human Spirit and the Natural World

from *Nature;* from *Self-Reliance,* "The Snowstorm," and "Concord Hymn"
by Ralph Waldo Emerson 58

from *Walden* and from *Civil Disobedience* by Henry David Thoreau 61

Part 4: Focus on Literary Forms: Poetry

"I heard a Fly buzz—when I died—"; "Because I could not stop for Death—";
"My life closed twice before its close—"; "The Soul selects her own Society—";
"There's a certain Slant of light,"; "There is solitude of space";
"The Brain—is wider than the Sky—"; "Water, is taught by thirst"
by Emily Dickinson..64

from *Preface to the 1855 Edition of Leaves of Grass*; from *Song of Myself*;
"I Hear Anerica Singing"; "A Noiseless Patient Spider"; "By the Bivouac's
Fitful Flame"; "When I Heard the Learn'd Astronomer" by Walt Whitman.................67

UNIT 4: DIVISION, RECONCILIATION, AND EXPANSION (1850–1914)

Part 1: The Emerging American Identity: A Nation Divided

"An Episode of War" by Stephen Crane
"Willie Has Gone to the War" by Stephen Foster, George Cooper 70

"Swing Low, Sweet Chariot" and "Go Down, Moses" Spirituals 73

from *My Bondage and My Freedom* by Frederick Douglass.....................................76

"An Occurrence at Owl Creek Bridge" by Ambrose Bierce 79

"The Gettysburg Address" and "Second Inaugural Address" by Abraham Lincoln
"Letter to His Son" by Robert E. Lee...82

Part 2: Focus on Literary Forms: Diaries, Journals, and Letters

from *Mary Chesnut's Civil War* by Mary Chesnut
"Recollections of a Private" by Warren Lee Goss
"A Confederate Account of the Battle of Gettysburg" by Randolph McKim
"An Account of the Battle of Bull Run" by Stonewall Jackson
"Reaction to the Emancipation Proclamation" by the Rev. Henry M. Turner
"An Account of an Experience With Discrimination" by Sojourner Truth...................85

Part 3: Forging New Frontiers

from *Life on the Mississippi, The Boys' Ambition* and
"The Notorious Jumping Frog of Calaveras County" by Mark Twain..........................88

"The Outcasts of Poker Flat" by Bret Harte 91

"Heading West" by Miriam Davis Colt
"I Will Fight No More Forever" by Chief Joseph 94

"To Build a Fire" by Jack London 97

Part 4: Living in a Changing World

"The Story of an Hour" by Kate Chopin 100

"April Showers" by Edith Wharton 103

"Douglass" and "We Wear the Mask" by Paul Laurence Dunbar 106

"Luke Havergal" and "Richard Cory" by Edwin Arlington Robinson
"Lucinda Matlock" and "Richard Bone" by Edgar Lee Masters 109

"A Wagner Matinée" by Willa Cather 112

UNIT 5: DISILLUSION, DEFIANCE, AND DISCONTENT (1914–1946)

Part 1: The Emerging American Identity: Facing Troubled Times

"The Love Song of J. Alfred Prufrock" by T. S. Eliot 115

"A Few Don'ts by an Imagiste," "The River-Merchant's Wife: A Letter," and
"In a Station of the Metro" by Ezra Pound
"The Red Wheelbarrow," "The Great Figure," and "This Is Just to Say"
by William Carlos Williams
"Pear Tree" and "Heat" by H. D. 118

"Winter Dreams" by F. Scott Fitzgerald 121

"The Turtle" by John Steinbeck 124

"anyone lived in a pretty how town" and "old age sticks" by E. E. Cummings
"The Unknown Citizen" by W. H. Auden 127

"The Far and the Near" by Thomas Wolfe 130

"Of Modern Poetry" and "Anecdote of the Jar" by Wallace Stevens
"Ars Poetica" by Archibald MacLeish
"Poetry" by Marianne Moore 133

Part 2: Focus on Literary Forms: The Short Story

"In Another Country" by Ernest Hemingway
"The Corn Planting" by Sherwood Anderson
"A Worn Path" by Eudora Welty 136

Part 3: From Every Corner of the Land

"Chicago" and "Grass" by Carl Sandburg 139

"The Jilting of Granny Weatherall" by Katherine Anne Porter 142

"Race at Morning" and "Nobel Prize Acceptance Speech" by William Faulkner.........145

"Birches," "Mending Wall," " 'Out, Out—',"
"Stopping by Woods on a Snowy Evening,"
"Acquainted With the Night," and "The Gift Outright" by Robert Frost 148

"The Night the Ghost Got In" by James Thurber
from *Here Is New York* by E. B. White...151

from *Dust Tracks on a Road* by Zora Neale Hurston...................................154

"Refugee in America," "Ardella," "The Negro Speaks of Rivers,"
and "Dream Variations" by Langston Hughes
"The Tropics in New York" by Claude McKay...157

"From the Dark Tower" by Countee Cullen
"A Black Man Talks of Reaping" by Arna Bontemps
"Storm Ending" by Jean Toomer 160

UNIT 6: PROSPERITY AND PROTEST (1946–PRESENT)

Part 1: Literature Confronts the Everyday

"The Life You Save May be Your Own" by Flannery O'Connor................................163

"The First Seven Years" by Bernard Malamud...166

"The Brown Chest" by John Updike 169

"Hawthorne" by Robert Lowell
"Gold Glade" by Robert Penn Warren
"The Light Comes Brighter" and "The Adamant" by Theodore Roethke
"Traveling Through the Dark" by William Stafford...172

"Average Waves in Unprotected Waters" by Anne Tyler.................................175

from *The Names* by N. Scott Momaday
"Mint Snowball" by Naomi Shihab Nye
"Suspended" by Joy Harjo...178

"Everyday Use" by Alice Walker..181

from *The Woman Warrior* by Maxine Hong Kingston.................................184

"Antojos" by Julia Alvarez..187

"Freeway 280" by Lorna Dee Cervantes
"Who Burns for the Perfection of Paper" by Martín Espada
"Hunger in New York City" by Simon Ortiz
"Most Satisfied by Snow" by Diana Chang
"What For" by Garret Hongo..190

Part 2: Focus on Literary Forms: Essay

from *The Mortgaged Heart* by Carson McCullers
"Onomatopoeia" by William Safire
"Coyote v. Acme" by Ian Frazier..193

"Straw Into Gold: The Metamorphosis of the Everyday" by Sandra Cisneros
"For the Love of Books" by Rita Dove
"Mother Tongue" by Amy Tan...196

Part 3: The Emerging American Identity: Social Protest

"The Rockpile" by James Baldwin...199

from *Hiroshima* by John Hersey
"Losses" and "The Death of the Ball Turret Gunner" by Randall Jarrell..............202

"Mirror" by Sylvia Plath
"In a Classroom" by Adrienne Rich
"The Explorer" by Gwendolyn Brooks
"Frederick Douglass" and "Runagate Runagate" by Robert Hayden.......................205

"For My Children" by Colleen McElroy
"Bidwell Ghost" by Louise Erdrich..208

"The Writer in the Family" by E. L. Doctorow..211

"Camouflaging the Chimera" by Yusef Komunyakaa
"Ambush" from *The Things They Carried* by Tim O'Brien........................214

The Crucible, Act I, by Arthur Miller..217

The Crucible, Act II, by Arthur Miller..220

The Crucible, Act III, by Arthur Miller..223

The Crucible, Act IV, by Arthur Miller..226

ANSWERS..229

"The Earth on Turtle's Back" (Onondaga), **"When Grizzlies Walked Upright"** (Modoc), **from *The Navajo Origin Legend*** (Navajo), **from The Iroquois Constitution**

Open-Book Test

Multiple Choice and Short Answer

Write your answers to all questions in this section on the lines provided.
For multiple-choice questions, circle the letter of the best answer.

1. In the box below, describe the location of the Chief's wife, the muskrat, and the turtle by placing them in/on/under Skyland, the Water, or the Earth according to how the Earth is created in "The Earth on Turtle's Back." Briefly summarize where the Chief's wife originally came from and how she arrived on Earth.

Skyland	
Water	
Earth	

_____

2. Choose two of the details from the beginning of "The Earth on Turtle's Back," and use them to explain the Onondaga tribe's cultural convictions about how the world is organized physically and spiritually.

_____

3. List animals from "The Earth on Turtle's Back" that exemplify the human characteristics of strength, courage, compassion, and intelligence, and use a few words from a quotation from the myth to support your answer.

_____

4. In "When Grizzlies Walked Upright," what can you infer from the Native American practice of burning a grizzly bear who had "killed an Indian"? Explain your answer.
    a. They were trying to erase a painful memory.
    b. They were trying to reunite the bear and the Native American spirit in death.
    c. They made the assumption that that particular bear could not have been their ancestor.
    d. They were expressing their anger at the grizzly bear and experiencing the catharsis of openly grieving.

_____

_____

5. Reread the paragraph from "When Grizzlies Walked Upright" that begins "The Sky Spirit broke off the small end . . . ." Which answer best traces the development of the grizzly bears from that point on? Explain your answer.
    a. They walked on the Earth. They were sent to live at the mountain's base. They interbred with the daughter of the Sky Spirit. They were burned by the Native Americans.
    b. They walked on the Earth. They were sent to live at the mountain's base. They interbred with the daughter of the Sky Spirit. They were ordered to walk on all fours.
    c. They lived in the sky. They were sent to live at the mountain's base. They interbred with the daughter of the Sky Spirit. They were ordered to walk on all fours.
    d. They walked on the Earth. They were sent to live in a lodge of ice and snow. They interbred with the daughter of the Sky Spirit. They were burned by the Native Americans.

    _____

    _____

6. Using details from the origin myth, explain why "The Indians living around Mount Shasta would never kill a grizzly bear" in "When Grizzlies Walked Upright."

    _____

    _____

7. In the first paragraph of *The Navajo Origin Legend*, the reader learns that "Soon after the *ablutions* were completed they heard the distant call of the approaching gods." What text from this paragraph indicates how important it is to perform ablutions on that day?

    _____

    _____

8. In *The Navajo Origin Legend*, there are significant elements of the natural world that were believed to have brought about the creation of human life. Which element created life? Support your answer choice with specifics from the text.
    a. Mirage People   b. buckskin   c. tips of the eagle feathers   d. the wind

    _____

    _____

9. The excerpt from the Iroquois Constitution shows a strong connection between items found in nature and what they symbolize. Wampum has been used by Native Americans for trading, but in this context, what else does it represent? Explain your answer.
    a. a confederate lord's newfound status
    b. a signal that all of the lords are connected to one another
    c. a promise that the lord will honor the constitution
    d. a promise that the lord will uphold the values of the confederate lords

    _____

    _____

10. Which of the following words would be the best synonym for *deliberation* as used in the Iroquois Constitution? Explain why each of the following answers is or is not an adequate synonym in the context of the excerpt.
    a. effort _____ b. consideration _____
    c. patience _____ d. tenderness _____

Extended Response

11. Based on your reading of the three Native American origin myths and the Iroquois Constitution, suggest inferences a reader might make about early Native American cultural beliefs about community, nature, or religion. Write one or two paragraphs using at least three substantiating details from the selections.

12. Using the chart below, list which animals, features of nature, people, and supernatural events are used to develop "The Earth on Turtle's Back," "When Grizzlies Walked Upright," and *The Navajo Origin Legend*. In a short essay, compare the effectiveness of each element in its ability to support the premise of each myth.

MYTH	ANIMALS	NATURE	PEOPLE	SUPERNATURAL EVENTS
"Earth on Turtle's Back"				
"When Grizzlies Walked . . .				
Navajo Origin Legend				

13. Part of the power of origin myths involves the images they use. In a short essay, select five or six visual or sound images from the myths, and describe what these images meant to you while you were reading the myths.

14. Select several principles outlined in the Iroquois Constitution that relate to current concepts of democracy, religion, or generally accepted standards of behavior in American society. Write an essay comparing them, and use specific concepts mentioned in the excerpt.

15. Write an essay in which you present some important characteristics of a good leader. Compare or contrast the characteristics you chose with characteristics that the Iroquois considered important for their leaders, as described in the Iroquois Constitution.

Oral Response

16. Go back to question 3, 4, 6, 11, or 13 or one assigned by your teacher, and take five to ten minutes to expand your answer and prepare an oral response. Find additional details in the myths or the Iroquois Constitution that will support your points. You may wish to make notes to guide your response.

Rubric for Evaluating Extended Responses

0	1	2	3	4
Blank paper	Incorrect purpose, mode, audience	Correct purpose, mode, audience	Correct purpose, mode, audience	Correct purpose, mode, audience
Foreign language	Brief, vague	Some elaboration	Moderately well elaborated	Effective elaboration
Illegible, incoherent	Unelaborated	Some details	Clear, effective language	Consistent organization
Not enough content to score	Rambling	Gaps in organization	Organized (perhaps with brief digressions)	Sense of completeness, fluency
	Lack of language control	Limited language control		
	Poor organization			

"A Journey Through Texas" from *The Journey of Alvar Núñez Cabeza de Vaca*
by Alvar Núñez Cabeza de Vaca
"Boulders Taller Than the Great Tower of Seville" by García López de Cárdenas
Open-Book Test

Multiple Choice and Short Answer

Write your answers to all questions in this section on the lines provided.
For multiple-choice questions, circle the letter of the best answer.

1. What is revealed in de Vaca's exploration narrative "A Journey Through Texas"? Support
   your answer with details from the narrative.
   a. how the Native Americans built their houses
   b. where the Native Americans found water
   c. the cooking of food
   d. the creation of warm weather garments

   _____

   _____

2. Which words or phrases from this short passage of "A Journey Through Texas" indicate
   the passage of time? Explain your answer.
   > . . . but they soon came to where I was, and remained awake all night in great
   > alarm, talking to me, saying how frightened they were.

   _____

   _____

3. List particular words or phrases that reveal the status of women in "A Journey Through
   Texas." Describe the implication of these words.

   _____

   _____

4. Use evidence from the selection in "A Journey Through Texas" to describe the reason for
   the change in how the explorers used the Native Americans to further their travels.

   _____

   _____

5. The purpose of an exploration narrative is usually to document a geographical journey.
   Where did de Vaca intend to explore, and how did he express his intent?

   _____

   _____

6. De Vaca writes that Native Americans *subsisted* on the same food as the explorers. Which
   answer gives the correct meaning of *subsisted*? Explain why each of the other answers is
   incorrect.
   a. They grew the same crops as the explorers.
   b. They stayed with the explorers in order to have the opportunity to try their food.
   c. They had the same food preferences as the explorers.
   d. They were able to stay alive by eating the same food as the explorers.

   _____

   _____

7. Paraphrase this passage from "Boulders Taller Than the Great Towers of Seville," and explain its meaning.

> They set out from there laden with provisions, because they had to travel over some uninhabited land before coming to settlements . . .

_____

_____

8. What is de Cárdenas's primary purpose in the exploration narrative "Boulders Taller Than the Great Towers of Seville"? Explain your answer choice, citing details from the selection.

   a. to find food sources for his companions
   b. to learn more about canyons and share his knowledge with people back in Spain
   c. to describe the difficulty of traveling over the terrain
   d. to improve relations with the Native Americans

_____

_____

9. In addition to information about the topography, what other information is included in "Boulders Taller Than the Great Towers of Seville" that might be helpful to future explorers? Explain the value of this information.

   a. the way in which water was stored for long journeys
   b. the language spoken by the Native Americans
   c. the different perspectives of the canyon as seen by many explorers
   d. the proper techniques for crossing a raging river

_____

_____

10. What is the most powerful impression of de Cárdenas's expedition that the reader retains after reading "Boulders Taller Than the Great Towers of Seville"? Cite three words or phrases from the narrative that support your answer.

_____

_____

Extended Response

11. In a brief essay, describe the attitudes of the Native Americans toward other tribal groups portrayed in "A Journey Through Texas." Support your opinions with two examples from the textbook.

12. Reread "A Journey Through Texas" to find attributes of de Vaca or his companions that the Native Americans might have valued most. Given the information in the narrative, explain in one paragraph why these attributes were of special value to the Native Americans.

13. There are several contrasting elements in the narratives of de Vaca and de Cárdenas. Using information from your textbook, write a short essay that examines the differences in the terrain, climate, and human interaction experienced by the two explorers.

14. In the chart below, list the information that was the focus of de Vaca's and de Cárdenas's narratives. Then, write a short analysis of the kind of information that seemed most critical to each expedition leader.

NARRATIVE	FACTUAL INFORMATION	PERSONAL INFORMATION
"A Journey Through Texas"		
"Boulders Taller . . . "		

15. Compare the attitudes of the Native Americans towards travel in both narratives. Write a short essay, using specifics from your textbook to support your comparison.

Oral Response

16. Go back to question 3, 5, 10, 13, or 15 or one assigned by your teacher, and take five to ten minutes to expand your answer and prepare an oral response. Find additional details in the exploration narratives that will support your points. If necessary, make notes to be clear about the order in which you want to present your points.

Rubric for Evaluating Extended Responses

0	1	2	3	4
Blank paper Foreign language Illegible, incoherent Not enough content to score	Incorrect purpose, mode, audience Brief, vague Unelaborated Rambling Lack of language control Poor organization	Correct purpose, mode, audience Some elaboration Some details Gaps in organization Limited language control	Correct purpose, mode, audience Moderately well elaborated Clear, effective language Organized (perhaps with brief digressions)	Correct purpose, mode, audience Effective elaboration Consistent organization Sense of completeness, fluency

6 Open-Book Test   © Prentice-Hall, Inc.

from *The Interesting Narrative of the Life of Olaudah Equiano*

Open-Book Test

Multiple Choice and Short Answer

Write your answers to all questions in this section on the lines provided.
For multiple-choice questions, circle the letter of the best answer.

1. At certain moments in *The Interesting Narrative of the Life of Olaudah Equiano*, Equiano was sufficiently ill and uncomfortable to make him feel _____. Cite details from the selection to support your answer choice.

   a. that he wished he could create a small area in which he could separate himself from others.

   b. that he wanted to be a fish or some other creature of the ocean.

   c. brave enough to ask to be brought upstairs to get some relief.

   d. that he wanted the comfort of having other children around him.

   _____

   _____

2. Which detail from the beginning of the selection could have been eliminated from Equiano's account without detracting from the power of the narrative? Explain your answer choice.
   a. Many slaves became ill and eventually died.
   b. The slaves were unable to see how the ship was being controlled.
   c. The stench of the hold was unbearable.
   d. The hold was exceedingly crowded.

   _____

   _____

3. Equiano was one of several enslaved people who chose to write about his experiences. What was the purpose of slave narratives? Explain your choice.
   a. to campaign for children's rights
   b. to encourage slave traders to be fair with one another
   c. to make the general public aware of the harsh conditions of slavery
   d. to create laws that would regulate trade between different countries

   _____

   _____

   _____

4. Select the answer that best describes the narrator's attitude about the occurrence of illness and death aboard the slave ship in *The Interesting Narrative of the Life of Olaudah Equiano*. What details support your answer choice?
   a. The slaves did not have the appropriate immunities to fight new diseases.
   b. Children would have fared better if they had not left Africa.
   c. The slaves were prepared to endure whatever occurred on the voyage.
   d. Their illness was, in part, a result of the greed of the traders who bought too many slaves and crowded them together.

   _____

   _____

5. Use context clues from the quote below to select the word that is the opposite of the underlined word. Define each answer choice.

> The close conditions and heat "produced copious perspirations, so that the air soon became unfit for respiration . . . "

a. abundant _____

b. exhausting _____

c. uninhabitable _____

d. meager _____

6. Equiano probably hoped that certain people would read his slave narrative. Who might be able to make the most use of it? Explain your answer choice.

a. other African Americans

b. legislators who opposed slavery

c. landowners

d. legislators who liked African Americans

_____

_____

7. Select the answer that best summarizes the main idea in the final paragraph of *The Interesting Narrative of the Life of Olaudah Equiano*. Explain your answer choice.

a. The slaves were treated like property or animals.

b A drum was used as a signal for slave traders to begin purchasing slaves.

c. The slaves were brought to the merchant's yard.

d. The merchants treated the slaves better than they had been treated aboard the ship.

_____

_____

8. Which word most powerfully describes the slaves' shipboard experience? Explain your answer choice.

a. loathsome

b. pestilential

c. copious

d. pacify

_____

_____

9. Cite an example from the narrative, describing Equiano's interests. How might he have made a contribution to society if he was not a slave?

_____

_____

_____

10. Which phrase best completes the following sentence? Explain why.

Equiano's narrative proved to be a useful document for readers, because _____

a. it taught them about sea travel.

b. it was autobiographical.

c. it represented actual proof of the horrors experienced by slaves.

d. it traced the significant events of Equiano's life.

_____

_____

_____

Extended Response

11. Using two details or quotations from *The Interesting Narrative of the Life of Olaudah Equiano*, write a short description of the assurances that the older slaves on Barbados gave to the newcomers. Include the reactions of the ships' slaves to these assurances.

12. In the chart below, list examples of the slave traders' varying treatment of the slaves. Then write a brief essay, stating which treatment was most dominant.

EXAMPLES OF SLAVE TRADERS' LACK OF CARING FOR SLAVES	EXAMPLES OF SLAVE TRADERS' CARING FOR SLAVES

13. Reread Equiano's narrative to discover how African Americans tried to escape their destiny as slaves. In one or two paragraphs, justify their reasoning, citing details of the conditions on board.

14. Select at least four words from *The Interesting Narrative of the Life of Olaudah Equiano* that emphasize the commercial nature of slave trade. Use these words in a short essay to discuss how African Americans were viewed by traders.

15. Write a short speech on behalf of the abolition of slavery. Select three examples from *The Interesting Narrative of the Life of Olaudah Equiano* and use them to make your speech dramatic and effective.

Oral Response

16. Go back to question 4, 7, 11, 13, or 14 or one assigned by your teacher, and take five to ten minutes to expand your answer and prepare an oral response. Find additional details in Equiano's narrative that will support your points. If necessary, make notes to be clear about the order in which you want to present your answer.

Rubric for Evaluating Extended Responses

0	1	2	3	4
Blank paper Foreign language Illegible, incoherent Not enough content to score	Incorrect purpose, mode, audience Brief, vague Unelaborated Rambling Lack of language control Poor organization	Correct purpose, mode, audience Some elaboration Some details Gaps in organization Limited language control	Correct purpose, mode, audience Moderately well elaborated Clear, effective language Organized (perhaps with brief digressions)	Correct purpose, mode, audience Effective elaboration Consistent organization Sense of completeness, fluency

from *Journal of the First Voyage to America*
by Christopher Columbus

Open-Book Test

Multiple Choice and Short Answer

Write your answers to all questions in this section on the lines provided.
For multiple-choice questions, circle the letter of the best answer.

1. Choose the answer that states the primary reason that Columbus kept a journal. Explain why your answer is correct and why each of the others is incorrect.

    a. He needed to keep the king and queen accurately informed about his progress.

    _____

    b. He hoped to establish a place in history for himself.

    _____

    c. Other navigators wanted to hear about his explorations.

    _____

    d. He wanted to teach himself a particular dialect of the Spanish language.

    _____

2. In his *Journal of the First Voyage to America*, Columbus was impressed by the beauty of the island of San Salvador. Find two quotations that are examples of the beauty he observed.

    _____

    _____

3. In one of the lakes he discovered, Columbus "saw a snake, which we killed, and I have kept the skin for your highnesses." Why did Columbus decide to keep the snakeskin? Choose the best answer and, explain your choice.
    a. He was interested in the natural world of reptiles.
    b. Before he became an explorer, he had been a collector by trade.
    c. He was hoping to sell the snakeskin to the natives or use it to barter with them.
    d. He thought it might be valuable in some manner and possibly worth money.

    _____

    _____

4. In *Journal of the First Voyage to America*, Columbus describes the birds' singing as "exquisite." Find two other attributes of the island that could be called "exquisite."

    _____

    _____

5. Queen Isabella and King Ferdinand financially supported the expeditions of Columbus. Does Columbus's experience at San Salvador justify their support of future explorations? Use details from *Journal of the First Voyage to America* to support your position.

    _____

    _____

6. "It was a great *affliction* for me to be ignorant of their [the trees'] natures, for I am very certain they are all valuable," wrote Columbus in *Journal of the First Voyage to America*. Use clues in this quotation to determine which answer best describes the word "affliction," and explain your answer.

    a. experience of loss or pain   b. experience of being wealthy
    c. feeling of embarrassment   d. experience of being well–educated

    _____

7. As *Journal of the First Voyage to America* begins, Christopher Columbus documents his journal entry with details about landing on the island. Briefly, explain why it was important to have such specific details.

    _____

    _____

8. Add two sentences to the following summary to make it more specific. Review Columbus's journal to make sure that your details are accurate.

    Columbus's exploration of San Salvador demonstrated that there was a hospitable environment for agricultural development. _____

    _____

9. Using the information provided in *Journal of the First Voyage to America*, choose the answer that best explains why Columbus visited other islands; then state why each answer choice is correct or incorrect.

    a. He felt that he had spent enough time on San Salvador._____

    b. His men were tired and hungry. _____

    c. The natives were unfriendly._____

    d. He was seeking more items of value._____

10. Which of the following journal notations would be the most important to King Ferdinand and Queen Isabella? Explain your answer choice.

    a. "This island even exceeds the others in bounty and fertility."
    b. "The natives . . . showed great pleasure in presenting us with it [water]."
    c. "[I will see the king of the island] in order to see if I can acquire any gold . . ."
    d. "It is my wish to fill all the water casks..."

    _____

    _____

Extended Response

11. Complete the Venn diagram to analyze which elements of Columbus's journal are important to Columbus, to King Ferdinand and Queen Isabella, and to both parties. Write one or two paragraphs explaining your answers.

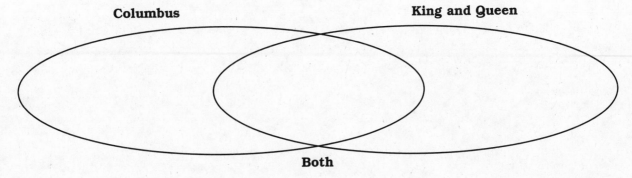

Columbus   King and Queen

Both

12. Columbus traded with the natives in order to get the water that he needed. Select three details from *Journal of the First Voyage to America* and write a short essay that indicates his respect for the natives' property and his desire to establish a relationship with them.

13. Columbus mentions in his journal that "we asked him [the native] . . . for water." It may be that Columbus and his shipmates conducted their business by making hand or body motions. In a paragraph, describe how the natives reacted to the concept of trading, using two details from the story.

14. In *Journal of the First Voyage to America*, Columbus provides specific information that supports the idea that San Salvador will be either a non–threatening or worthwhile place for explorers to visit. Write an essay using journal quotations to support both of these points.

15. Imagine that Columbus has decided he would benefit from knowing more about San Salvador before he investigates other islands. Using a few specifics from *Journal of the First Voyage to America*, create a short argument that justifies Columbus's opinion to Queen Isabella and King Ferdinand.

Oral Response

16. Go back to question 1, 5, 11, 12, or 15 or one assigned by your teacher, and take five to ten minutes to expand your answer and prepare an oral response. Find additional details in the journal entry that will support your points. You may wish to make notes to guide your response.

Rubric for Evaluating Extended Responses

0	1	2	3	4
Blank paper Foreign language Illegible, incoherent Not enough content to score	Incorrect purpose, mode, audience Brief, vague Unelaborated Rambling Lack of language control Poor organization	Correct purpose, mode, audience Some elaboration Some details Gaps in organization Limited language control	Correct purpose, mode, audience Moderately well elaborated Clear, effective language Organized (perhaps with brief digressions)	Correct purpose, mode, audience Effective elaboration Consistent organization Sense of completeness, fluency

Name _____ Date _____

from *The General History of Virginia* by John Smith
from *Of Plymouth Plantation* by William Bradford

Open-Book Test

Multiple Choice and Short Answer

Write your answers to all questions in this section on the lines provided.
For multiple-choice questions, circle the letter of the best answer.

1. What were the problems experienced by settlers in the beginning of *The General History of Virginia*? Explain your answer and identify the cause of their problems.
   a. The natives were hostile to the newcomers.
   b. There had been several accidents aboard the ship.
   c. The settlers were unable to plant food because the soil was poor.
   d. There was insufficient food and housing for the settlers.

   _____

   _____

2. Compare John Smith's opinion of his leadership abilities with those of President Ratcliffe, described in *The General History of Virginia*. Cite two details from Smith's account to support your point of view.

   _____

   _____

3. In *The General History of Virginia*, John Smith's captors are impressed by certain features of his compass. Name at least three facts they were probably unaware of until he showed them the instrument.

   _____

   _____

4. Whom does John Smith blame for his men's lack of preparedness? Explain your answer choice.
   a. the Council that sent them on the overseas voyage
   b. President Ratcliffe
   c. the people who transported them across the ocean
   d. the Native Americans whom they met

   _____

5. Break down this passage to figure out the primary idea of the sentence. Then fill in the chart below with the appropriate information.

   > But now was all our provisions spent, the sturgeon gone, all helps abandoned, each hour expecting the fury of the savages; when God the patron of all good endeavors, in that desperate extremity so changed the hearts of the savages that they brought such plenty of their fruits and provision as no man wanted.

What happened (what was the main action)?
To whom does John Smith give credit for the settlers' change in luck?
What does Smith mean by "desperate extremity"?

6. Throughout William Bradford's account in *Of Plymouth Plantation*, he attributes every success to the same source. Explain who is given this credit, and what this tells you about the settlers. Cite three examples of favorable incidents that resulted.

_____

_____

7. One of the most valuable aspects of Bradford's account is his description of the growing relationship between the settlers and the Native Americans. Explain why the following agreement is unusual for both groups.

> If any did unjustly war against him, they would aid him; if any did war against them, he should aid them.

_____

_____

8. Examine the following passage from *Of Plymouth Plantation*, and decide which answer choice reflects the most essential information. Explain the reasons for your choice.

> But that which was most sad and lamentable was, that in two or three months' time half of their company died, especially in January and February, being the depth of winter, and wanting houses and other comforts: being infected with the scurvy and other diseases which their long voyage and their inaccommodate condition had brought upon them.

a. Some settlers survived the winter.
b. Half of the group perished from illness.
c. The settlers needed to build homes.
d. January and February were difficult months.

_____

_____

9. Reread the sentence from *Of Plymouth Plantation* that begins "But in examining of all opinions . . . . " Then break down the sentence into smaller, more understandable parts. Which statement best expresses the main idea? Explain your answer choice.

a. The master knew the ship was strong.
b. The travelers steadied the main beam.
c. Two passengers had brought a strong metal screw from Holland.
d. The ship's carpenter was a hard worker.

_____

_____

10. Reread the sentence that precedes the line below to retrieve context clues for the meaning of the word *homely*. Which word is the best synonym for *homely*?

> In a word, [they] did all the homely and necessary offices for them [the sick] . . . "

a. horrific   b. important
c. vulgar   d. domestic

Explain your answer choice.

_____

_____

Extended Response

11. Explain in a brief essay the reason John Smith was not killed, and the possible value that Chief Powhatan may have perceived in him. Cite details from *The General History of Virginia* to support your premises.

12. At the end of Smith's account, he has a narrow escape. He also has some positive experiences that convince him to stay in Virginia. Reread the last several paragraphs of *The General History of Virginia*. In a short essay, describe his narrow escape and cite at least two reasons that he decides to stay.

13. In a brief essay, identify and describe what you believe to be the most important of the six agreements reached by the Native Americans and the settlers in *Of Plymouth Plantation*.

14. What types of information did John Smith and William Bradford learn that would be of value to those who chose to venture across the ocean from Europe? Write a brief essay, using at least two examples from each account to support your statements.

15. In the chart below, list significant experiences from *The General History of Virginia* and *Of Plymouth Plantation* that early settlers had with Native Americans. Then, in a few paragraphs, compare the experiences from both accounts, making sure to mention whether they are positive or negative.

The General History of Virginia Settlers' Experience with Native Americans	*Of Plymouth Plantation* Settlers' Experience with Native Americans

Oral Response

16. Go back to question 1, 6, 7, 13, or 14 or one assigned by your teacher, and take five to ten minutes to expand your answer and prepare an oral response. Find additional details in the two narrative accounts that will support your points. If necessary, make notes to be clear about the order in which you want to present your response.

Rubric for Evaluating Extended Responses

0	1	2	3	4
Blank paper Foreign language Illegible, incoherent Not enough content to score	Incorrect purpose, mode, audience Brief, vague Unelaborated Rambling Lack of language control Poor organization	Correct purpose, mode, audience Some elaboration Some details Gaps in organization Limited language control	Correct purpose, mode, audience Moderately well elaborated Clear, effective language Organized (perhaps with brief digressions)	Correct purpose, mode, audience Effective elaboration Consistent organization Sense of completeness, fluency

Name _____ Date _____

"To My Dear and Loving Husband" by Anne Bradstreet
"Huswifery" by Edward Taylor

Open-Book Test

Multiple Choice and Short Answer

Write your answers to all questions in this section on the lines provided.
For multiple-choice questions, circle the letter of the best answer.

1. Which line from "To My Dear and Loving Husband" helps you identify the speaker?
   Explain.
   a. "If ever two were one, then surely we"
   b. "If ever man were lov'd by wife than thee"
   c. "I prize thy love more than whole mines of gold"
   d. "My love is such that rivers cannot quench"

   _____

   _____

2. Which statement best presents the main idea of "To My Dear and Loving Husband"?
   Explain why, using a quotation from the poem.
   a. A husband loves his wife.
   b. A wife wants her husband to be rewarded.
   c. A husband and wife may both die soon.
   d. A wife is expressing the depth of her love for her husband.

   _____

3. Which answer best completes this sentence from Bradstreet's poem?
   "Nor aught but love from thee, give recompense" means that nothing but the love of her
   husband can _____.
   a. quench the wife's thirst   c. repay her love
   b. ever be good enough to please her d. repay her hard work and courage
   Explain your answer choice.

   _____

4. Find an example of Puritan Plain Style writing—the use of short words, direct statements,
   or references to everyday items—in "To My Dear and Loving Husband." Explain why the
   example you chose fits the definition of Puritan Plain Style.

   _____

   _____

5. Paraphrase—restate in your own words—the following lines from Bradstreet's poem:
       Then while we live, in love let's so persevere,
       That when we live no more, we may live ever.

   _____

   _____

6. In "Huswifery," Taylor uses the metaphor of a spinning wheel and its components to
   represent himself and his attempts to be more worthy. Which of these images may be
   another metaphor that could be used for the same purpose? Explain your choice.
   a. a home   b. an apple   c. a piece of candy   d. a stone

   _____

7. Find an example of a reference to an everyday object in "Huswifery." Explain what the object represents in the context of the poem.

_____

_____

8. Paraphrase—restate in simpler words—the following lines from "Huswifery":
        [Then clothe] My words, and actions, that their shine may fill
        My ways with glory and Thee glorify.

_____

_____

9. In the context of Taylor's poem, what does the word *affections* mean? Explain why the speaker wants his affections to be part of a holy spinning wheel.
    a. feelings of tenderness   c. illnesses
    b. emotions   d. directions

_____

_____

10. For what purpose does Taylor diverge from Puritan Plain Style to become fancier and more elaborate? Explain why this change is acceptable to the Puritans.
    a. He needs to be able to express himself more elegantly.
    b. He needs to create an elaborate metaphor, so that he will feel more artistic.
    c. He needs to fully express his devotion to God.
    d. He needs to express his involvement with sewing chores.

_____

_____

Extended Response

11. Why does the speaker in "To My Dear and Loving Husband" want "the heavens [to] reward thee manifold"? In a short essay, answer this question with details from the poem and discuss what form that reward might take.

12. Rewrite "To My Dear and Loving Husband" in a more modern style. Try to maintain the length of the poem, but you do not need to rhyme.

13. Fill in the following chart. For each poem, list at least two references to God, holiness, or large concepts about life and death. Then, in an essay, write about the importance of religion to Puritans.

"To My Dear and Loving Husband" REFERENCES TO GOD/LIFE AND DEATH	"Huswifery" REFERENCES TO GOD/LIFE AND DEATH

14. Restructure one of the stanzas in "Huswifery" to change it into a prose paragraph in modern English. Try to keep the length approximately the same as the original.

15. In the chart below, list at least four examples of repetition—of words, phrases, rhythms, ideas, or themes—that occur in Bradstreet's and Taylor's poems. Choose one of the poems and, in one or two paragraphs, discuss why the use of repetition is effective.

"To My Dear and Loving Husband" EXAMPLES OF REPETITION	"Huswifery" EXAMPLES OF REPETITION

Oral Response

16. Go back to question 4, 6, 8, 13, or 15 or one assigned by your teacher, and take five to ten minutes to expand your answer and prepare an oral response. Find additional details in the poems that will support your points. If necessary, make notes to be clear about the order in which you want to present your response.

Rubric for Evaluating Extended Responses

0	1	2	3	4
Blank paper Foreign language Illegible, incoherent Not enough content to score	Incorrect purpose, mode, audience Brief, vague Unelaborated Rambling Lack of language control Poor organization	Correct purpose, mode, audience Some elaboration Some details Gaps in organization Limited language control	Correct purpose, mode, audience Moderately well elaborated Clear, effective language Organized (perhaps with brief digressions)	Correct purpose, mode, audience Effective elaboration Consistent organization Sense of completeness, fluency

from *Sinners in the Hands of an Angry God* by Jonathan Edwards

Open-Book Test

Multiple Choice and Short Answer

Write your answers to all questions in this section on the lines provided.
For multiple-choice questions, circle the letter of the best answer.

1. What is the most important message of Edwards's sermon? Use a quotation from the text in your explanation.
    a. People should open themselves to God and Christian beliefs.
    b. People should fear the wrath of God.
    c. People should resign themselves to eternal damnation.
    d. People should be more aware of how stubborn they are.

    _____

    _____

2. Using a quotation from the sermon, explain which answer best completes the sentence below.

    > In *Sinners in the Hands of an Angry God*, Jonathan Edwards is speaking to the members of his congregation as though they are:

    a. children   b. sinners who need conversion
    c. insensitive to others in their community   d. strangers

    _____

    _____

3. Reread the first two paragraphs of Edwards's sermon. For which purpose does Edwards use these words? Explain your answer, using a quotation from *Sinners in the Hands of an Angry God*.
    a. He is scaring his congregation so they will fear him.
    b. He is upset with the congregation and wishes they would take better care of themselves.
    c. He is scaring the congregation with an image of Hell so they will pay attention to all of his sermon.
    d. He is reminding the congregation that they are dependent upon his good will.

    _____

    _____

4. *Sinners in the Hands of an Angry God* is an illustration of persuasion—using repetition, emotional appeal, or rational appeal to convince others. In the chart below, provide at least three examples of repetition and appealing to the emotions.

REPETITION IN *Sinners in the Hands of an Angry God*
USE OF EMOTIONAL APPEAL IN *Sinners in the Hands of an Angry God*

5. Reread the paragraph that begins: "The God that holds you over the pit of Hell . . . abhors you and is dreadfully provoked." In the context of the paragraph, what is the meaning of *abhors* and *provoked*?

_____

_____

6. Which word best replaces the underlined word in the following sentence? (You may need to reread the entire sentence.) Explain your choice.

When God beholds the <u>ineffable</u> extremity of your case, and sees your torment . . .

a. inexcusable   b. beautiful   c. inexpressible   d. inexhaustible

_____

_____

7. Use clues in the text to determine the sense of the phrase, "out of Christ," in the first sentence of the selection and in the last paragraph of the selection. Then answer the following questions: What is the meaning of this expression? What can those congregants who are "out of Christ" do to change their status?

_____

_____

8. Where does Jonathan Edwards change the tone of his sermon? Explain the quotation you selected.

a. "Here you are in the land of the living and in the house of God, and have an opportunity to obtain Salvation."
b. "You have reason to wonder that you are not already in Hell."
c. "Their case is past all hope . . ."
d. "Your damnation does not slumber . . ."

_____

_____

9. What is the congregants' "extraordinary opportunity" to which Edwards refers in the next to the last paragraph? Explain your answer with details or quotations.

a. to become rich instead of poor
b. to enter a nearby kingdom
c. to experience a great feast
d. to experience the mercy of Christ

_____

_____

_____

10. Instead of a sermon, Edwards could have written a newspaper article, an essay, or given a speech in public. Was a sermon the most effective way for him to deliver his message? If so, explain why, or suggest another method of presentation and why it may be better.

_____

_____

_____

Extended Response

11. Edwards uses many metaphors and imaginative expressions of speech to dramatize *Sinners in the Hands of an Angry God.* Select at least three of these expressions. In a short essay, explain why they are powerful and what effect they might have on listeners.

12. What results did Edwards warn the listeners could happen if they did not heed his sermon? In one or two paragraphs, choose at least three details from the selection that describe what could happen to those who did not "[press] into the kingdom of God." Include the impression that these words may have made on Edwards's congregrants.

13. Imagine that you are a speaker who is creating a persuasive argument for or against something. In the chart below, list the important parts of your speech. Then write the first two or three sentences of the speech.

TOPIC	TONE	PURPOSE	IMPORTANT POINTS

14. *Sinners in the Hands of an Angry God* changes in tone on the last page, as Edwards switches to a different mood and uses different arguments. In a brief essay, identify the change, using details from the text. In addition, explain why he may have chosen to change the delivery style of his sermon.

15. Although Edwards delivered his six-hour sermon in a quiet, calm tone, his listeners became terrified. If you were preaching this sermon, would you have chosen: 1) the same content; 2) the same length; and 3) the same delivery style? In two or three paragraphs, explain your answer. Use details from the text to support your position.

Oral Response

16. Go back to question 1, 3, 4, 11, or 14 or one assigned by your teacher, and take five to ten minutes to expand your answer and prepare an oral response. Find additional details in the sermon that will support your points. If necessary, make notes to be clear about the order in which you want to present your response.

Rubric for Evaluating Extended Responses

0	1	2	3	4
Blank paper Foreign language Illegible, incoherent Not enough content to score	Incorrect purpose, mode, audience Brief, vague Unelaborated Rambling Lack of language control Poor organization	Correct purpose, mode, audience Some elaboration Some details Gaps in organization Limited language control	Correct purpose, mode, audience Moderately well elaborated Clear, effective language Organized (perhaps with brief digressions)	Correct purpose, mode, audience Effective elaboration Consistent organization Sense of completeness, fluency

Name _____ Date _____

from *The Autobiography* and from *Poor Richard's Almanack*
by Benjamin Franklin

Open-Book Test

Multiple Choice and Short Answer

Write your answers to all questions in this section on the lines provided.
For multiple-choice questions, circle the letter of the best answer.

1. On the first page of *The Autobiography*, Benjamin Franklin mentions three instances that "might lead me into" faults he does not wish to commit. What are the three instances? Choose the answer that has the correct information. Explain what each of these words or phrases means. Use the context clues in the account to help you.
   a. natural inclination, the customs of the time, and rough company
   b. natural inclination and custom
   c. natural inclination, the phases of the moon, and bad judgment
   d. natural inclination, custom, and the time of the year

   _____

2. There is another reason that Franklin decided to organize his day by writing in a book. Examine the selection for additional details. Choose the best answer below. Explain what this information reveals about Franklin's personality.
   a. He knew he would be famous someday, and he wanted people to read about him.
   b. He wanted the book kept by his grandchildren for posterity.
   c. He wanted to be encouraged by being able to read about his own progress.
   d. He wanted something he could easily hide from his family.

   _____

3. What was Franklin's plan in trying "to acquire the habitude of these virtues"? Choose the best answer. Explain why you did or did not choose each answer.
   a. He wanted to, occasionally, forget all about them, hoping it would renew his motivation to try harder.
   b. He wanted to work on all thirteen at once, so he could achieve his goal more quickly.
   c. He wanted to begin by practicing silence, so he could listen to the thoughts in his mind more effectively.
   d. He wanted to focus his attention on one virtue at a time, hoping to master each one and proceed to the next.

   _____

4. In *The Autobiography*, why does Franklin say that in regard to the virtue of temperance, "constant vigilance was to be kept up"? Explain his reasoning. Use the context clue that appears later in this same sentence to understand the word "vigilance." Be sure to include this meaning in your explanation.

   _____

5. One technique used in aphorisms is rhyming, because it helps people to remember the saying. Choose at least four examples from *Poor Richard's Almanack*, and write the words that rhyme on the lines below. Also tell why you think Franklin chose the words he did.

_____

_____

6. Benjamin Franklin expresses the opinion that he was not very successful at achieving the virtue of becoming more orderly. Use three details from this autobiographical account to agree or disagree with Franklin's opinion of this quality in himself.

_____

_____

7. Franklin may be revealing some of his basic beliefs about the nature of human beings in *Poor Richard's Almanack*. If so, explain what you think his opinion of people might be. Use one of the aphorisms to support your view.

_____

_____

8. Franklin is exceptionally modest when he acknowledges that he may have been tackling too large a task by attempting to achieve the thirteen virtues. Find the detail that reveals how he thought he might appear to others if he actually had achieved all of them. Choose the best answer. Explain why he came to this conclusion.
   a. He might be seen as too intimidating to others.
   b. He might be admired so much as to make him feel uncomfortable.
   c. He might become too famous and lose his privacy.
   d. He might become the object of hatred and envy.

_____

_____

9. *The Autobiography* is, of course, written from Benjamin Franklin's subjective point of view. As an objective observer, a reader has a different perspective. Refer to the text and list at least five of the virtues Franklin says he has achieved. Then, for each virtue, give examples of the ways in which Franklin demonstrated this achievement.

_____

_____

10. Benjamin Franklin would place several of his aphorisms on the pages of *Poor Richard's Almanack*, along with the other practical information it contained. What was his purpose in including these sayings on each page? Choose the best answer. Offer an opinion as to why people enjoyed reading Franklin's aphorisms.
    a. He was trying to use up space on the top and bottom of the page.
    b. He was not a person with much to say.
    c. He believed that he knew better than others how they should live their lives.
    d. He was trying to teach about life in an entertaining way, and he knew that a brief, humorous saying would be the best method for getting his message across.

_____

_____

Extended Response

11. We have the benefit of history to tell us that Benjamin Franklin was held in high esteem both in our own country and abroad. He was a success as a writer, advice giver, printer, scientist, statesman, and diplomat. In a short essay, choose three of the thirteen virtues and discuss how they may have helped Franklin to become the great man he was.

12. In *The Autobiography*, Franklin uses an analogy about a "speckled ax." In a few paragraphs, explain the analogy and how it relates to Franklin's attempts at self-improvement. Use at least two details the from text.

13. Which of the thirteen virtues would it have been reasonable for Franklin to expect to achieve? Are there any that seem unreasonable? In a short essay, justify your answer with at least two details from the autobiography that support either the reasonableness—or the unreasonableness—of Franklin's attempts to become a better human being.

14. Franklin makes a comparison between weeding a garden and improving oneself. In a short essay, extend this comparison by using details from the autobiography. If you prefer, you may create another comparison, using a model other than the process of weeding a garden.

15. Write three aphorisms about subjects you believe to be important. Use Franklin's techniques of rhyme, repetition, metaphor, and any other methods that seem appropriate. In a short essay, explain what the metaphors mean, and why your aphorisms are important.

Oral Response

16. Go back to question 5, 6, 7, 12, or 14 or one assigned by your teacher, and take five to ten minutes to expand your answer and prepare an oral response. Find additional details in the autobiography that will support your points. If necessary, make notes to guide your response.

Rubric for Evaluating Extended Responses

0	1	2	3	4
Blank paper Foreign language Illegible, incoherent Not enough content to score	Incorrect purpose, mode, audience Brief, vague Unelaborated Rambling Lack of language control Poor organization	Correct purpose, mode, audience Some elaboration Some details Gaps in organization Limited language control	Correct purpose, mode, audience Moderately well elaborated Clear, effective language Organized (perhaps with brief digressions)	Correct purpose, mode, audience Effective elaboration Consistent organization Sense of completeness, fluency

Name _____   Date _____

The Declaration of Independence by Thomas Jefferson
from **The Crisis, Number 1** by Thomas Paine

Open-Book Test

Multiple Choice and Short Answer

Write your answers to all questions in this section on the lines provided.
For multiple-choice questions, circle the letter of the best answer.

1. In *The Declaration of Independence,* Jefferson lists many English abuses of the colonists.
    Among these abuses is a long list of military actions that he feels are unwarranted. Fill in
    the two charts below as follows: In the first chart, give five examples of military actions
    taken by the English. In the second chart, give five examples of the impact military action
    had on the colonists. Use details from the text for both charts.

MILITARY ACTION TAKEN BY ENGLAND

IMPACT ON THE COLONISTS

2. Jefferson uses the explosive power of particular words to convey the seriousness of the
    situation in which the colonists find themselves. To whom does he refer in the following
    quotation: "A prince whose character is thus marked by every act which may define a
    tyrant is unfit to be the ruler of a free people," and what is the strong negative label he
    uses to define this person?

    _____

    _____

3. In addition to citing the abuses of the English government in *The Declaration of
    Independence,* Jefferson specifically notes the lengths to which the colonists have gone
    to avoid war. Which answer identifies one of the colonists' positive actions? Give the
    quotation in the text that describes this action. Explain the reaction by the British.
    a. The colonists have tried to ignore British intrusions into their freedom.
    b. The colonists have sent appeals to the English to stop their abuses.
    c. The colonists have explored an alliance with Canada.
    d. The colonists have looked for other lands to settle, in order to allow British rule to
       continue in the colonies.

    _____

    _____

    _____

4. Jefferson's mission is to convince the legislators in the colonies to sign this document and send it to the King of England. In order to accomplish this task, he structures the document in a certain manner. State the main themes of each section of *The Declaration of Independence* that, when added together, become an effective and persuasive document.

Section 1: _____

_____

Section 2: _____

_____

Section 3: _____

_____

Section 4: _____

_____

Section 5: _____

5. One of the most famous quotations from *The Declaration of Independence* contains the message that all people "are endowed by their creator with certain unalienable rights; that among these are life, liberty, and the pursuit of happiness." Which word most closely matches the meaning of "unalienable"? Explain why you did or did not choose each answer.
   a. unable to be taken away; undeniable
   b. unable to be given to more than a few people at a time
   c. unable to be supported by law
   d. unable to be defined

_____

6. Thomas Paine, in *The Crisis*, is able to use quotations effectively to persuade his readers to adopt his viewpoint. By using quotations, he makes his writing seem closer to the reader, more personal. Which quotation reveals the purpose of the British government? Translate the quotation into modern language.
   a. "[Give] me peace in my day!"
   b. "If there be trouble let it be in my day . . . "
   c. "[Show] your faith by your works"
   d. "to bind . . . in all cases whatsoever"

_____

7. Give the meaning for the word *infidel* in the following quotation. Explain the meaning of the quotation and what Thomas Paine is saying about himself.

> Neither have I so much of the infidel in me, as to suppose that [God] has relinquished the government of the world, and given us to the care of devils . . .

_____

8. Using a quotation from *The Crisis*, define the people who might not end up serving their country. Explain what will happen to those who agree to serve the colonies in their time of need.

_____

9. Thomas Paine intentionally uses the highly charged words *impious* and *infidel*. Find the sentence containing the word "impious" and define it. Then describe why both of these words contain exceptional power as used in this context.

_____

_____

10. Thomas Paine concludes *The Crisis* with a call to action. Reread the selection. Choose the answer that names the group he expects to act and the action that he expects them to take. Explain your choice, using a quotation from the article.
   a. all of the colonists; he expects them to protect their families
   b. all of the colonists; he wants them to support a declaration of war against the British
   c. the British; he wants them to stop the abuses
   d. the colonists who are strong and most able; he wants them to start an army

_____

_____

Extended Response

11. Name at least four of the worst British offenses described in *The Declaration of Independence*. Explain, in a brief essay, why you consider these actions to be the most horrendous of those committed against the colonies.

12. Part of the anger expressed by Thomas Jefferson concerns not only the outright abuses by the British King, but the ways in which he has neglected the colonies regarding the law. In one or two paragraphs, provide at least three examples of this neglect, using details or quotations from *The Declaration of Independence*.

13. In *The Crisis*, Thomas Paine makes two appeals by using emotional, dramatic analogies. One is based on a story about a father and son, and on a description of a thief. Choose either of these analogies, and in an essay, explain why you think the comparison to the colonists' situation is or is not effective.

14. Jefferson and Paine wanted the colonists to contemplate a dangerous course of action. They painted a very bleak picture so that the colonists would realize that they had no alternative. Overall, which do you find more persuasive as a call to action—*The Declaration of Independence* or *The Crisis*? In an essay, support your opinion by comparing aspects of the two selections, offering details and quotations from both.

15. *The Declaration of Independence* and *The Crisis* demonstrate the different appeals used by Jefferson and Paine—emotion and reason. In a short essay, analyze which style is more appropriate for each document. Cite examples from both texts to support your analysis.

Oral Response

16. Go back to question 1, 3, 9, 11, or 14 or one assigned by your teacher, and take five to ten minutes to expand your answer and prepare an oral response. Find additional details in the selections to support your points. If necessary, make notes to guide your response.

"To His Excellency, General Washington" and **"An Hymn to the Evening"**
by Phillis Wheatley

Open-Book Test

Multiple Choice and Short Answer

Write your answers to all questions in this section on the lines provided.
For multiple-choice questions, circle the letter of the best answer.

1. What is the primary purpose of Wheatley's poem "To His Excellency, General Washington"? Choose the best answer. Explain why you did or did not choose each answer.
    a. She wants George Washington to know that she admires him.
    b. Wheatley is hoping that Washington will be impressed by her poetry.
    c. Wheatley is encouraging Washington in the war against Great Britain.
    d. Wheatley is trying to get her work seen by a prospective publisher.

    _____

    _____

2. Wheatley has a particular message that she is trying to get across in "To His Excellency, General Washington." Choose the answer that best expresses her message. Offer a quotation from the poem that supports your answer.
    a. The gods and goddesses of the heavens may influence the outcome of the Revolutionary War.
    b. Great Britain and France were once allies with America.
    c. George Washington will need to inspire his demoralized troops to fight.
    d. The American military is fierce and has demonstrated excellence in battle.

    _____

    _____

3. Go back to the poem and determine the meaning of *pensive* in the following line:
    > Anon [soon] Britannia droops the pensive head.

    On the lines below, explain the meaning of the word and why Britannia has become "pensive." Use lines from the poem to help you.

    _____

    _____

4. Translate the quotation "Fix'd are the eyes of nations on the scales" by rearranging the line and changing some of the words into more updated language. Choose the answer that makes the meaning of the line clear. Explain why, according to Wheatley, other nations are concerned with the outcome of this war.
    a. Other nations are partial to Great Britain, because it is such a powerful nation.
    b. Other nations support the colonies in their drive for independence.
    c. Other nations are thinking of forming a European alliance against America.
    d. Other nations wonder whether the balance of trade will be affected by the outcome.

    _____

    _____

5. Wheatley creates powerful imagery by using personification—giving human characteristics to an object, part of nature, or an idea. List four examples of personification in
"To His Excellency, General Washington." Underline the key word. In addition, explain
which characteristic is given and to what object it is given.

_____

6. What is your interpretation of the imagery used to describe the fighting power of America
in "To His Excellency, General Washington"? Choose the best answer. Use a detail from
the poem to support your choice.
a. The army is as powerful as the light in the skies.
b. The army is as angry as the deepest sorrow of the dark night.
c. The army is as silent in its movement as a mother who moves quietly in her child's
bedroom.
d. The army is as powerful as the storms that cause waves in the ocean to rise up.

_____

7. Clarify the change in tone of "An Hymn to the Evening" from its beginning to its ending.
Choose the answer that best describes this change. Support your answer with two
quotations from the poem.
a. Wheatley's tone changes from admiration of the sunset's beauty to a sense of calm, as
she anticipates an evening's rest.
b. Wheatley's tone changes from admiration of the sunset's beauty to a sense of fear, as
the night becomes darker.
c. Wheatley's tone changes from admiration of the sunset's beauty to a sense of
anticipation, as she imagines the work of the coming day.
d. Wheatley's tone changes from despair at day's end to a sense of hope about the new
day that will come tomorrow.

_____

8. Reread the following quotation from Wheatley's "An Hymn to the Evening":

    Filled with the praise of him who gives the light;
  And draws the sable curtains of the night.

Who represents the personification of "him," and which two actions is "he" described to
be engaged in?

_____

9. Why will the next day begin with the speaker awakening "more pure, more guarded from
the snares of sin"? Find a detail in the first stanza of the text that explains the reason.

_____

10. What does "night's leaden scepter seals my drowsy eyes" imply? Choose the correct
answer. Explain the action that is taking place.
a. the eyes   b. the night   c. the poet   d. sleep

_____

Extended Response

11 Of these two poems written by Phillis Wheatley—"To His Excellency, General Washington" and "An Hymn to the Evening," which is the more powerful? Use two or three details to write a short essay that validates your opinion.

12. In "To His Excellency, General Washington," Wheatley makes excellent use of adjectives. Complete the chart below with five powerful adjectives from the poem. Include the nouns they modify. In a short essay, select two or three of these examples, and describe why they work effectively in the poem.

ADJECTIVES					
NOUNS MODIFIED					

13. "To His Excellency, General Washington" and "An Hymn to the Evening" make excellent use of the technique of contrasting one element with another to provide the reader with a vivid image. For each poem, describe the contrasts that Wheatley draws.

14. The weather and the skies are used to paint vibrant pictures in both of Wheatley's poems. Write a brief essay using at least two details from each poem that exemplify how these natural features are well-used in Wheatley's poetry.

15 Phillis Wheatley wrote both of these poems when she was fairly young. What do the style and content of each poem reveal about her personality and her interests? In one or two paragraphs, select at least two examples—details or quotations—from each poem that tell you something about the poet.

Oral Response

16. Go back to question 2, 5, 7, 12, or 13 or one assigned by your teacher, and take five to ten minutes to expand your answer and prepare an oral response. Find additional details in the poems that will support your points. If necessary, make notes to guide your response.

Rubric for Evaluating Extended Responses

0	1	2	3	4
Blank paper Foreign language Illegible, incoherent Not enough content to score	Incorrect purpose, mode, audience Brief, vague Unelaborated Rambling Lack of language control Poor organization	Correct purpose, mode, audience Some elaboration Some details Gaps in organization Limited language control	Correct purpose, mode, audience Moderately well elaborated Clear, effective language Organized (per-haps with brief digressions)	Correct purpose, mode, audience Effective elaboration Consistent organization Sense of completeness, fluency

Name _____ Date _____

Speech in the Virginia Convention by Patrick Henry
Speech in the Convention by Benjamin Franklin

Open-Book Test

Multiple Choice and Short Answer

Write your answers to all questions in this section on the lines provided.
For multiple-choice questions, circle the letter of the best answer.

1. In his speech, what is Patrick Henry's opinion about how far-ranging and extensive the debate about war should be? Choose the best answer. Find a quotation from text page 169, and use it to support your answer.
    a. The debate should be controlled, with comments limited to a few minutes.
    b. The debate should be very free, to appropriately match the importance of the subject matter.
    c. The debate should be very free, because he wants to invite the public to participate.
    d. The debate should be controlled, because he is concerned that the proceedings may get out of hand.

    _____

    _____

2. Choose the answer that best completes this thought. Then, use a detail from the myth in Henry's speech that justifies your answer.

    > Henry draws an analogy between reality and myth to bolster his arguments. By using a myth as an example, he implies that Americans must

    a. face the reality of war, although it is painful.
    b. speak freely, even though it is an unpopular thing to do.
    c. behave exactly as the men in the myth behaved.
    d. maintain their sense of hope against all odds.

    _____

    _____

3. Judging from the context of the paragraph in which this sentence is contained, what is the meaning of *insidious*? Choose the best meaning, and explain why you did or did not choose each answer.

    > Is it that insidious smile with which our petition has been lately received?

    a. receptive   b. loyal   c. deceitful   d. happy

    _____

    _____

4. A technique often used in speeches is repetition. Find five examples of words, phrases, or sentence structure that reveal the effective use of repetition in Henry's speech.

    _____

    _____

    _____

5. In an appeal to the reason of his listeners, Henry mentions in "Speech in the Virginia Convention" that while the English have pretended to respond to American concerns, their behavior demonstrates a very different attitude. Find the specifics that Henry uses to document his charge.

_____

_____

6. Franklin begins his speech by humbly describing his own faults. Interpret this section, and state how it applies to his purpose.

_____

_____

7. Choose the answer that best completes the thought below. Then, justify your answer with a detail from the text.

Franklin addresses the delegates as thoughtful individuals by making an appeal to reason. He asks them to adopt the Constitution in its current form, because

a. he is old and growing somewhat impatient with the difficult process of achieving a unanimous vote.

b. he is concerned that as the delegates become more tired, they will become careless and make mistakes in the document.

c. he realizes that the document is not perfect, but it contains the combined efforts of many people, who are by nature imperfect.

d. he is concerned that if the delegates need to meet at another time, they may reverse their decision.

_____

_____

8. Franklin acknowledges that there may still be differences among the delegates concerning the perfection of the Constitution. He urges them to sign it anyway, for a particular reason. He also shows—for his time—an astute awareness of the importance of public perception. Find a detail or quotation that offers his reasoning.

_____

_____

9. While Franklin does not expect the Constitution to be flawless, he does have a high opinion of its creators. He believes that they have characteristics that will be important to the success of the document. He also notes that outsiders may have different expectations. List two good attributes of the delegates, and two or three expectations that others may have of them.

_____

_____

10. The style of Franklin's speech at the Constitutional Convention was calm and carefully stated. Is this an appropriate style for an event of this magnitude? Choose the best answer, and explain why you did or did not choose each answer.

a. Yes, because everyone was tired from the endless debate.

b. Yes, because he was old and needed to keep his strength intact.

c. No, because he should have reinforced his message with strong words against their enemy, England.

d. Yes, because the war was over, and the discussion needed to be resolved so that America could feel united.

_____

_____

Extended Response

11. Patrick Henry's statement, " . . . give me liberty or give me death!" is his most famous quotation. Find three other examples of his willingness to take up arms for his cause. In a short essay, explain what the examples demonstrate about his commitment.

12. One of Patrick Henry's appeals to his audience was to convince them that those who fought for freedom were morally correct. Find three quotations that support this idea. In one or two paragraphs, explain why they were effective.

13. Patrick Henry makes extensive use of the technique of delivering rhetorical questions— those to which the listener already knows the answer. Complete the chart below with three examples of rhetorical questions used in his speech. Then, in a brief essay, discuss why they are a useful technique for speech.

RHETORICAL QUESTIONS (EXAMPLES)
1.
2.
3.

14. In Franklin's speech, he issues a warning to the delegates about speaking of their deliberations elsewhere. Find details that express his concerns. In a short essay, analyze these concerns, and include the way in which Franklin has set an example of the behavior he hopes the delegates will observe.

15. Many quotations still used today have come to us from the founders of our government, including both Patrick Henry and Benjamin Franklin, who were masters of writing and speaking. Find a quotation from each of the two speeches that could be applied today. (The quotations you select do not need to be famous.) Then, in a short essay, explain how they could be best used for a modern cause.

Oral Response

16. Go back to question 1, 4, 8, 13, or 15 or one assigned by your teacher, and take five to ten minutes to expand your answer and prepare an oral response. Find additional details in the speeches that will support your points. If necessary, make notes to guide your response.

Rubric for Evaluating Extended Responses

0	1	2	3	4
Blank paper Foreign language Illegible, incoherent Not enough content to score	Incorrect purpose, mode, audience Brief, vague Unelaborated Rambling Lack of language control Poor organization	Correct purpose, mode, audience Some elaboration Some details Gaps in organization Limited language control	Correct purpose, mode, audience Moderately well elaborated Clear, effective language Organized (perhaps with brief digressions)	Correct purpose, mode, audience Effective elaboration Consistent organization Sense of completeness, fluency

"Letter to Her Daughter from the New White House"
by Abigail Adams
from *Letters from an American Farmer*
by Michel-Guillaume Jean de Crèvecoeur

Open-Book Test

Multiple Choice and Short Answer

Write your answers to all questions in this section on the lines provided.
For multiple-choice questions, circle the letter of the best answer.

1. How does the reader become aware that Abigail Adams' "Letter to Her Daughter from the New White House" is a personal rather than a public communication? Find details that support this observation.

   _____

   _____

2. What are the main things that Adams feels she must have immediately for her new home? Choose the correct answer. Explain why you did or did not choose each answer.
   a. more servants to keep the house in proper order

   _____

   b. more stables in which to house their horses

   _____

   c. more windows so she can see the river better

   _____

   d. wood for fires and bells to ring for assistance

   _____

3. Some of Adams's statements reflect her opinion, while others contain the basic facts about her new environment. Is her statement about Georgetown a fact or an opinion? What does she think about Georgetown, and how does it fare in comparison to another town with which she is familiar? Find details that answer these questions.

   _____

   _____

   _____

4. Why is there no wood available for the fires in the various fireplaces of the Adams home? Choose the correct answer. Explain why this is an ironic situation.
   a. The wood is being used to heat fires for the poor in the streets of the city.
   b. There are buildings in the forest that have used up the available wood.
   c. It is a problem to find the labor to cut and carry the wood to the house.
   d. It is being used to dam up the river nearby.

   _____

   _____

5. In her personal correspondence, Adams continually refers to her new home in a somewhat casual manner. However, although her daughter—the recipient of the letter—knows exactly where her mother is, to an outside reader it is not immediately apparent. What is the new "house" to which she refers, and where is it? As you answer these questions, include a detail that offers clues to the reader.

_____

_____

6. In "Letter to Her Daughter from the New White House," Adams says that she and her husband seem to have arrived in a "new country." What does she mean by this comment? Find at least three details that support her opinion. Why is her term "new country" ironic, given her status?

_____

_____

_____

7. Why does Crèvecoeur call America an "asylum"? Define "asylum," and use three details from his epistle that support this perception of America.

_____

_____

_____

8. Give three facts and three opinions from *Letters from an American Farmer*. Keep in mind that facts can be proven, and opinions cannot be proven.

_____

_____

9. What does Crèvecoeur mean when he refers to the concept of "self-interest"? Choose the best answer. Use details from his epistle to explain why he believes self-interest is a good attribute.
   a. being unaware of others' needs
   b. being motivated by personal achievement and success
   c. being selfish
   d. being absorbed only in the progress of one's own family

_____

_____

10. Reread the sentence that begins "Can a wretch who wanders about . . . whose life is a continual scene of sore affliction or pinching *penury* . . . " Choose the answer that defines the word "penury." Use context clues from the sentence to assist you. Offer additional clues in the text that further emphasize the meaning of the word.
   a. physical illness   c. unbearable pain
   b. nomadic lifestyle   d. lack of money or basic necessities

_____

_____

Extended Response

11. Crèvecoeur has a very particular concept of what it means to consider oneself as having a "country." Why does he say that Europeans cannot call their homelands their countries? Write a short essay to answer this question. Use at least three details from *Letters from an American Farmer* to support his opinion.

12. At the end of her letter, Abigail Adams experiences a change in her attitude. Using details from the text, write a short essay that describes her initial attitude toward her new surroundings. Explain how the change in her attitude comes about.

13. In *Letters from an American Farmer*, Crèvecoeur is extravagant in his praise of America, sometimes seeming to exaggerate. Choose three examples from his epistle, and rewrite them in a more subdued manner so that they appear to be more objective. Then, in one or two paragraphs, compare the old and new versions.

14. The personal letter of Abigail Adams and the epistle of Crèvecoeur—written in a personal style, but intended to be read by the public—have very different writing styles. Complete the chart below by taking two sentences from each work and rewriting them in the other author's style. Then, in a few paragraphs, compare the styles, and discuss which style is most effective for each subject.

Adams's Style	Adams Rewritten	Crèvecoeur's Style	Crèvecoeur's Rewritten

15. In both "Letter to Her Daughter from the New White House" and *Letters from an American Farmer*, the authors offer praise for aspects of America. Discuss some of this praise in a short essay. Using two or three details from each work, analyze whether the praise is valid in light of your knowledge of American history.

Oral Response

16. Go back to question 1, 3, 7, 12, or 13 or one assigned by your teacher, and take five to ten minutes to expand your answer and prepare an oral response. Find additional details in the selections that will support your points. If necessary, make notes to guide your response.

Rubric for Evaluating Extended Responses

0	1	2	3	4
Blank paper Foreign language Illegible, incoherent Not enough content to score	Incorrect purpose, mode, audience Brief, vague Unelaborated Rambling Lack of language control Poor organization	Correct purpose, mode, audience Some elaboration Some details Gaps in organization Limited language control	Correct purpose, mode, audience Moderately well elaborated Clear, effective language Organized (perhaps with brief digressions)	Correct purpose, mode, audience Effective elaboration Consistent organization Sense of completeness, fluency

"The Devil and Tom Walker" by Washington Irving

Open-Book Test

Multiple Choice and Short Answer

Write your answers to all questions in this section on the lines provided.
For multiple-choice questions, circle the letter of the best answer.

1. In the first few pages of "The Devil and Tom Walker," the narrator very effectively sets the tone of the home of Tom Walker. What can the reader conclude about the main characters of this story, Tom Walker and his wife, and the environment in which they live?

    _____

    _____

2. Find the clue in the story that describes the level of selfishness to which Tom and his wife had sunk. Explain how far his wife was willing to go in her meanness.
    a. They would hide their belongings from the neighbors.
    b. The two of them tried to cheat one another.
    c. Their children had only one outfit of clothing to wear.
    d. They would hide their valuables in the swamp.

    _____

    _____

3. In the beginning of "The Devil and Tom Walker," Washington Irving gives the reader some background about the treasure of the pirate Captain Kidd. What can the reader infer is Irving's purpose in providing these details? Explain why you did or did not choose each answer.
    a. He is trying to create a scary atmosphere for the rest of the story.

    _____

    b. He is hinting at Tom Walker's strong appetite for ill-gotten money.

    _____

    c. He is foreshadowing the appearance of the Devil.

    _____

    d. He is taking the opportunity to describe the swamp in great detail.

    _____

4. What does the following phrase tell you about the cultural attitudes of the people Irving is writing about?
    > . . . just at the time that earthquakes were prevalent in New England, and shook
    > many tall sinners down upon their knees . . .

    _____

    _____

5. Washington Irving writes as the omniscient narrator—that is, he is able to tell us what is going on inside his characters' heads. Complete the diagram below, indicating Tom's attitudes towards his wife, his getting lost in the swamp, and the appearance of the Devil.

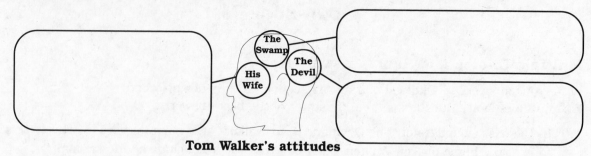

Tom Walker's attitudes

6. Reread the paragraph that begins, "It was late in the dusk of evening . . ." Then reread the passage that begins: "I am he to whom the red men consecrated this spot . . ." Whose attitudes toward Native Americans are expressed in each passage?

_____

_____

7 Irving describes Tom Walker's wife by writing that "All her avarice was awakened at the mention of hidden gold . . . " Which word below is a synonym for *avarice*? List two other details in the story that emphasize the avarice of Tom Walker's wife.
   a. energy   b. feminine   c. work   d. greed

_____

_____

8. In "The Devil and Tom Walker," the narrator offers the reader a glimpse of the intense hostility between Tom Walker and his wife. Which quotation describes the extent to which Tom Walker will go in order to avoid agreeing with his wife?

_____

_____

9. Cite two quotations that give the reader insight into Tom's feelings about his wife.

_____

_____

10. Reread the paragraph that begins, "His reputation for a ready-moneyed man . . ." What is Washington Irving telling the reader about people's attitudes toward money in the early 1700s?

_____

_____

_____

Extended Response

11. Tom Walker feared the future he might have to face, owing to his deal with the Devil. Cite at least three examples from "The Devil and Tom Walker" of Tom's newfound attention to religion. In a short essay, examine whether his new religious efforts had an impact on his life.

12 Reread the passage that begins, "Some say that Tom grew a little crack-brained . . . " What does this paragraph tell you about the growing state of Tom Walker's mind? Use this passage and at least one other example from the text to describe Tom's confusion about how he was going to save himself.

13. Complete the story diagram below by filling in the details of "The Devil and Tom Walker." In finding details, try to choose those that clearly and directly build to, and descend from, the climax of the story.

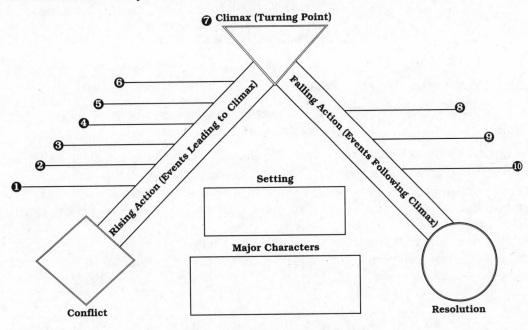

The Devil and Tom Walker

14. Using the chart you completed above, write a brief essay that analyzes the most important events. Explain why these events are important. For example, they may add to the story's suspense, they may help to define the characters, or they may help to foreshadow the action that comes next.

15. "The Devil and Tom Walker," like other similar tales, is a fable that contains a message. Using details from the story, analyze the most unrealistic aspects of the fable. In a brief essay, discuss how effective they are. Do these unusual occurrences make the message stronger for the reader?

Oral Response

16. Go back to question 6, 8, 10, 12, or 13 or one assigned by your teacher, and take five to ten minutes to expand your answer and prepare an oral response. Find additional details in the story that will support your points. Make notes to guide your response.

Rubric for Evaluating Extended Responses

0	1	2	3	4
Blank paper Foreign language Illegible, incoherent Not enough content to score	Incorrect purpose, mode, audience Brief, vague Unelaborated Rambling Lack of language control Poor organization	Correct purpose, mode, audience Some elaboration Some details Gaps in organization Limited language control	Correct purpose, mode, audience Moderately well elaborated Clear, effective language Organized (perhaps with brief digressions)	Correct purpose, mode, audience Effective elaboration Consistent organization Sense of completeness, fluency

"A Psalm of Life" and **"The Tide Rises, The Tide Falls"**
by Henry Wadsworth Longfellow

Open-Book Test

Multiple Choice and Short Answer

Write your answers to all questions in this section on the lines provided.
For multiple-choice questions, circle the letter of the best answer.

1. How does the title "A Psalm of Life" relate to the main message of Longfellow's poem?
   Explain your answer choice, citing one line of the poem as support.
   a It says that we should concern ourselves with the condition of our souls.
   b. It says that we should make the most of the lives we have and pass on our experience
   to others.
   c. It says that we should treat life as though it is a battle to be won.
   d. It says that we should mourn the dead for a long period of time.

   _____

   _____

2. Complete the chart below by first paraphrasing Longfellow's message and then listing
   four quotations that either restate or amplify his primary thoughts in "A Psalm of Life."

LONGFELLOW'S MESSAGE:
1.
2.
3.
4.

3. Longfellow uses images in "A Psalm of Life" that contain larger meanings. Choose one
   image from the poem that relates to any of the five senses—sight, smell, taste, touch, or
   sound—and explain what it means.

   _____

   _____

4. Notice that in each stanza of "A Psalm of Life," there is a central idea. Longfellow has
   chosen to express each of his main ideas in a structured rhyming pattern. Select one of
   the stanzas, and rewrite it in prose to express the same idea without rhyme.

   _____

   _____

   _____

   _____

5. Interpret the fifth stanza from "A Psalm of Life," making sure to address these questions: Why does Longfellow draw an analogy with a battle? Which other symbols of battle does he use, and what do they represent? What is the usefulness of mentioning "dumb, driven cattle"?

_____

_____

6. What is the primary image of "The Tide Rises, The Tide Falls," and what does it represent? Cite a line from the poem that supports your answer choice.
   a. The image is the ocean, and it represents the calm, cooling force of nature.
   b. The image is the ocean, and it represents the violent, unpredictable aspects of nature.
   c. The image is the beach, and it represents the need for people to relax.
   d. The image is the ocean, and it represents a call that comes at the ending of a life.

_____

_____

7. Which word is a synonym for _efface_ in the following line?
   Efface the footprints in the sands . . .
   Describe the image that effaces the footprints.
   a. deepen   b. surround   c. explore   d. erase

_____

_____

8. Describe the rhyming pattern in "The Tide Rises, the Tide Falls". How is this pattern effective in supporting the main theme of the poem?

_____

_____

9. Which images of life are conveyed by the following lines? Explain how they differ from the rest of the poem.
   The morning breaks; the steeds in their stalls
   Stamp and neigh, as the hostler calls . . .

_____

_____

10. What image is conveyed by the "calling" of the sea, and the waves with their "soft, white hands" in "The Tide Rises, the Tide Falls"? How does this image relate to the theme, and is it effective?

_____

_____

Extended Response

11. What is the main theme of each of Longfellow's poems? Select a line from each poem that supports the two themes, and in a few paragraphs, discuss whether the themes are alike and different, and how they are related to one another.

12. In "A Psalm of Life," why does Longfellow encourage his readers to make their lives "sublime"? In a short essay, examine the message in the seventh and eighth stanzas. Cite two details from the poem to support your answer.

13. Complete the chart below with four images of the ocean environment from either of Longfellow's two poems. In the chart, explain the meaning of each image.

OCEAN IMAGES	MEANING
1.	
2.	
3.	
4.	

14. Footprints have two different symbolic meanings in "A Psalm of Life" and "The Tide Rises, The Tide Falls." In a few paragraphs, describe what footprints symbolize in each poem. Cite details from both selections to support your interpretation.

15. In "The Tide Rises, The Tide Falls," there are many voices that "call." Two of these voices, the "curlew" and the "hostler," contradict each other. Explain, in a short essay, what the curlew and the hostler represent and how they are at odds. Use details from the poem to support your explanation.

Oral Response

16. Go back to question 3, 4, 12, 13, or 14 or one assigned by your teacher, and take five to ten minutes to expand your answer and prepare an oral response. Find additional details in the poems that will support your points. If necessary, make notes to guide your response.

Rubric for Evaluating Extended Responses

0	1	2	3	4
Blank paper	Incorrect purpose, mode, audience	Correct purpose, mode, audience	Correct purpose, mode, audience	Correct purpose, mode, audience
Foreign language	Brief, vague	Some elaboration	Moderately well elaborated	Effective elaboration
Illegible, incoherent	Unelaborated	Some details	Clear, effective language	Consistent organization
Not enough content to score	Rambling	Gaps in organization	Organized (perhaps with brief digressions)	Sense of completeness, fluency
	Lack of language control	Limited language control		
	Poor organization			

Name _____ Date _____

"Thanatopsis" by William Cullen Bryant
"Old Ironsides" by Oliver Wendell Holmes
"The First Snowfall" by James Russell Lowell
from Snowbound by John Greenleaf Whittier

Open-Book Test

Multiple Choice and Short Answer

Write your answers to all questions in this section on the lines provided.
For multiple-choice questions, circle the letter of the best answer.

1. Which statement summarizes the two primary messages in "Thanatopsis"? Explain your answer choice, citing details from the poem as support.
   a. Death is something that only the old and ill have to face; the rest of us do not need to fear it.
   b. Life is to be embraced, because the beauty of nature is all around us.
   c. Death is part of nature and should be accepted; it will come to all of us at some point.
   d. We are all equals in death.

   _____

   _____

2. The title "Thanatopsis" refers to a vision of death. Bryant includes many symbols associated with death throughout the poem, even though he infrequently mentions the actual words "death" or "dead." Complete the chart below, listing several of these symbols that convey the poem's theme to the reader.

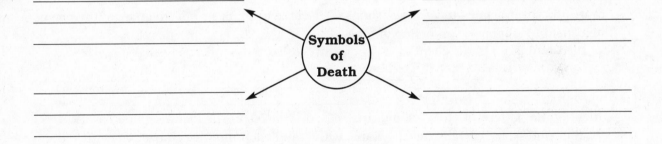

3. Reread the section that begins, "So shalt thou rest, ..." In this context, what can the reader assume is Bryant's intent in the following lines of his poem?
   > The speechless babe, and the gray-headed man—
   > Shall one by one be gathered to thy side,
   > By those, who in their turn shall follow them.
   a. We should try not to worry about death, since it can happen to people at any age.
   b. We should try to make an impact upon the world, so that when we die, people will notice we are gone.
   c. We should be happy that when we die, we escape the cares of life.
   d. We should take some comfort in knowing that all humans will die—that this is part of nature.

   Cite a detail from the poem that supports your answer choice.

   _____

4. "Old Ironsides" points out many of the effects *The Constitution* had on people. Which statement describes one of the ship's good attributes? Explain why you chose your answer.
   a. The ship has a beautiful flag that is still in excellent condition.
   b. The ship brings back historical memories that stir people's emotions and national pride.
   c. The ship reminds people of the harshness of war and battle.
   d. The ship reminds people to protect their own possessions from disrepair.

   _____

   _____

5. Why did Holmes suggest that the government "tear her tattered ensign down" and "give [Old Ironsides] to the god of storms"?

   _____

   _____

6. In "The First Snowfall," there is a distinct rhythmic pattern of meter—stressed and unstressed syllables. Reread the following stanza, identifying which sounds are emphasized. Then, mark each stressed syllable with ´, and each unstressed syllable with ˘. The first ones are done for you.

   > I stood and watched by the window/ The noiseless work of the sky
   > And the sudden flurries of snowbirds,/ Like brown leaves whirling by.

7. As he explains the falling snowflakes to his daughter, the speaker in "The First Snowfall" is thinking of an event from his past. Summarize his experience by describing what makes his thoughts change. What is the memory that comes into his mind?

   _____

   _____

8. Reread the beginning of the first stanza of *Snowbound*. Using context clues, choose the word that best defines the word *ominous*. Cite three examples from this part of the poem that help to emphasize an ominous tone.
   a. threatening   b. silent   c. unrevealed   d. magical

   _____

   _____

9. Identify the pattern of stressed and unstressed syllables in the following lines from *Snowbound*. Mark each stressed syllable with ´, and each unstressed syllable with ˘. The first ones have been done for you.

   > A prompt, decisive man, no breath/ Our father wasted: "Boys, a path!"
   > Well pleased (for when did farmer boy/ Count such a summons less than joy?)
   > Our buskins on our feet we drew . . .

10. How does the ending of *Snowbound* contrast in tone with the beginning? Cite two quotations from the poem to emphasize the difference.

    _____

    _____

Extended Response

11. The poets who wrote "Thanatopsis" and "Old Ironsides" deal with the theme of change through time. In a short essay, contrast the way in which each poet deals with change and death, citing details from the poems.

12. Select a stanza from any one of the four poems, and write it in prose. Then, in a brief essay, explain whether you think the new version is more or less powerful than the original poetry. Keep the poet's purpose in mind as you write your essay.

13. Some of the four poems use animals as part of the imagery or as part of setting a scene. Select two examples from the poems. In a brief essay, discuss the images and ideas that come to mind as the reader thinks about these animals.

14. In a brief essay, explore the variety in Whittier's descriptions of a wintry scene in *Snowbound*. Identify how he conveys the intensity of the snowstorm in colorful language that helps the reader to picture the storm.

15. In *Snowbound*, the poet and his brothers are given a task. In a short essay, describe the task, why they need to accomplish it, and their attitude. Cite three details from the poem, explaining the results of their task.

Oral Response

16. Go back to question 3, 7, 10, 14, or 15 or one assigned by your teacher, and take five to ten minutes to expand your answer and prepare an oral response. Find additional details in the poems that will support your points. Make notes to guide your response.

Rubric for Evaluating Extended Responses

0	1	2	3	4
Blank paper Foreign language Illegible, incoherent Not enough content to score	Incorrect purpose, mode, audience Brief, vague Unelaborated Rambling Lack of language control Poor organization	Correct purpose, mode, audience Some elaboration Some details Gaps in organization Limited language control	Correct purpose, mode, audience Moderately well elaborated Clear, effective language Organized (perhaps with brief digressions)	Correct purpose, mode, audience Effective elaboration Consistent organization Sense of completeness, fluency

"Crossing the Great Divide" by Meriwether Lewis
"The Most Sublime Spectacle on Earth" by John Wesley Powell

Open-Book Test

Multiple Choice and Short Answer

Write your answers to all questions in this section on the lines provided.
For multiple-choice questions, circle the letter of the best answer.

1. What is the focus of Lewis's account in "Crossing the Great Divide"? Explain your answer choice, citing a detail from the selection.
   a. the explorers' lack of food and desperate need to find some food quickly
   b. the explorers' ability to establish a camp quickly in unfamiliar territory
   c. the difficulty of the explorers' communication with the Native Americans
   d. the progress of the communication between the explorers and the Native Americans

   _____

   _____

2. Reread the first long paragraph of "Crossing the Great Divide." Identify descriptive details that show the close relationship among the various Native Americans in Lewis's account.

   _____

   _____

3. Lewis communicates important information to the Native Americans concerning the westward travel of the explorers. Complete the chart below, listing specific details from his account.

INFORMATION LEWIS TELLS TO THE NATIVE AMERICANS
1.
2.
3.
4.

4. "Crossing the Great Divide" describes how Lewis and the rest of his company set the stage for a negotiation with the Native Americans. What tone does he convey in describing his actions? Find details that suggest Lewis's approach.

   _____

   _____

   _____

5. Which word is a synonym for *conspicuous*? Use context clues from the quotation below to help you. Then, explain why Lewis may have wanted to be "conspicuous" in his friendliness.

    > . . . in which we took care to make them a conspicuous object of our own good wishes and the care of our government.

    a. careful   b. primary   c. obvious   d. suspicious

    _____

    _____

6. In "The Most Sublime Spectacle on Earth," what is the feature of the Grand Canyon that immediately grabs the reader's attention and evokes in the reader a mental picture of the canyon? Cite details from the account that supports your answer.
    a. the steepness of the walls
    b. the unusually large size of the canyon
    c. the comparison with the gorge at the base of Niagara Falls
    d. the dam in the canyon

    _____

    _____

7. In "The Most Sublime Spectacle on Earth," Powell writes descriptively to convey the greatness of the Grand Canyon. List at least three descriptive details from the selection.

    _____

    _____

8. How does Powell convey information that helps the reader to imagine a variety of clouds and their effects on the canyon? Identify four physical aspects of the clouds' size, distance, location, or relationships in space that make the scene come to life.

    _____

    _____

9. Powell titles his piece "The Most Sublime Spectacle on Earth." Which word is a synonym for *sublime*? Cite a detail that supports Powell's claim.
    a. relaxing   b. frightening   c. awe-inspiring   d. enormous

10. In addition to noting the geological impact of the clouds in "The Most Sublime Spectacle on Earth," Powell goes to some lengths to give them almost human attributes, thus making them appear more interesting to the reader. Provide four quotations that describe the clouds in a lively or human manner.

    _____

    _____

Extended Response

11. How are the two explorers' accounts of newly discovered territory similar, and how are they different? Select an important detail or two from each account, and, in a short essay, compare and contrast them.

12. Why does Lewis take such pains to create and maintain a good relationship with the Native Americans? Write a short essay in which you offer an opinion about his purpose. Cite details from "Crossing the Great Divide" and from the introductory material to support your opinion.

13. Fill in the diagram below by reviewing the different aspects of Powell's description of the Grand Canyon. Some of your answers may be based on your own experiences with nature that you can compare with Powell's account.

"The Most Sublime Spectacle on Earth"

| **Describe it.** | How does it look, sound, smell, feel or taste? | **Compare it.** | What is it similar to? Different from? |

_____   _____
_____   _____

| **Associate it.** | What does it make you think of? | **Analyze it.** | How is it made? How does it work? |

_____   _____
_____   _____

14. Using the information you completed in the diagram above, write a paragraph or two about the ways in which Powell's writing is most effective. Include a quotation or two that makes the experience of the Grand Canyon come alive for the reader.

15. The tone of "The Most Sublime Spectacle on Earth" changes from the beginning to the end. In an essay, use details from the account to describe the change and evaluate its effectiveness.

Oral Response

16. Go back to question 4, 8, 11, 12, or 15 or one assigned by your teacher, and take five to ten minutes to expand your answer and prepare an oral response. Find additional details in the accounts that will support your points. If necessary, make notes to guide your response.

Rubric for Evaluating Extended Responses

0	1	2	3	4
Blank paper	Incorrect purpose, mode, audience	Correct purpose, mode, audience	Correct purpose, mode, audience	Correct purpose, mode, audience
Foreign language	Brief, vague	Some elaboration	Moderately well elaborated	Effective elaboration
Illegible, incoherent	Unelaborated	Some details	Clear, effective language	Consistent organization
Not enough content to score	Rambling	Gaps in organization	Organized (perhaps with brief digressions)	Sense of completeness, fluency
	Lack of language control	Limited language control		
	Poor organization			

Name _____ Date _____

"The Fall of the House of Usher" and "The Raven"
by Edgar Allan Poe

Open-Book Test

Multiple Choice and Short Answer

Write your answers to all questions in this section on the lines provided.
For multiple-choice questions, circle the letter of the best answer.

1. Which action does the narrator take in the beginning of "The Fall of the House of Usher,"
   to change his first impression of the House of Usher? Explain whether his action works,
   citing details from the story.
   a. He closes his eyes several times, and then re-opens them.
   b. He tries to imagine the house in a more picturesque setting.
   c. He positions himself, upon his horse, at the edge of a lake.
   d. He climbs upon a nearby hill to get a different vantage point.

   _____

   _____

2. As the narrator enters the House of Usher, his sense of apprehension increases. Cite
   details that suggest the "fancy" to which the narrator succumbs.

   _____

   _____

3. Poe was working to achieve what he termed a "single effect" in "The Fall of the House of
   Usher"—a singular impression to which every element of the story contributes. Fill in the
   chart below by stating the single effect of this story; list several physical details of the
   house and the area surrounding it that contribute to this effect.

SINGLE EFFECT OF "THE FALL OF THE HOUSE OF USHER":
CONTRIBUTING DETAILS
1.
2.
3.
4.
5.

4. Reread the sentence that begins, "While the objects around me . . . ," and break down
   this long sentence into smaller, simpler ideas. Rewrite the sentence as three or four
   sentences. If you wish, you may re-order their sequence for clarity.

   _____

   _____

   _____

5. How does Poe's presentation of the character of Roderick Usher add to the overall effect he is trying to achieve? Cite four details from the story that contribute to this effect.

_____

_____

_____

6. In contrast to Roderick Usher, the narrator presents himself as someone who values _____ .

a. reason   b. money   c. nature   d. a juicy horror tale

Explain your answer choice, citing details from the story.

_____

_____

7. There are several rhyming and rhythmic techniques that Poe uses in "The Raven" to create a sense of impending doom. Reread one or two stanzas of the poem, and cite two lines or portions of lines that contain these sound qualities.

_____

_____

8. Use the context clues from lines 36–41 of "The Raven" to determine the meaning of *obeisance*. Select the best meaning of *obeisance*; then explain how context clues helped you to arrive at the correct meaning of the word.

a. gesture of respect   b. noise
c. promise   d. reference to the past

_____

_____

9. Reread lines 66–70 of "The Raven." These lines are essentially one long sentence. Break down the lines into three or four smaller sentences, having a clearer meaning.

_____

_____

10. Reread lines 43–47 of "The Raven." What does the narrator mean when he acknowledges that the bird is "sure no craven"? What is the best meaning of *craven*? Explain how you arrived at your answer, citing context clues from the poem.

a. The bird is surely not lost.
b. The bird is not accustomed to socializing.
c. The bird does not lack courage.
d. The bird is not old enough to be wandering around in strange quarters.

_____

_____

Extended Response

11. What is the narrator's perception of his own responsibility toward Roderick Usher in "The Fall of the House of Usher"? How does he fulfill that responsibility? In a short essay, discuss this issue, citing details from Poe's story.

12. In a few paragraphs, analyze two of the main influences that have caused Roderick Usher's decline over several years. Provide details from "The Fall of the House of Usher" to substantiate your point of view.

13. There were two forms of artistic expression in which Roderick Usher was able to work with some success. In a short essay, cite details from the story to describe how his state of mind is revealed in each artistic form.

14. In both "The Fall of the House of Usher" and "The Raven," there is a strong impact on the narrator as he proceeds to tell his tale. In a brief essay, consider the effect on the narrator in each selection, using examples to support your opinions.

15. Poe employs certain symbols in both selections. Complete the chart below, listing three symbols from "The Fall of the House of Usher" and "The Raven," and explain how they are used in the story and the poem.

SYMBOL #1:	
USE IN STORY:	**USE IN POEM:**

SYMBOL #2:	
USE IN STORY:	**USE IN POEM:**

SYMBOL #3:	
USE IN STORY:	**USE IN POEM:**

Oral Response

16. Go back to question 6, 7, 11, 13, or 14 or one assigned by your teacher, and take five to ten minutes to expand your answer and prepare an oral response. Find additional details in the selections that will support your points. If necessary, make notes to guide your response.

Rubric for Evaluating Extended Responses

0	1	2	3	4
Blank paper	Incorrect purpose, mode, audience	Correct purpose, mode, audience	Correct purpose, mode, audience	Correct purpose, mode, audience
Foreign language	Brief, vague	Some elaboration	Moderately well elaborated	Effective elaboration
Illegible, incoherent	Unelaborated	Some details	Clear, effective language	Consistent organization
Not enough content to score	Rambling	Gaps in organization	Organized (perhaps with brief digressions)	Sense of completeness, fluency
	Lack of language control	Limited language control		
	Poor organization			

"The Minister's Black Veil" by Nathaniel Hawthorne

Open-Book Test

Multiple Choice and Short Answer

Write your answers to all questions in this section on the lines provided.
For multiple-choice questions, circle the letter of the best answer.

1. What is the initial reaction to the minister's veil-covered appearance on the Sabbath morning? Cite two comments about the minister's black veil expressed by the townspeople at the beginning of the story.

   _____

   _____

2. What moral is Hawthorne trying to communicate to the reader by mentioning the townspeople's reactions? Explain why your answer choice is correct, citing details from the story.
   a. Hawthorne is trying to represent triviality, because they are slightly amused by the veil.
   b. Hawthorne is trying to represent innocence, because they aren't terribly concerned about the veil.
   c. Hawthorne is trying to represent ignorance and superstition, because they become upset and alarmed.
   d. Hawthorne is trying to represent immaturity, because they tend to make fun of things they do not understand.

   _____

   _____

3. There are several clues in "The Minister's Black Veil" that suggest possibilities for what the black veil might mean to Mr. Hooper. Fill in the chart below, listing the quotation and possible meaning of the veil in different parts of the story.

THE SYMBOLISM OF THE BLACK VEIL FOR MR. HOOPER	
QUOTATION	MEANING

4. As the parishioners listen to Mr. Hooper's service, they feel a stronger power from his words than ever before. What does the symbol of the black veil reveal about their characters? Cite details from the story and the chart in question #3 to support your answer.

   _____

   _____

5. In "The Minister's Black Veil," there is a reference to a "fancy" that two of the townspeople experience—a feeling or vision that the minister and the spirit of a young dead woman are "walking hand in hand." What is a reasonable interpretation of this imagined moment? Support your answer, citing a detail from the story.
   a. The minister is calmer when he is with the dead than with the living.
   b. The minister's black veil permits him to view the afterlife and allows the dead to see him.
   c. The minister is embarrassed to be near anyone who is living.
   d. The two townspeople were carried away by the minister's funeral oration.

   _____

   _____

6. The relationship between Mr. Hooper and his fiancée has become complicated by the presence of the black veil. Find instances in the story where this can be seen. Then, explain Elizabeth's feelings toward the minister, citing two details from the text.

   _____

   _____

   _____

7. Reread the paragraph from "The Minister's Black Veil" that begins, "Among all its bad influences . . ." Explain the one beneficial result of the veil, and the message that Hawthorne may be trying to convey. Cite a quotation from the text to support your opinion.

   _____

   _____

   _____

8. Hawthorne makes the townspeople a symbol of faults he finds among many humans. Reread the Guide for Interpreting to obtain more background for the story. Then cite three faults that Hawthorne highlights. Use examples from the story to support your answer.

   _____

   _____

9. In the sentence "But the bride's cold fingers quivered in the tremulous hand of the bridegroom . . . ," what is the meaning of the word *tremulous*? Reread the sentence in its entirety, and cite the clue in the sentence that suggests the correct meaning.
   a. cold   b. large, heavy
   c. compassionate; sympathetic   d. trembling; shaking with fear

   _____

   _____

10. Reread the paragraph that begins, "It was remarkable that of all the busybodies and impertinent people in the parish . . . " What is the meaning of the word *impertinent*? Cite evidence of the impertinence of the townspeople.
    a. gossipy   b. cowardly   c. disrespectful   d. annoying

   _____

   _____

Extended Response

11. What is the overall impression that the reader receives about the character of Mr. Hooper? Select several details from "The Minister's Black Veil," and, in a few paragraphs, make a case for whether Mr. Hooper is basically a good person, an evil person, or some combination of both.

12. The Reverend Mr. Clark enters the final scene of "The Minister's Black Veil" as a newcomer, with his own perceptions of Mr. Hooper, and his own biases. Fill in the diagram below listing three of Reverend Clark's opinions of Mr. Hooper's character, using details from the text.

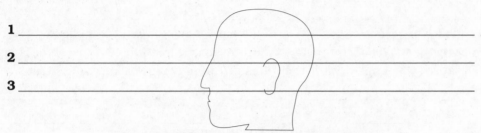

1 _____

2 _____

3 _____

Reverend Clark's Opinion of Mr. Hooper

13. Using the above diagram and information from the text to support your opinions, write a paragraph or two that describes the Reverend Clark's wishes for Mr. Hooper. In addition, discuss his assumptions when Mr. Hooper resists him.

14. In the story, there are references to the "veil of eternity," a slightly different veil than the material one worn by Mr. Hooper. Reread the conversation between Reverend Clark and Mr. Hooper. In a short essay, describe the symbolic meaning of this other veil, and why Mr. Hooper is ready to have that veil lifted. Include details from the text.

15. The paragraph that begins, "Why do you tremble at me alone?" contains the climax of "The Minister's Black Veil" and Hawthorne's broader message to the reader. In a short essay, cite details from the paragraph to convey Hawthorne's larger message, both about the meaning of the veil and about the people of the minister's town.

Oral Response

16. Go back to question 3, 6, 8, 11, or 15 or one assigned by your teacher, and take five to ten minutes to expand your answer and prepare an oral response. Find additional details in the story that will support your points. If necessary, make notes to guide your response.

Rubric for Evaluating Extended Responses

0	1	2	3	4
Blank paper Foreign language Illegible, incoherent Not enough content to score	Incorrect purpose, mode, audience Brief, vague Unelaborated Rambling Lack of language control Poor organization	Correct purpose, mode, audience Some elaboration Some details Gaps in organization Limited language control	Correct purpose, mode, audience Moderately well elaborated Clear, effective language Organized (perhaps with brief digressions)	Correct purpose, mode, audience Effective elaboration Consistent organization Sense of completeness, fluency

from *Moby-Dick* by Herman Melville

Open-Book Test

Multiple Choice and Short Answer

Write your answers to all questions in this section on the lines provided.
For multiple-choice questions, circle the letter of the best answer.

1. What do Captain Ahab's pacing and the mark of his footprints on the deck represent?
   Cite details from the story to support your answer.
   a. his need to be up and about on deck
   b. his continuing obsession with Moby-Dick
   c. his desire to be at home in a country garden
   d. his need to exercise his false leg

   _____

   _____

2. Why does Captain Ahab decide to offer his men a gold piece for finding the great whale?
   Provide details about his possible motivation.

   _____

   _____

3. Starbuck has very particular objections to the pursuit of Moby-Dick. Find the details that
   outline his objections, and explain how Ahab persuades Starbuck to help him.

   _____

   _____

4. What are some of the warning signs in *Moby-Dick* that there is danger to come, even after
   Starbuck agrees to help Ahab? Cite two details that foreshadow coming events.

   _____

   _____

5. As the men toast the coming fight with the whale and anticipate their victory, Ahab grabs
   the intersection of the steel weapons and twists and shakes them at Starbuck, Stubbs,
   and Flask. What is Ahab trying to accomplish with this action? Cite a detail from the
   selection that supports your answer.
   a. He is conducting an electrical experiment.
   b. He wants them to feel a sense of brotherhood with him.
   c. He is trying to infuse them with the magnitude of his own passion to kill Moby-Dick.
   d. He wants the other men to see that he has substantial support for his mission, so they
      will not rebel.

   _____

   _____

6. In the section of *Moby-Dick* entitled "The Chase—Third Day," Captain Ahab delivers a monologue. In the following chart, focus on the aspects of thought and thinking that Ahab mentions. On line 1 of your answer, provide the detail or quotation on the subject of his thinking. On line 2 of your answer, explain what this detail reveals about Ahab.

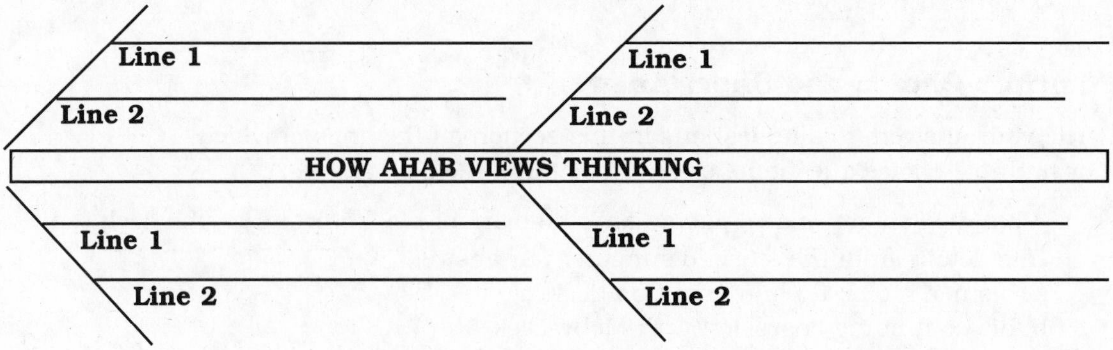

Line 1 _____   Line 1 _____
Line 2 _____   Line 2 _____

HOW AHAB VIEWS THINKING

Line 1 _____   Line 1 _____
Line 2 _____   Line 2 _____

7. Melville describes different aspects of the wind to express the theme of humans versus nature. Using details from the selection text of *Moby-Dick*, explain Ahab's opinion of the wind.

_____

_____

8. What is the implication of Starbuck's comment, "I misdoubt me that I disobey my God in obeying him!"? Cite a quotation that supports this meaning.
   a. He is concerned that he has disobeyed the will of Captain Ahab and will suffer the consequences.
   b. He is concerned that he has thought about his conscience too much and is getting confused.
   c. He fears that in obeying Ahab, he has gone against the will of God.
   d. He doubts that God will help him in his quest to convince others to help him mutiny against Ahab.

_____

_____

9. Sharks appear twice in this selection from *Moby-Dick*. They have a symbolic meaning. What do they represent, and what message is Melville trying to convey? Cite details from either or both pages to substantiate your response.

_____

_____

10. As the men toast the demise of Moby-Dick, they yell "cries and maledictions against the white whale . . . " Define *maledictions*, and cite other details from the rest of this sentence to help suggest the tone of this moment in *Moby-Dick*.

_____

_____

Extended Response

11. Fill in the diagram below listing several of Captain Ahab's qualities. Then, in a short essay, state whether you think Ahab is an effective captain. Cite details from *Moby-Dick* to support your opinions.

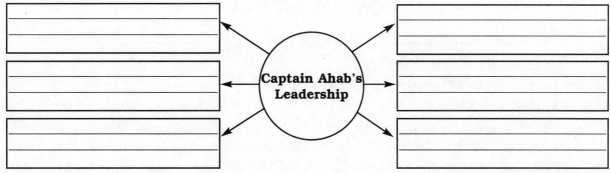

12. Starbuck and Stubbs, as they face the white whale and probable death, communicate their feelings to one another and the world at large (text pages 343–344). In a short essay, compare their reactions. How are they similar, and how do they differ? Use details from the text to support your point of view.

13. Melville uses a very descriptive passage about "a red arm and a hammer hovered backwardly uplifted in the open air, in the act of nailing the flag . . ." to communicate both a specific action and a larger meaning. In a few paragraphs, use details from the text to define who and what Melville is specifically describing. In addition, identify the larger theme that he is trying to convey.

14. In this excerpt from *Moby-Dick*, the fate of the sky hawk becomes intermingled with the fate of Ahab and the men aboard his ship. In a brief essay, discuss the symbolism of this action and the way in which it pertains to Melville's theme of humankind versus nature.

15. Melville offers an ironic sentiment in the last paragraph of *Moby-Dick* when he writes, " . . . the great shroud of the sea rolled on as it rolled five thousand years ago." In a short essay, use this comment, and choose one of the two events that occur on the last page of the selection, to discuss the irony of people's actions in *Moby-Dick*.

Oral Response

16. Go back to question 1, 3, 4, 12, or 14 or one assigned by your teacher, and take five to ten minutes to expand your answer and prepare an oral response. Find additional details in the book excerpt that will support your points. If necessary, make notes to guide your response.

Rubric for Evaluating Extended Responses

0	1	2	3	4
Blank paper Foreign language Illegible, incoherent Not enough content to score	Incorrect purpose, mode, audience Brief, vague Unelaborated Rambling Lack of language control Poor organization	Correct purpose, mode, audience Some elaboration Some details Gaps in organization Limited language control	Correct purpose, mode, audience Moderately well elaborated Clear, effective language Organized (perhaps with brief digressions)	Correct purpose, mode, audience Effective elaboration Consistent organization Sense of completeness, fluency

from *Nature*, from *Self-Reliance*, "The Snowstorm," and "Concord Hymn"

by Ralph Waldo Emerson

Open-Book Test

Multiple Choice and Short Answer

Write your answers to all questions in this section on the lines provided.
For multiple-choice questions, circle the letter of the best answer.

1. In *Nature*, Emerson uses many different visual images to state the Transcendentalist concept that nature and the human spirit are linked. Select one of these images and explain what he means.

   _____

2. Do you agree with Emerson's statement that "Nature is a setting that fits equally well a comic or mourning piece"? Explain what he means, and use details from *Nature* to agree or disagree with this idea.

   _____

3. Sometimes, according to Emerson, he is so absorbed by the beauty of nature that he is less in touch with his everyday reality of people and places. Find a detail or quotation from *Nature* that supports this observation.

   _____

4. Reread the sentence in *Self-Reliance* that begins, "Great men have always done so. . . ." What basis of Transcendental philosophy is revealed in this statement? Cite details from the sentence that support your answer.
   a. Humans have always relied on their own abilities, particularly those who are geniuses.
   b. Great achievers can sometimes appear distracted.
   c. Great achievers have felt the power of nature and God in their own work.
   d. Great achievers are independent thinkers.

   _____

5. Emerson states in *Self-Reliance* that society values conformity above all else. Do you accept his statement, or do you find it inaccurate? Use details from the excerpt to support your response.

   _____

6. What does Emerson mean in *Self-Reliance* when he says that "God will not have his work made manifest by cowards"? Cite a detail or quotation from the excerpt that helps the reader interpret Emerson's concept.

   _____

7. Who or what is the "fierce artificer," molding and shaping the snow, in "The Snowstorm"? Provide the detail in this poem that lets the reader know the identity of the "artificer."
   a. the traveler, who is stopped with his sled
   b. the north wind
   c. the farmer, who is furious at the impact of the snowstorm
   d. the courier, who is angry that he cannot complete his rounds

   _____

   _____

8. What are Emerson's impressions of the result of "The Snowstorm"? Find details that give clues to his reaction. Fill in the diagram below to provide your answers. Describe his attitude that is supported by your diagram.

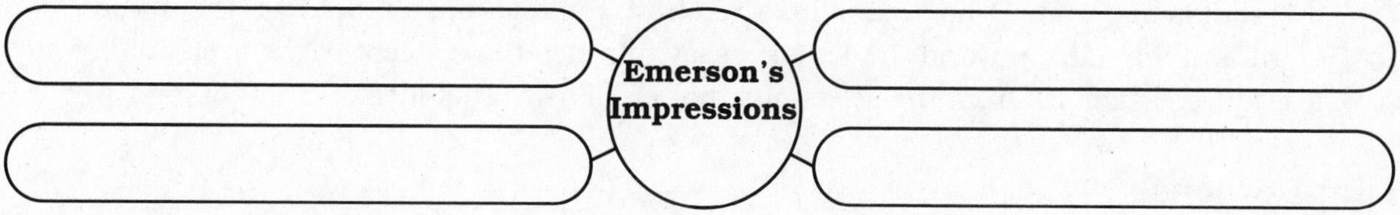

   ```
   (          )          (          )
             Emerson's
             Impressions
   (          )          (          )
   ```

   _____

9. In "Concord Hymn," Emerson refers to a "rude" bridge that stood at the time of the American Revolution but has since disintegrated "down the dark stream." What does the word "rude" mean in this context? Review the poem, and explain what event took place near the bridge.
   a. uncomfortable   b. high   c. silent   d. crude, rough

   _____

   _____

10. In "Concord Hymn," Emerson refers to the "farmers" who stood on the spot he is writing about. Why is it important that he mentions their occupation, considering the purpose of his poem? Use details or quotations from the poem to support your opinion.

    _____

    _____

Extended Response

11. Fill in the chart below. List examples from two of Emerson's writings to provide a detailed picture of Emerson's feelings toward nature.

WRITING #1: EMERSON ON NATURE	WRITING #2: EMERSON ON NATURE
1.	1.
2.	2.
3.	3.

12. In "The Snowstorm," an element of nature is portrayed as a human being with a particular occupation. Write a few paragraphs that describe the element of nature, the human occupation, and how they are revealed by examples from the poem.

13. What is the purpose of "Concord Hymn"? On what occasion was it used? Refer back to the poem. In a short essay, discuss whether it achieves its purpose, using examples from the poem.

14. One of the key concepts in Emerson's writing is about the individual and how she or he sees herself or himself in relation to nature and society. In a brief essay, discuss how Emerson views the individual, using at least three examples from *Nature*, *Self-Reliance*, "The Snowstorm," or "Concord Hymn."

15. In addition to the significance of the individual, the Transcendental concept of the oversoul is important. The oversoul derives from the relationship between the human spirit and the natural world. In a short essay, discuss the concept of the oversoul. Give at least three examples from the selections that emphasize this idea.

Oral Response

16. Go back to question 2, 4, 10, 14, or 15 or one assigned by your teacher, and take five to ten minutes to expand your answer and prepare an oral response. Find additional details in the selections that will support your points. If necessary, make notes to guide your response.

Rubric for Evaluating Extended Responses

0	1	2	3	4
Blank paper Foreign language Illegible, incoherent Not enough content to score	Incorrect purpose, mode, audience Brief, vague Unelaborated Rambling Lack of language control Poor organization	Correct purpose, mode, audience Some elaboration Some details Gaps in organization Limited language control	Correct purpose, mode, audience Moderately well elaborated Clear, effective language Organized (perhaps with brief digressions)	Correct purpose, mode, audience Effective elaboration Consistent organization Sense of completeness, fluency

from *Walden* and from *Civil Disobedience*
by Henry David Thoreau

Open-Book Test

Multiple Choice and Short Answer

Write your answers to all questions in this section on the lines provided.
For multiple-choice questions, circle the letter of the best answer.

1. What does Thoreau mean when he writes, " . . . a man is rich in proportion to the things
   he can afford to let alone"? Provide a detail from the text that gives you a clue about
   where Thoreau is heading with this statement.
   a. Rich men can hire others to do their work.
   b. A man is rich by virtue of his appreciation of things in their natural state.
   c. Thoreau was so wealthy he could afford to take his time deciding what needed to be
      refurbished.
   d. Thoreau was perceived as rich by all of his friends.

   _____

   _____

2. Part of Thoreau's style is to build an argument to support his premise. Reread the
   paragraph that begins, "I have frequently seen . . . " in which Thoreau compares an
   artist's and a farmer's perceptions of the value of a farm. Explain the traditional view of
   value in this context, and explain Thoreau's view.

   _____

   _____

3. Thoreau states in *Walden*, "As long as possible live free and uncommitted." Although he
   may seem to be making an analogy between a farm and a jail, he is speaking of larger
   issues. Explain what his analogy means, and evaluate his advice in light of your own
   experiences.

   _____

   _____

4. As part of the construction of his argument for simplicity, Thoreau uses repetition to
   state both what people should do, and what they should avoid. Fill in the chart below
   listing four examples of each, using the text to assist you with details.

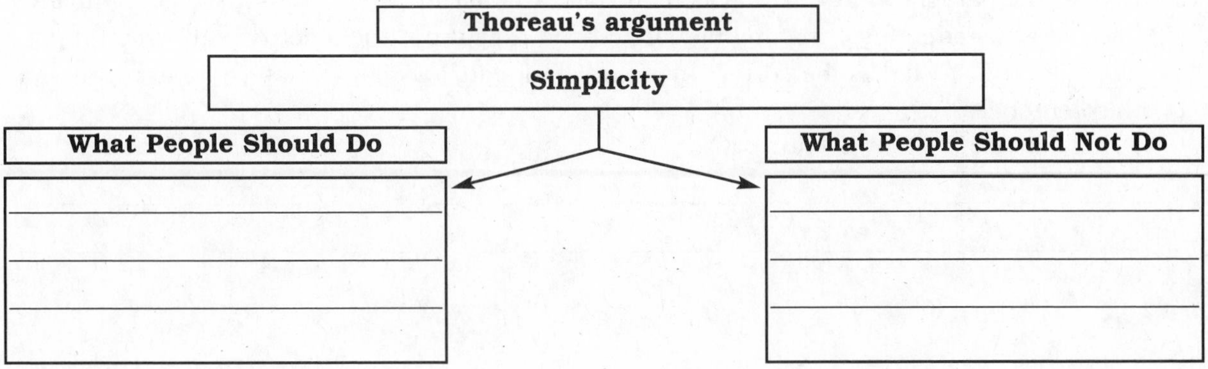

Thoreau's argument
Simplicity

What People Should Do	What People Should Not Do

5. In *Walden*, Thoreau describes a well-known story about a bug. Why does he think this story needs to be retold here? Explain its significance, using a detail from the text.
   a. He wants to demonstrate the power of oral history.
   b. He thinks people should treasure their memories.
   c. He is encouraging people to allow their natural inner growth to take place in its own time.
   d. He wants people to realize that there is value in keeping and maintaining old possessions, such as furniture.

   _____

   _____

6. Thoreau presents his philosophy of government in *Civil Disobedience*. What is his essential belief? State whether you agree or disagree with his point of view. Use a detail or quotation from *Civil Disobedience* to support your stance.
   a. He believes there should be no government.
   b. He believes that government is the tool of the most evil people in the country.
   c. He believes that government can be effective in the area of trade.
   d. He believes that the less government there is, the better off the country will be.

   _____

   _____

7. What does Thoreau mean when he refers to a "wooden gun" in *Civil Disobedience*? Explain his reference in the context of his larger opinion about the use of government.

   _____

   _____

8. Thoreau writes in *Civil Disobedience*, "This American government—what is it but a tradition . . . endeavoring to transmit itself unimpaired to posterity . . . " What does the word *posterity* mean? Give the context clue that helps the reader determine the meaning of this word.
   a. future generations   b. another country
   c. people who need assistance   d. the most intelligent and well-educated people

   _____

   _____

9. What is Thoreau's expectation of what a "citizen" such as he can reasonably ask of the government? What is his expectation of other citizens? Provide the quotation from *Civil Disobedience* that supports your answer.

   _____

   _____

10. Reread the paragraph in *Civil Disobedience*, in which Thoreau says that the government has not assisted in fostering any useful activity, except by "the alacrity with which it got out of its way." What is the correct meaning of *alacrity*? Explain what Thoreau means in this sentence.
    a. persistence   b. courtesy   c. speed   d. enthusiasm

    _____

    _____

Extended Response

11. How do you think Thoreau might survive in modern America? What might be his occupation, and how would he live? In a few paragraphs, use details from *Walden* and *Civil Disobedience* to support your opinion.

12. What does Thoreau convey to the reader when he says, "I have always been regretting that I was not as wise as the day I was born"? Does he really feel as though he is an unwise person? Is he speaking sarcastically? In a short essay, examine this quotation, using details from the text to support your interpretation.

13. How does Thoreau reveal his feelings about spiritual matters in *Walden*? In a brief essay, explain his attitude, using his analogies where necessary.

14. Thoreau's writings have often been used as sources for quotations. Fill in the chart by choosing four quotations from *Walden* or *Civil Disobedience* that could be used as mottoes. Then explain their meanings in a modern context.

QUOTATION	MEANING
1.	1.
2.	2.
3.	3.
4.	4.

15. Thoreau writes about two very different subjects in *Walden* and *Civil Disobedience*, seeming to be writing from the perspectives of two different people, living in almost opposite worlds. Nonetheless, certain aspects of his philosophy remain constant. In a short essay, examine the consistency of his philosophy in these essays.

Oral Response

16. Go back to question 2, 3, 6, 12, or 14 or one assigned by your teacher, and take five to ten minutes to expand your answer and prepare an oral response. Find additional details in the essays that will support your points. Make notes to guide your response.

Rubric for Evaluating Extended Responses

0	1	2	3	4
Blank paper Foreign language Illegible, incoherent Not enough content to score	Incorrect purpose, mode, audience Brief, vague Unelaborated Rambling Lack of language control Poor organization	Correct purpose, mode, audience Some elaboration Some details Gaps in organization Limited language control	Correct purpose, mode, audience Moderately well elaborated Clear, effective language Organized (perhaps with brief digressions)	Correct purpose, mode, audience Effective elaboration Consistent organization Sense of completeness, fluency

Emily Dickinson's Poetry

Open-Book Test

Multiple Choice and Short Answer

Write your answers to all questions in this section on the lines provided.
For multiple-choice questions, circle the letter of the best answer.

1. In "I heard a Fly buzz—when I died—," what does the image of the fly seem to convey?
    Explain why you did or did not choose each answer.

    a. the annoyance of having people around her as she lay dying _____

    _____

    b. the windows being open by mistake, allowing a fly to enter _____

    _____

    c. her amazement that she could hear so well _____

    _____

    d. her intense awareness at the moment of death, including the ongoing everyday life of

    nature _____

    _____

2. In "Because I could not stop for Death—," Dickinson uses several slant rhymes. These
    pairs do not rhyme by using precise sound but by using approximate sound. Sometimes,
    one of the words in the slant rhyming pattern will have more syllables than the other
    word. Provide four examples of pairs with slant rhymes from the poem.

    _____

    _____

3. In "My life closed twice before its close—," Dickinson writes that "Parting is all we know of
    heaven, And all we need of hell." What do these two lines imply? Select the answer that
    best interprets the lines. Give the quotation from another part of the poem that reveals
    Dickinson's attitude.
    a. Parting gives us a glimpse of what heaven may be like.
    b. Parting gives us a glimpse of what hell may be like.
    c. Parting is a part of life that we should learn to accept.
    d. Parting, as in the death that leads to heaven, is painful to human beings.

    _____

    _____

4. Choose four examples of pairs of slant rhymes (approximate) or exact (precise) rhymes
    from "The Soul selects her own Society—." Fill in the chart below, and label each type of
    rhyme.

SLANT / EXACT RHYMES: "THE SOUL SELECTS HER OWN SOCIETY—"	
1.	1.
2.	2.
3.	3.
4.	4.

5. In "There's a certain Slant of light," Dickinson uses a visual image to capture a larger idea. Reread the poem, and provide the image. Then, define the abstract concept to which Dickinson refers.

_____

_____

6. Dickinson refers to a light "That oppresses, like the Heft / Of Cathedral Tunes." What is the meaning of *oppresses*? Reread the poem, and circle the letter of the answer. On the lines below, add two details, including the context clue that provides the reader with the meaning of the word, and give the reason that the word *oppresses* is so effective in this poem.
   a. embraces the mind with warmth   b. weighs heavily on the mind
   c. surrounds the mind with pleasantness   d. conquers the mind's unruly thoughts

_____

_____

7. In "There is a solitude of space," what does Dickinson suggest about the depth of one's soul compared to other experiences of vastness? Reread the poem and interpret the comparisons and what you perceive to be her attitude toward the soul.

_____

_____

8. Reread "There is a solitude of space." What does *finite* mean? Explain why you did or did not choose each answer.
   a. the crowded feeling of society _____
   b. uncomfortable _____
   c. limited _____
   d. thoughtless _____

9. Reread the first stanza of "The Brain—is wider than the Sky—." Which of these, the brain or the sky, contains the other "with ease"? Is this what we would ordinarily expect? Why, or why not?

_____

_____

10. There are three concrete images and abstract concepts that are paired in "Water, is taught by thirst." Find the three pairs, labeling each word in the pair as concrete (experienced through the five senses) or as abstract (experienced through thought or feeling).

_____

_____

Extended Response

11. What is the overall concept that Dickinson seems to be dealing with in her poetry? In a brief essay, examine three ways she expresses this concept. Use details from her poetry in your response.

12. Compare the way in which Dickinson analyzes the soul and the brain in "There is a solitude of space" and "The Brain—is wider than the Sky—." In a few paragraphs, analyze the value that Dickinson places on each, in reference to the other elements in the two poems.

13. Reread the background information about Emily Dickinson. With this understanding of her personality in mind, write a brief essay about how her poetry reveals her personality. Choose at least three examples from her poetry to justify your premise.

14. Choose examples of slant (approximate) and precise rhymes from several of the Dickinson poems in your text. Complete the chart below, listing five pairs of each, and cite the poem in which they are used. Then, in a short paragraph, offer an opinion about why the use of slant rhymes is or is not effective in Dickinson's poetry. Use an example to support your opinion.

15. What are the particular images of aspects of nature that Dickinson seems to rely on most

SLANT RHYMING PAIRS	POEM TITLE
1.	1.
2.	2.
3.	3.
4.	4.
5.	5.

EXACT RHYMING PAIRS	POEM TITLE
1.	1.
2.	2.
3.	3.
4.	4.
5.	5.

in the poems presented in the text? Choose three images. In a short essay, discuss their effectiveness for Dickinson's purpose in each particular poem.

Oral Response

16. Go back to question 5, 7, 9, 11, or 13 or one assigned by your teacher, and take five to ten minutes to expand your answer and prepare an oral response. Find additional details in the poems that will support your points. Make notes to guide your response.

Rubric for Evaluating Extended Responses

0	1	2	3	4
Blank paper Foreign language Illegible, incoherent Not enough content to score	Incorrect purpose, mode, audience Brief, vague Unelaborated Rambling Lack of language control Poor organization	Correct purpose, mode, audience Some elaboration Some details Gaps in organization Limited language control	Correct purpose, mode, audience Moderately well elaborated Clear, effective language Organized (perhaps with brief digressions)	Correct purpose, mode, audience Effective elaboration Consistent organization Sense of completeness, fluency

Walt Whitman's Poetry

Open-Book Test

Multiple Choice and Short Answer

Write your answers to all questions in this section on the lines provided.
For multiple-choice questions, circle the letter of the best answer.

1. How do the ideas expressed in the first paragraph of the preface to *Leaves of Grass* act as a helpful defense for Whitman's use of free verse in his poetry? Use a detail from the paragraph to support your answer.
   a. He is concerned that Americans are obsessed with the past.
   b. He suggests that Americans throw away past notions of politics and religion.
   c. He likens the past to a corpse that has been around too long.
   d. He suggests that we learn from the past and then move forward to use what is appropriate for the present.

   _____

   _____

2. In Whitman's descriptive choices for the imagery in the preface to *Leaves of Grass*, he uses the United States as an example of a particular kind of nation. Provide three examples of images of America that contribute to his overall positive impression.

   _____

   _____

3. Reread section 1 in "Song of Myself." How is Whitman's emphasis on the individual confirmed by the style in which he writes? Cite examples of his content as well as the rhythm of his writing.

   _____

   _____

4. In "Song of Myself," Whitman mentions "creeds and schools in abeyance." What is the meaning of the word *abeyance*? Explain why you did or did not choose each answer.
   a. abundance _____
   b. temporary suspension or stopping _____
   c. part of his everyday life _____
   d. a period of revolt _____

5. What can you assume about Whitman's attitude in section 17 of "Song of Myself"? What type of person does he seem to be? Explain the answer you have chosen by using a quotation from the poem.
   a. He is unconcerned about others.
   b. He thinks he is the only person in the universe.
   c. He is conceited.
   d. He values his individuality and that of others.

   _____

   _____

6. Who or what might the "listener" represent in section 51 of "Song of Myself"? Explain what a reader might infer about the listener's identity, using a detail to support your opinion.

_____

_____

7. In "I Hear America Singing," Whitman offers examples of the people who contribute to the American spirit. Complete the diagram below, listing examples of these individuals on the diagonal lines, and, on the horizontal lines, add the descriptions that Whitman provides for each of them.

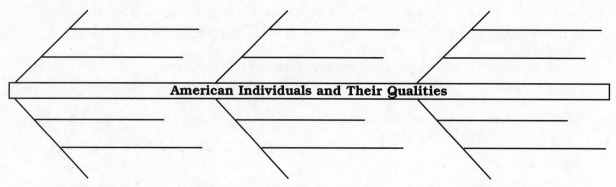

American Individuals and Their Qualities

8. Whitman's portrayal of people all over America, singing as they are engaged in their daily tasks, describes an energetic nation of individuals. In addition, he uses adjectives to strengthen his imagery. Cite five of these adjectives that add to his portrait of a young and vital country.

_____

_____

9. How do the images in "A Noiseless Patient Spider" and "By the Bivouac's Fitful Flame" relate to similar ideas? Give details from each poem that support your answer choice.
   a. Each poem represents humans dealing with nature.
   b. Each poem addresses itself to the futility of life.
   c. Each poem depicts a human being who is searching.
   d. Each poem depicts an anguished struggle.

_____

_____

10. How can one account for Whitman's feelings of illness as he listens to an astronomy lecture? How does he help himself to feel better? Use details from "When I Heard the Learn'd Astronomer" to validate your answer.

_____

_____

Extended Response

11. In the chart below, list some of the many animals Whitman describes in section 14 of "Song of Myself." Then, in a short essay, use two details from the poem to suggest Whitman's feelings toward nature and the outdoor life.

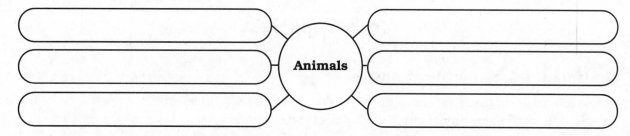

12. What does section 6 of "Song of Myself" demonstrate about Whitman's attitude toward death? In a few paragraphs, discuss his philosophy concerning death. Use examples from the poem.

13. In his preface to *Leaves of Grass*, Whitman calls America "essentially the greatest poem." To prove his claim, he cites several examples of what he perceives to be the poetic nature of the United States. In a short essay, choose and write about examples from *Leaves of Grass* and "I Hear America Singing" that demonstrate the poetry—the inspiration, the excitement, the largeness of spirit—that Whitman sees in America.

14. In "A Noiseless Patient Spider," is the comparison of a spider to a person's soul effective? Why or why not? Use details from the poem, including Whitman's choice of a title, to respond to this question in a brief essay.

15. In a brief essay based upon your reading of Whitman's work, describe what seems to be his primary philosophy. Select a few examples from his writing that most strongly represent his main ideas, and discuss their effectiveness.

Oral Response

16. Go back to question 5, 6, 10, 11, or 15 or one assigned by your teacher, and take five to ten minutes to expand your answer and prepare an oral response. Find additional details in the writings that will support your points. Make notes to guide your response.

Rubric for Evaluating Extended Responses

0	1	2	3	4
Blank paper Foreign language Illegible, incoherent Not enough content to score	Incorrect purpose, mode, audience Brief, vague Unelaborated Rambling Lack of language control Poor organization	Correct purpose, mode, audience Some elaboration Some details Gaps in organization Limited language control	Correct purpose, mode, audience Moderately well elaborated Clear, effective language Organized (perhaps with brief digressions)	Correct purpose, mode, audience Effective elaboration Consistent organization Sense of completeness, fluency

"An Episode of War" by Stephen Crane
"Willie Has Gone to the War," words by George Cooper,
music by Stephen Foster

Open-Book Test

Multiple Choice and Short Answer

Write your answers to all questions in this section on the lines provided.
For multiple-choice questions, circle the letter of the best answer.

1. What is the most likely interpretation of why Crane has the officer set out coffee for his men at the beginning of "An Episode of War"? Explain why you chose your interpretation.

   a. Crane wants to show that it is important for men to have energy to fight.

   b. Crane is drawing a contrast between the mundane act of drinking coffee and the reality of war.

   c. Crane is trying to show that the officer is unintelligent.

   d. Crane is showing that the men are basically greedy.

   _____

   _____

   _____

2. Often, the word *inscrutable* is used to describe someone's facial expression. Reread the word in its context. Which definition best fits this use of the word? Give the context clues that help the reader determine the meaning of this word.
   a. extremely far away   c. blazing, smoking
   b. can be measured easily   d. impossible to see; mysterious

   _____

   _____

3. Crane makes a special point of mentioning twice that the orderly-sergeant "leaned nervously backward." Reread this section of "An Episode of War," and explain the orderly-sergeant's actions, using details from the text.

   _____

   _____

4. Crane describes the lieutenant as he takes his leave from the battle scene as "precisely like a historical painting." Complete the chart below with details of the battle scene from this page that would work well in a painting of the event.

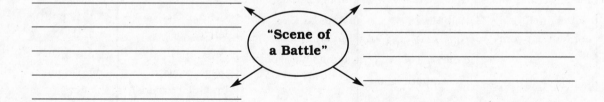

© Prentice-Hall, Inc.

5. Which of the sentences below lets the reader know that, besides being a realistic portrait of a battle, Crane's writing here is also naturalistic (suggesting forces beyond one's control that the character has to deal with)? Explain your answer with a detail from the text.
   a. The lieutenant watches the battle as an observer, as he walks away.
   b. The lieutenant is annoyed with his fellow soldiers when he gets shot.
   c. The lieutenant minimizes the loss of his arm by telling his family it doesn't matter that much.
   d. The lieutenant does not immediately understand the consequences of this battle.

   _____

   _____

6. For what reason do you think the doctor in "An Episode of War" says he will not need to amputate the officer's arm? Use information from Crane's scene of a war-torn battle—as well as your own knowledge about the way in which people sometimes react to medical information.

   _____

   _____

7. If realism portrays life faithfully and accurately, "Willie Has Gone to the War" paints a more idealized picture of war and its effects. Give a few examples of the romantic nature of this song.

   _____

   _____

8. Using your own knowledge about the horrors of war, why do you think Cooper and Foster chose to write "Willie Has Gone to the War" in a more romantic style?

   _____

   _____

9. Which is the best meaning for *glade*? List several context clues in the song that suggest the meaning of this word.
   a. river   b. bird's nest   c. sky   d. open space in a forest

   _____

   _____

10. Repetition is often used to help establish a particular kind of tone. Cite repetitive words and phrases from "Willie Has Gone to the War," and describe the way in which they set the tone for the song.

    _____

    _____

    _____

Extended Response

11. After the officer is wounded in "An Episode of War," several comments are made that refer to his condition. Complete the chart below by listing those comments.

Speaker	Comments to the Lieutenant
1. An officer from the brigade	
2. The surgeon (first comment)	
3. The surgeon (later comments)	
4. The officer himself	

12. Write a brief essay, discussing the meaning of the various comments in question 11. Include some reference in your essay—a detail or quotation from the text—about how these comments made the lieutenant feel.

13. Reread the sentence from "An Episode of War" that begins "Sitting with his back against a tree . . . " Why does the lieutenant have this burst of feeling? Offer your opinion in a short essay, and use details from the text to support your stance.

14. Which is the most realistic part of "Willie Has Gone to the War"? Select a few lines from the song; then, in a short essay, explain why they capture the realities of war.

15. Reread the first two pages of "An Episode of War." What do these pages imply about the relationship between the lieutenant and his men? In a few paragraphs, discuss how they feel about each other. Use details from the story to support your opinion.

Oral Response

16. Go back to question 1, 4, 12, 13, or 15 or one assigned by your teacher, and take five to ten minutes to expand your answer and prepare an oral response. Find additional details in the selections that will support your points. If necessary, make notes to guide your response.

Rubric for Evaluating Extended Responses

0	1	2	3	4
Blank paper Foreign language Illegible, incoherent Not enough content to score	Incorrect purpose, mode, audience Brief, vague Unelaborated Rambling Lack of language control Poor organization	Correct purpose, mode, audience Some elaboration Some details Gaps in organization Limited language control	Correct purpose, mode, audience Moderately well elaborated Clear, effective language Organized (perhaps with brief digressions)	Correct purpose, mode, audience Effective elaboration Consistent organization Sense of completeness, fluency

"Swing Low, Sweet Chariot" and "Go Down, Moses"
Spirituals

Open-Book Test

Multiple Choice and Short Answer

Write your answers to all questions in this section on the lines provided.
For multiple-choice questions, circle the letter of the best answer.

1. The theme of "Swing Low, Sweet Chariot" can refer to more than one experience. Which answer best states the theme or themes of this spiritual? Explain your answer.
    a. The theme is about crossing over to heaven in a beautiful manner.
    b. The theme is about crossing over to freedom from slavery and about going to heaven.
    c. The theme is about the difficulties of slavery and the struggle to be free.
    d. The theme is about a young slave who wants to go home to his parents.

    _____

    _____

2. What does the use of "a band of angels" imply in "Swing Low, Sweet Chariot"? In what manner would the angels be likely to "come after" the singer? Use detail from the text to explain your answer.

    _____

    _____

3. The repetition of the word *home* in "Swing Low, Sweet Chariot" tells the reader that this word has special meaning. In the context of slaves who live on plantations, think of several meanings for the word *home*, and enter them in the diagram below.

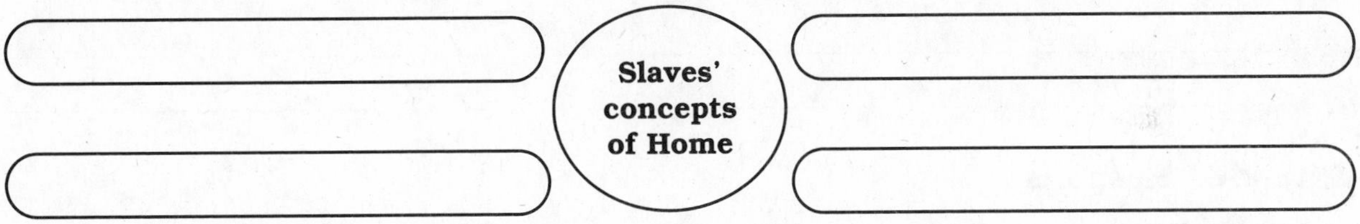

    Slaves' concepts of Home

4. Why does the speaker in "Swing Low, Sweet Chariot" ask that the chariot be "low"? Explain why you chose your answer.

    a. because the speaker is small

    b. to rhyme with the rest of the song

    c. because the speaker is sad

    d. so that the speaker can easily get onto the chariot

    _____

    _____

5. The refrain of "Swing Low, Sweet Chariot" uses repetition to emphasize the main theme of the song. Which lines of the refrain most strongly emphasize the theme? Why?

    _____

    _____

6. Which of these lines is the most powerful in the refrain of "Go Down, Moses"? Explain your answer.
   a. Tell old Pharaoh
   c. Way down in Egypt land
   b. Go down, Moses
   d. To let my people go

   _____

7. "Let my people go" is repeated several times in the spiritual "Go Down, Moses." Why might the creator or creators of this spiritual have wanted to repeat this particular line? Whom might they have been addressing?

   _____

8. The people in "Go Down, Moses" have been "oppressed." Select the meaning for *oppressed.* Define the two different oppressors and the two different groups of enslaved people.
   a. kept down by cruel or unjust powers
   c. given opportunities
   b. beaten
   d. found to be threats to society

   _____

9. Reread the following line from "Go Down, Moses." Which word offers the best meaning for the word "smite"? Explain your choice, using context clues from the spiritual.

   If not I'll smite your first-born dead

   a. torture   b. obey   c. kill   d. enslave

   _____

10. "Egypt land" is used several times in "Go Down, Moses." What is the effect on the listener of the repetition of "Way down in Egypt land"?

   _____

Extended Response

11. Both of these spirituals use several examples of repetition. In the following chart, list the repeated words or phrases that seem the most significant. Then write a brief essay, in which you discuss what makes them significant.

"SWING LOW, SWEET CHARIOT"	"GO DOWN, MOSES"
1.	
2.	
3.	

12. There are several religious references in both of these spirituals. In a short essay, describe how religion or God is used in each, and where it is most effective.

13. Imagine that there are slave owners still living. Which song would they prefer to hear the slaves singing in their fields? Why? Write a short essay that compares the power of the two spirituals, and the effect each might have on a plantation filled with working slaves.

14. Each of these two spirituals is addressed to a specific listener or listeners. In a paragraph or two, discuss who the listener(s) might be, both in the refrains (repeated sections) and the verses. Use details from the text to support your opinion.

15. If only one of these two songs could be placed in a time capsule to represent the period of the late 1800s, which would better represent the mood of the times and the condition of slavery? In a short essay, make a case for choosing one spiritual over the other. Use the text to amplify your response.

Oral Response

16. Go back to question 1, 6, 10, 12, or 15 or one assigned by your teacher, and take five to ten minutes to expand your answer and prepare an oral response. Find additional details in the spirituals that will support your points. If necessary make notes to guide your response.

Rubric for Evaluating Extended Responses

0	1	2	3	4
Blank paper Foreign language Illegible, incoherent Not enough content to score	Incorrect purpose, mode, audience Brief, vague Unelaborated Rambling Lack of language control Poor organization	Correct purpose, mode, audience Some elaboration Some details Gaps in organization Limited language control	Correct purpose, mode, audience Moderately well elaborated Clear, effective language Organized (perhaps with brief digressions)	Correct purpose, mode, audience Effective elaboration Consistent organization Sense of completeness, fluency

Name _____ Date _____

from *My Bondage and My Freedom* by Frederick Douglass

Open-Book Test

Multiple Choice and Short Answer

Write your answers to all questions in this section on the lines provided.
For multiple-choice questions, circle the letter of the best answer.

1. Which clues immediately tell the reader that he or she is reading both an autobiography and the story of a person who had been enslaved? Reread the first paragraph, and list the words or phrases that provide this information.

   _____

   _____

2. According to Douglass, it was not in Mrs. Auld's original nature to act as a slaveholder who denied rights to slaves. Which answer mentions the ingredients that she initially lacked? Use a quotation from the text to explain which element she needed to acquire.
   a. She lacked a strong character.
   b. She lacked kindness.
   c. She lacked the perception that a woman's place was in the home.
   d. She lacked an innate wickedness or a corrupt personality.

   _____

   _____

3. Douglass writes that he "was more than that [a slave]." How is he correct, or incorrect, in making this statement?

   _____

   _____

4. Using a quotation from the text, explain what happened to change Mrs. Auld.

   _____

   _____

5. Douglass describes Mrs. Auld's earlier behavior as "Christian"—charitable and good-hearted. Fill in the diagram below with the evidence of her Christian behavior, upon which he bases this description.

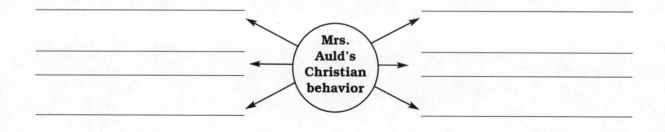

6. Interpret the passage that starts with "Slavery soon . . ." and ends on textbook page 460 with " . . . riveted to her position." What does Frederick Douglass imply about the changes that have taken place in Mrs. Auld, and about how they affect her?

    _____

    _____

7. In the following sentence, use context clues to determine the meaning of *benevolent*.

    > My mistress—who had begun to teach me—was suddenly checked in her benevolent design, by the strong advice of her husband.

    Which is the correct meaning of the word? Write the context clues that help the reader.
    a. threatening   c. kindly, charitable
    b. unpleasant   d. forbidden

    _____

8. In his autobiography, Frederick Douglass expresses an awareness of his intelligence. Give several examples from *My Bondage and My Freedom* that show his desire to learn.

    _____

    _____

9. Mrs. Auld, upon discovering Frederick Douglass reading in a corner, rushed at him "with something of the wrath and consternation" of a spy who had just found a traitor. Reread the entire sentence. What is the correct meaning of *consternation?* Offer the context clues that help to determine the word's meaning.
    a. pride   c. embarrassment
    b. great fear or shock   d. humor

    _____

10. In *My Bondage and My Freedom*, Douglass acknowledges that he was treated well by Mrs. Auld in many respects. On the same page, find the reasoning that demonstrates his overall objection to his situation. Explain which aspects of slavery he minds the most, using details from this page.

    _____

    _____

    _____

Extended Response

11. Douglass is very specific in relating the attitudes that youngsters had toward him. Using details from the text, explain, in a few paragraphs, the ways in which the children's attitudes differed from those of the adults.

12. How does Douglass demonstrate in *My Bondage and My Freedom* that "education and slavery are incompatible with each other"? In a short essay, use examples that explain this concept, and describe how he managed to get around Mrs. Auld's restrictions.

13. Douglass describes Mrs. Auld's behavior both early in his life and as he was growing up. In the following chart, offer several details from *My Bondage and My Freedom* that show examples of these two stages of his life, as shown by her behavior.

MRS. AULD'S EARLY BEHAVIOR	MRS. AULD'S LATER BEHAVIOR
1.	
2.	
3.	
4.	

14. In a short essay, take a position on what you believe to be Mrs. Auld's true nature, as shown in *My Bondage and My Freedom.* Was she basically a good soul, or was she a vengeful person who had once appeared kind? Use details from the chart in question 13 and the text to help you substantiate your opinion.

15. Douglass writes, "knowledge only increased my discontent." Since he sought learning in such an earnest manner, this phrase would seem to be a contradiction. Using details from the text, write a short essay that explains this statement.

Oral Response

16. Go back to question 3, 4, 11, 12, or 14 or one assigned by your teacher, and take five to ten minutes to expand your answer and prepare an oral response. Find additional details in the autobiography that will support your points. If necessary make some notes to guide your response.

Rubric for Evaluating Extended Responses

0	1	2	3	4
Blank paper	Incorrect purpose, mode, audience	Correct purpose, mode, audience	Correct purpose, mode, audience	Correct purpose, mode, audience
Foreign language	Brief, vague	Some elaboration	Moderately well elaborated	Effective elaboration
Illegible, incoherent	Unelaborated	Some details	Clear, effective language	Consistent organization
Not enough content to score	Rambling	Gaps in organization	Organized (perhaps with brief digressions)	Sense of completeness, fluency
	Lack of language control	Limited language control		
	Poor organization			

Name _____ Date _____

Open-Book Test

Multiple Choice and Short Answer

Write your answers to all questions in this section on the lines provided.
For multiple-choice questions, circle the letter of the best answer.

1. What might seem strange to a reader about the tone at the beginning of "An Occurrence at Owl Creek" ? Taking into consideration the subject matter, might the reader expect a different tone?

   _____

   _____

2. Bierce has chosen a particular point of view with which to open his story. Is it objective (does not reveal any character's thoughts and feelings) or in the first-person (reveals the thoughts and feelings of one character)? Give evidence from the story to support your answer.

   _____

   _____

3. In the story, there is a reference to how people in the military view death. Find the reference. Which answer depicts their attitude? Explain how they demonstrate their attitude.
   a. They are fearful of death.
   b. They feel a sense of respect towards death.
   c. They do not fear death.
   d. They are scornful of death.

   _____

   _____

4. At a certain point, there is a shift in the point of view. Which answer shows the change? Explain why you did or did not choose each answer.

   a. "He was a civilian . . ." _____

   _____

   b. "The sergeant turned to the captain . . ." _____

   _____

   c. "How slowly it appeared to move!" _____

   _____

   d. "His face had not been covered, nor his eyes bandaged." _____

   _____

5. Bierce has the doomed man express certain thoughts that give the reader a sense of his terror. Give two examples of his reactions, as he is about to be hanged.

   _____

   _____

6. There are several places in "An Occurrence at Owl Creek Bridge" where there is a change in the time sequence. Identify one of these places, and note the effect it has on the story.

_____

7. Reread the sentence that contains this phrase: ". . . he swung through unthinkable arcs of oscillation, like a vast pendulum." Which is the correct meaning of *oscillation*? Give the context clues that assist the reader in determining the meaning of this word.
   a. darkness   c. act of swinging back and forth
   b. feeling like a large heart   d. feeling of being on fire

_____

8. What surprising piece of information is revealed about the grey-clad horseman)? What does this information imply about Farquhar and his responsibility for his deed?

_____

_____

9. In "An Occurrence at Owl Creek Bridge," Farquhar's wife expresses herself with an "ineffable" kind of feeling. Which answer gives the best meaning of *ineffable*? Provide the clues for this meaning.
   a. enormous   c. warm
   b. dignified   d. too overwhelming to be described by words;
                                            inexpressible

_____

10. Bierce experiments in "An Occurrence at Owl Creek Bridge" with shifting the time sequence among several different time periods. Remember the following events in the actual sequence in which they happen in the story. Write the numbers on the lines provided.

   1. Farquhar has a conversation with a Federal scout. _____

   2. Farquhar sees his wife waiting for him at home. _____

   3. The sergeant releases the plank on which Farquhar is standing. _____

   4. The soldiers stand at parade rest. _____

   5. Farquhar dies. _____

   6. Farquhar is strung up in preparation for being hanged. _____

Extended Response

11. In a short essay, explain how Bierce supports the concept that "all is fair in love and war." Include an explanation of the irony concerning the character who expresses this opinion.

© Prentice-Hall, Inc.

12. There are several instances in "An Occurrence at Owl Creek Bridge" where Bierce attributes a heightened awareness of one or more of the senses—taste, touch, smell, sound, or sight—to Farquhar. In the chart below, list some of these perceptions, and include the sense that they represent.

PERCEPTION	ONE OF THE FIVE SENSES

13. Using the chart from question 12, write a short essay that explains the way in which one or more of these sensory descriptions are useful in showing the point of view Bierce is using. Do the descriptions contrast with, or match, the descriptions of the military presence in the story?

14. In a few paragraphs, describe the critical object that the Union army wants to protect (and that Farquhar wants to destroy). Why was this particular thing so important?

15. In a paragraph or two, discuss the elements of fantasy used in "An Occurrence at Owl Creek Bridge." Include the way in which they contribute to the story's effectiveness.

Oral Response

16. Go back to question 2, 5, 11, 12 or 15 or one assigned by your teacher, and take five to ten minutes to expand your answer and prepare an oral response. Find additional details in the story that will support your points. If necessary make notes to guide your response.

Rubric for Evaluating Extended Responses

0	1	2	3	4
Blank paper Foreign language Illegible, incoherent Not enough content to score	Incorrect purpose, mode, audience Brief, vague Unelaborated Rambling Lack of language control Poor organization	Correct purpose, mode, audience Some elaboration Some details Gaps in organization Limited language control	Correct purpose, mode, audience Moderately well elaborated Clear, effective language Organized (perhaps with brief digressions)	Correct purpose, mode, audience Effective elaboration Consistent organization Sense of completeness, fluency

An Occurrence at Owl Creek Bridge **81**

Name _____   Date _____

"The Gettysburg Address" and **"Second Inaugural Address"**
by Abraham Lincoln
"Letter to His Son" by Robert E. Lee

Open-Book Test

Multiple Choice and Short Answer

Write your answers to all questions in this section on the lines provided.
For multiple-choice questions, circle the letter of the best answer.

1. Reread the first paragraph of "The Gettysburg Address," beginning with "Four score and
    seven years ago" and ending with "equal." Why is this an especially effective way for
    Lincoln to begin his speech?

    _____

    _____

2. Study the sentence that begins: "But, in a larger sense. . . ." Which answer contains the
    meaning of *consecrate*? Give the context clues that suggest the meaning for this word.
    a. deface   c. dig up
    b. cause to be honored   d. stand upon

    _____

    _____

3. Why does Lincoln say that he and the observers "cannot consecrate this ground"? Which
    answer best describes what is he trying to imply about both himself and his listeners?
    Explain your answer.
    a. He and they are not serving in enough of an official capacity.
    b. He and they would be traitors.
    c. He and they are less able to consecrate it than the soldiers who have already made it
       sacred through their bloodshed.
    d. He and they are less able to consecrate it than someone else, because they are not
       clergymen.

    _____

    _____

4. Whom would you assume was the audience for Lincoln's "Gettysburg Address"? What
    might be the purpose of this address, given during the Civil War?

    _____

    _____

5. In his "Second Inaugural Address," Lincoln uses several references to God or religion. For
    what purpose does he choose these words, and this kind of emphasis, in his speech?

    _____

    _____

6. The final paragraph of Lincoln's "Second Inaugural Address" begins, "With malice toward none. . . ." Which answer gives the correct meaning of the word *malice*? Give the clues that suggest the meaning of the word.

   a. favoritism   b. memory   c. remembrance   d. ill will, spite

   _____

   _____

   _____

7. It is clear from reading Lincoln's "Second Inaugural Address" that his sense of responsibility for the nation is very strong, and that he is using this speech to inspire a sense of national responsibility in his listeners. Complete the chart below with three quotations about responsibility that he feels, or hopes that his listeners will share with him.

QUOTATIONS ABOUT RESPONSIBILITY
1.
2.
3.

8. In contract to Lincoln's style of oration, Lee has chosen to use a far more informal tone in his personal "Letter to His Son." Give two or three examples of words or phrases that convey this informality.

   _____

   _____

   _____

9. Which answer best expresses Lee's basic opinion concerning secession, expressed in "Letter to His Son"? Explain Lee's reasoning.

   a. He sees it as a possible option.   c. He hopes it will happen.

   b. He sees it as inevitable.   d. He sees it as an act of war.

   _____

   _____

   _____

10. Why does Lee write that he will "draw my sword on none"? What is the one exception to this statement? How does this statement express his feelings about "strife and civil war"?

   _____

   _____

   _____

Extended Response

11. In what ways do Lincoln and Lee agree with each other about the Civil War? In what ways do they disagree? Write a brief essay, analyzing their points of agreement and difference. Use details from the writings to help you.

12. Lincoln wrote and said many phrases that have since become familiar as quotations. Select five phrases from "The Gettysburg Address" and the "Second Inaugural Address" that could be quotations for posterity, and explain why they are important in the context of American history.

QUOTATION	IMPORTANCE
1.	
2.	
3.	
4.	
5.	

13. In his speeches, Lincoln makes several references to the Civil War, stating his perceptions about what he believes to be the purpose of the war, as well as his opinions about its outcome. Write a short essay, citing at least four of these references to the war. In your essay, explore his opinions, and analyze whether Lincoln casts any blame in his speeches.

14. Lincoln and Lee make use of faith or religion in their writings. How would you characterize their usage? In a paragraph or two, select examples from Lincoln and Lee, and describe how they were able to use religious references effectively.

15. Unlike the times during which Lincoln and Lee were writing, the modern era focuses on short phrases that can be used to capture sentiments and philosophies, popularly known as "sound bites." From these three writings, choose two "sound bites" to encapsulate the thoughts of feelings of each of these two men. In a short essay, explain why these examples are meaningful.

Oral Response

16. Go back to question 1, 3, 8, 11, or 13 or one assigned by your teacher, and take five to ten minutes to expand your answer and prepare an oral response. Find additional details in the selections that will support your points. If necessary, make notes to guide your response.

Rubric for Evaluating Extended Responses

0	1	2	3	4
Blank paper Foreign language Illegible, incoherent Not enough content to score	Incorrect purpose, mode, audience Brief, vague Unelaborated Rambling Lack of language control Poor organization	Correct purpose, mode, audience Some elaboration Some details Gaps in organization Limited language control	Correct purpose, mode, audience Moderately well elaborated Clear, effective language Organized (perhaps with brief digressions)	Correct purpose, mode, audience Effective elaboration Consistent organization Sense of completeness, fluency

from Civil War Diaries, Journals, and Letters

Open-Book Test

Multiple Choice and Short Answer

Write your answers to all questions in this section on the lines provided.
For multiple-choice questions, circle the letter of the best answer.

1. In *Mary Chesnut's Civil War,* there are factual observations of the early events of the Civil War, along with more personal information that contains opinion. Which of the following statements is an example of opinion? Choose the best answer. Explain why you did or did not choose each answer.

   a. Mrs. Hayne called to tell Mrs. Chesnut that she felt bad for "those who are not here."

   _____

   b. "Today at dinner there was no allusion to things as they stand in the harbor." _____

   c. ". . . our two governors dined with us . . ."   _____

   d. John Manning was "pleased as a boy to be on Beauregard's staff . . ."   _____

2. *Mary Chesnut's Civil War* offers significant information about the attack on Fort Sumter. In addition, there are several glimpses of the ways in which civilians were affected during the beginning days of the Civil War. Give one example of the impact on the everyday lives of people in Charleston.

   _____

   _____

3. Reread the sentence that states that Colonel Chesnut was "more unruffled than usual in his serenity. . . ." Circle the letter of the meaning for *serenity.* On the line below, give the context clues that suggest the meaning of the word.
   a. exhaustion   b. shyness   c. calmness   d. spirituality

   _____

   _____

4. Goss presents his early days as a private with interesting recollections. In *Recollections of a Private,* humor and exaggeration are used to present a contrast to the seriousness of war. In the following chart, list examples of either humor and exaggeration.

   _____   _____

   _____   _____

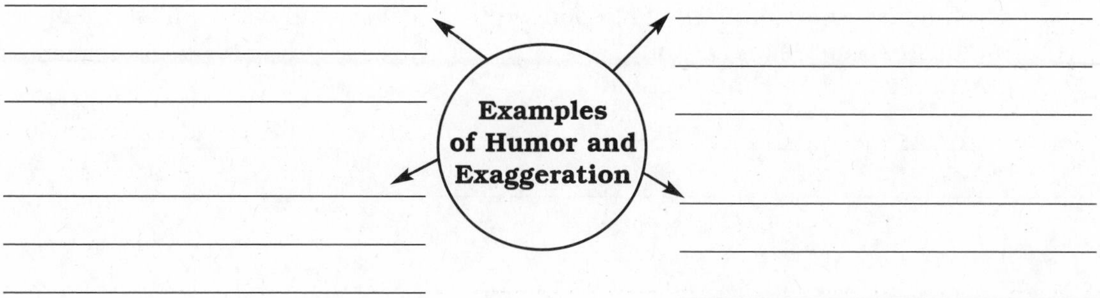

   _____   **Examples   _____
                              of Humor and**
   _____   **Exaggeration**   _____

   _____   _____

   _____   _____

5. Goss was entranced by the advertising poster encouraging men to enlist in the army. What is the main message that he is trying to convey to the reader about his state of mind at the time he enlisted? Choose the best answer, and explain it with details from the text.
   a. He was an inexperienced youth looking for excitement.
   b. He believed fervently in the Union and its mission.
   c. He was keeping alive a family tradition of serving his country.
   d. He thought enlisting might be peculiar.

   _____

   _____

6. In *A Confederate Account of the Battle of Gettysburg*, McKim provides an eyewitness account of a failed attack mounted by Robert E. Lee. Parts of his account are factual— they can be proved or supported—and other parts represent McKim's personal opinion. Complete the chart below with examples of the facts and the opinions.

EXAMPLES OF FACTS	EXAMPLES OF OPINIONS
1.	
2.	
3.	

7. In the letter to his wife entitled *An Account of the Battle of Bull Run*, Jackson repeats several times that he gives credit primarily to God for the success of his troops. In fact, he specifically asks his wife not to discuss the battle or the victory, saying "Let others speak praise, not myself." What might be the reason for his request? Give evidence from the letter that supports your conclusion.

   _____

   _____

8. In his *Reaction to the Emancipation Proclamation*, Turner writes from a personal point of view that captures, in a short amount of space, the dramatic response both races had to the announcement that slaves would become free. Choose three reactions to the proclamation that demonstrate the overwhelming response.

   _____

   _____

9. What seems to be the primary purpose of *An Account of an Experience With Discrimination*? Choose the best answer and use details from the account to support your answer.
   a. to complain about mistreatment
   b. to carefully document abuses of freedom so the legal system can address them
   c. to establish an anti-slavery group
   d. to get train conductors into trouble

   _____

   _____

10. In addition to providing valuable information, *"An Account of an Experience With Discrimination"* suggests some of Sojourner Truth's personal traits. Describe the kind of person she seems to be, using details from her account.

_____

_____

Extended Response

11. In the selections, there are two accounts of the experiences of people during the period of history when slavery was ending. Using examples from each account, explain the ways in which they represent different viewpoints.

12. Using two of the accounts of the Civil War as your sources, list the elements that are similar or different. Pay attention to the tone of the writer (humorous, objective, fearful, solemn), the perspective from which he or she is writing (as an experienced or inexperienced soldier, or as a soldier or a civilian) the number of facts and opinions, and the purpose of the account (to stimulate action on the part of others, or to express one's feelings and thoughts).

13. Use the list you made for the previous question to help you write a short essay comparing the two accounts of the Civil War. Examine the areas in which the two accounts are similar, and analyze the ways in which they are different.

14. The Civil War was fought for particular reasons—values that were held to be important by both the North and the South. It was also fought because many of the participants had personal reasons. Using examples from at least two of the accounts, write a paragraph or two that discusses some of the reasons that people fought in the war.

15. What might be the value for the modern reader in reading firsthand accounts of the Civil War, its battles, and its effects? Using details from two or three of these accounts, explain whether you believe they contain valuable information, and how it might be helpful to readers of this century.

Oral Response

16. Go back to question 2, 4, 10, 11, or 14 or one assigned by your teacher, and take five to ten minutes to expand your answer and prepare an oral response. Find additional details in the accounts that will support your points. If necessary, make notes to guide your response.

Rubric for Evaluating Extended Responses

0	1	2	3	4
Blank paper Foreign language Illegible, incoherent Not enough content to score	Incorrect purpose, mode, audience Brief, vague Unelaborated Rambling Lack of language control Poor organization	Correct purpose, mode, audience Some elaboration Some details Gaps in organization Limited language control	Correct purpose, mode, audience Moderately well elaborated Clear, effective language Organized (perhaps with brief digressions)	Correct purpose, mode, audience Effective elaboration Consistent organization Sense of completeness, fluency

**"The Boys' Ambition" from *Life on the Mississippi* and
"The Notorious Jumping Frog of Calaveras County"**
by Mark Twain

Open-Book Test

Multiple Choice and Short Answer

Write your answers to all questions in this section on the lines provided.
For multiple-choice questions, circle the letter of the best answer.

1. In the first few paragraphs of "The Boys' Ambition," what does Twain imply about the expectations that young boys might have regarding their future careers? Select the best answer. Explain why you did or did not choose each answer.

    a. They all had a burning desire to become clowns in the traveling circus. _____

    _____

    b. They felt the pain of African Americans' difficult lives. _____

    _____

    c. In general, their ambitions tended to change, but they consistently wanted to be involved with steamboats. _____

    d. None of them could settle on one ambition. _____

2. What general impression of the town of Hannibal does Twain portray in "The Boys' Ambition," especially before the steamboat arrives, and after it has left? Use a quotation from the textbook to support your answer.

    _____

    _____

    _____

3. In certain descriptions in "The Boys' Ambition," Twain uses humorous exaggeration to emphasize his thoughts and feelings, either about himself or others, as he was growing up. Find an example that demonstrates Twain's use of humor through overstatement.

    _____

    _____

    _____

4. Reread the sentence in "The Boys' Ambition" that describes the drayman's "prodigious voice." What is the meaning of this word? Provide the context clues that suggest the meaning of *prodigious.*
    a. fast-talking   c. laughing
    b. low   d. strong in size or power

    _____

    _____

5. In addition to expressing expressing jealousy toward the boy who apprentices aboard a steamboat, Twain discovers a positive result of the boy's occupation. Reread the last page of "The Boys' Ambition," and describe how the town boys benefitted.

_____

_____

6. What evidence is there in the first few paragraphs of "The Notorious Jumping Frog of Calaveras County" that tells the reader this is going to be a humorous story? Find at least two details or quotations that foreshadow Twain's intent to entertain his readers.

_____

_____

7. In "The Notorious Jumping Frog of Calaveras County," there are several examples of regional dialect used by Wheeler. Reread the dialect, using the context of the sentences to determine its meaning. Complete the chart below by selecting expressions and translating them into words or phrases that are more understandable.

DIALECT	ACTUAL WORD OR PHRASES
1.	
2.	
3.	

8. In Twain's "The Notorious Jumping Frog of Calaveras County," determine the meaning of the word *ornery.* Provide the context clues that help suggest the meaning of the word.
   a. sleepy   b. mean   c. lazy   d. superior

_____

9. Reread the following sentence to review its meaning: "Well, thish-yer Smiley had rat terriers, and chicken cocks, and tomcats and all them kind of things, till you couldn't rest, and you couldn't fetch nothing for him to bet on but he'd match you." On the lines below, translate the dialect of the following phrases into plainer language: a) "thish-yer"; b) "till you couldn't rest"; and c) "you couldn't fetch nothing for him to bet on but he'd match you."

   a. _____

   b. _____

   c. _____

10. What conclusion does Twain finally arrive at concerning the likelihood of finding information about Leonidas W. Smiley? Give evidence from either the beginning or the end of "The Notorious Jumping Frog of Calaveras County" that shows what Twain's expectations were.

_____

_____

Extended Response

11. In a short essay, discuss what the reader can infer about Twain's attitude toward the steamboat and its effect upon the town. Select at least four descriptive phrases from "The Boys' Ambition" to support your discussion.

12. Imagine that you have a window into the mind of Twain as a young boy in Hannibal, Missouri. Twain's mind is filled with ambitions, confusion, and feelings of envy. Fill in the diagram below with details or quotations from "The Boys' Ambition" that reveal Twain's inner thoughts.

Mark Twain's Thoughts

13. Using the completed diagram from question 12 to assist you, write a short essay in which you fully discuss Twain's thoughts and feelings. Analyze which of Twain's feelings are valid, and which of them represent the exaggerated reaction of a young boy.

14. Reread Twain's descriptions about St. Louis and elements of travel that the apprenticed boy had experienced in "The Boys' Ambition." Using details from this section, write a paragraph or two that describes Twain's level of worldliness and the amount of experience he and the other boys from Hannibal had with traveling.

15. Select a passage from "The Notorious Jumping Frog of Calaveras County" that contains a lot of Wheeler's particular dialect. Reread the passage, using context clues—and the sound of words that seem familiar—to help you to determine the meaning of words or phrases you do not understand. Rewrite the passage in language more familiar to the modern reader. Then, briefly explain why Twain's use of dialect is effective as a humorous device.

Oral Response

16. Go back to question 2, 3, 6, 13, or 15 or one assigned by your teacher, and take five to ten minutes to expand your answer and prepare an oral response. Find additional details in the stories that will support your points. If necessary, make notes to guide your response.

Rubric for Evaluating Extended Responses

0	1	2	3	4
Blank paper Foreign language Illegible, incoherent Not enough content to score	Incorrect purpose, mode, audience Brief, vague Unelaborated Rambling Lack of language control Poor organization	Correct purpose, mode, audience Some elaboration Some details Gaps in organization Limited language control	Correct purpose, mode, audience Moderately well elaborated Clear, effective language Organized (perhaps with brief digressions)	Correct purpose, mode, audience Effective elaboration Consistent organization Sense of completeness, fluency

© Prentice-Hall, Inc.

"The Outcasts of Poker Flat" by Bret Harte

Open-Book Test

Multiple Choice and Short Answer

Write your answers to all questions in this section on the lines provided.
For multiple-choice questions, circle the letter of the best answer.

1. In the first few pages of "The Outcasts of Poker Flat," the reader becomes quickly aware that Mr. Oakhurst assumes that the inhabitants of Poker Flat are out to do him some harm. Is Mr. Oakhurst correct? Choose the best answer and provide the quotation that supports your answer.
   a. He is incorrect. No one is after him.
   b. He is partly correct. They are not after him; they are after his brother, who is a gambler.
   c. He is partly correct. They are not after him; they are after his sister, for disgraceful behavior.
   d. He is correct. He is a gambler.

   _____

   _____

   _____

   _____

2. Harte provides certain clues in "The Outcasts of Poker Flat" to let the reader know immediately that it takes place in the far west. What aspect of the way in which the "moral atmosphere" is enforced informs the reader that Poker Flat is in an area that is not very civilized, and its inhabitants are quick to judge others?

   _____

   _____

   _____

3. Reread the character descriptions in "The Outcasts of Poker Flat." As you read the descriptions of Uncle Billy, there are several references to his reaction to banishment from the town. At one point, he "included the whole party in one sweeping anathema." Using clues from elsewhere on this page, determine the meaning of "anathema." Select the best answer and cite the context clues that helped you to arrive at this answer.
   a. hug   c. curse
   b. declaration   d. request to bring him back to town

   _____

   _____

   _____

   _____

4. Harte may have a particular purpose in describing Mr. Oakhurst's companions in such an unflattering manner. Complete the diagram below to show how Harte chooses to view the character of Mr. Oakhurst, and how he wants the reader to view him. Base your information on story details from this page, as well as from the beginning of the story.

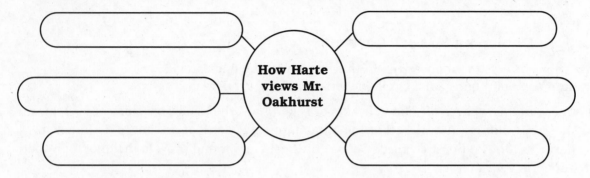

5. As "The Outcasts of Poker Flat" leave the town and make their way onward, they experience a physical environment that is different from the one they left behind. Using details from the story, describe at least one way in which their new environment presents a challenge and demonstrates that they are in undiscovered western territory.

_____

_____

6. There are a few instances in "The Outcasts of Poker Flat" when Mr. Oakhurst feels the need to discipline Uncle Billy. Describe the manner in which he exerts this discipline and the apparent reasons for Mr. Oakhurst's strictness.

_____

_____

7. Harte provides evidence of a growing bond between members of the newly formed camp companions. Cite one of the ways in which the group becomes closer.

_____

_____

8. On what basis did the Duchess and Mother Shipton call Piney "the child," since she was not really a youngster anymore? In what ways did they treat her as a child? Use details from "The Outcasts of Poker Flat" to help you to answer these questions.

_____

_____

9. Mother Shipton directs a "last vituperative attempt" toward the chimney smoke that she sees, as it rises from the town of Poker Flat. Reread the passage that begins: "The third day came . . . ," and determine the meaning of the word *vituperative*. Choose the best answer and provide the context clues in the passage that suggest the word's meaning.
   a. loud enough so that all can hear clearly   c. encouraging and helpful
   b. pleading for mercy   d. abusive (such as a curse)

_____

_____

10. In what way is Tom Simson's recitation of *The Iliad*, told as though it is a modern tale, helpful to the group of companions in "The Outcasts of Poker Flat"? Use details from the story to explain your answer.

_____

_____

Extended Response

11. In the final sentence of "The Outcasts of Poker Flat," Harte describes Mr. Oakhurst as "at once the strongest and yet the weakest" of the small group. In a brief essay, use at least four details from the story to describe ways in which Mr. Oakhurst is both strong and weak.

12. There are relationships that develop in "The Outcasts of Poker Flat," especially between the older and younger members of the group. In a short essay, use at least four details from the story to describe the relationships. Include your opinion of how the behavior of any of the characters seems ironic or surprising.

13. There are several instances that show how Mr. Oakhurst uses card games as an analogy for life. List examples of quotations from the story about card-playing, and explain how they relate to an overall philosophy of life that Mr. Oakhurst possesses.

14. Based on your knowledge of the characters in the story, identify the people in "The Outcasts of Poker Flat" whom you judge to be the least ethical. In a short essay, use details from the story to support your analysis of the characters you have identified as being morally weak.

15. There are several examples of either description or irony that Harte wishes to impart in "The Outcasts of Poker Flat." Some of these examples are contained in place names, and some are contained in names or descriptions of people. Find at least four examples of labels or names that seem to be either descriptive or ironic. In a short essay, use details from the story to substantiate your opinion.

Oral Response

16. Go back to question 4, 5, 11, 12, or 14 or one assigned by your teacher, and take five to ten minutes to expand your answer and prepare an oral response. Find additional details in the story that will support your points. If necessary, make notes to guide your response.

Rubric for Evaluating Extended Responses

0	1	2	3	4
Blank paper

Foreign language

Illegible, incoherent

Not enough content to score | Incorrect purpose, mode, audience

Brief, vague

Unelaborated

Rambling

Lack of language control

Poor organization | Correct purpose, mode, audience

Some elaboration

Some details

Gaps in organization

Limited language control | Correct purpose, mode, audience

Moderately well elaborated

Clear, effective language

Organized (perhaps with brief digressions) | Correct purpose, mode, audience

Effective elaboration

Consistent organization

Sense of completeness, fluency |

"Heading West" by Miriam Davis Colt
"I Will Fight No More Forever" by Chief Joseph

Open-Book Test

Multiple Choice and Short Answer

Write your answers to all questions in this section on the lines provided.
For multiple-choice questions, circle the letter of the best answer.

1. In the beginning of "Heading West," Colt says that it will be best for her family to settle in Kansas with an already established group. On what basis does she come to this conclusion?

    _____

    _____

2. Compare the tone of Colt's journal entry from January 15th with the entry from April 22nd. What kinds of emotions and thoughts does each entry express—are they similar or different in tone?

    _____

    _____

3. In her entry dated May 1st, Colt reveals some of her deep emotional reactions to this journey. As a reader, choose the section of this entry that you personally respond to most strongly. What impression does Colt give of her state of mind?

    _____

    _____

4. Colt describes "grasshoppers in profusion" in "Heading West." Reread the selection to determine the meaning of *profusion.* Select the correct meaning, then provide the context clue that suggests the meaning.
    a. abundance, rich supply   c. a variety of colors
    b. a mating ritual   d. the horse-drawn wagons

    _____

5. Reread the first paragraph of Colt's entry on May 3rd. She expresses certain fears about the Georgians. Does her opinion seem to be accurate? Why or why not?

    _____

    _____

6. In a description from near the middle of "Heading West," Colt uses the word *depredations.* Which answer best describes its meaning? Provide the context clues that help you determine the meaning.
    a. deprivations   b. bribery   c. acts of robbery   d. persuasion

    _____

    _____

7. Explain Colt's feelings upon her arrival in Kansas. Express whether her response to her new surroundings affected you as a reader.

_____

_____

8. In "I Will Fight No More Forever," Chief Joseph lists several individuals and groups of people who have died. What can the reader infer from his use of repetition? Select the best answer and list at least two of Chief Joseph's references to those who died.
   a. Chief Joseph is unable to think of other things to say.
   b. Chief Joseph is trying to send a coded message to other Native Americans.
   c. Chief Joseph was a highly emotional individual.
   d. Chief Joseph is trying to emphasize the excessive loss of Native Americans.

_____

_____

_____

9. There are many statements in "I Will Fight No More Forever" that evoke a strong response on the part of the reader. In the diagram below, list the quotations that are most effective in helping the reader to feel the plight of the Native Americans in Chief Joseph's tribe.

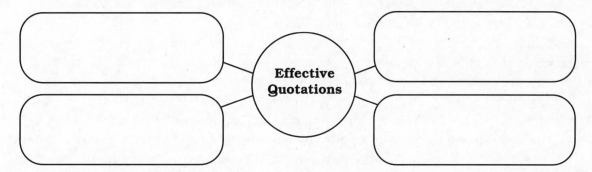

10. What can the reader infer that Chief Joseph means when he says: "I want to have time to look for my children . . ."? Why does he think he may not have time? Choose the best answer and provide the context clues that suggest this answer.
    a. He is afraid that they have gone to another territory.
    b. He is afraid he may die before he finds them.
    c. He does not want the army to find them.
    d. He is afraid he is too old to remember how to find them.

_____

_____

_____

Extended Response

11. From the journal entries in "Heading West," select the one that seems to be the most positive account. In a short essay, analyze the examples in this entry to show which details support Colt's optimistic perspective.

12. Colt expresses a fear about her possible future when she asks herself, "Is that what I have got to come to?" She is referring here to the appearance and manner of the woman who lives in a log cabin, but Colt has other intense fears. Complete the chart below as though you are able to read her thoughts. Then write a brief description of Holt's fears, using details from the text.

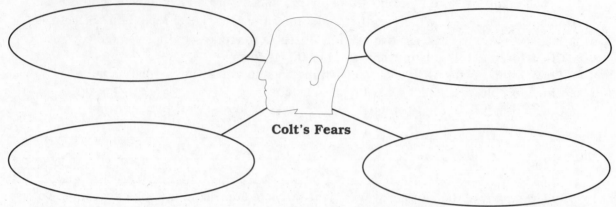

Colt's Fears

13. Reread the final entries in Colt's journal from May 12th and May 13th, in which she describes the conclusion of her family's journey. In a short essay, offer an opinion about what you perceive to be the worst reality that she and her family will have to face. Support your opinion with details from "Heading West."

14. "Heading West" and "I Will Fight No More Forever" represent different viewpoints on the development of the American frontier. In a brief essay, offer a contrast between the perspectives of Colt and Chief Joseph. Explain the differences with details from both selections.

15. Chief Joseph's statement "From where the sun now stands I will fight no more forever" has passed through the ages as a powerful, enduring symbol. Using details from the text, discuss this statement in a short essay. Analyze both its obvious and possible meanings.

Oral Response

16. Go back to question 3, 5, 9, 14, or 15 or one assigned by your teacher, and take five to ten minutes to expand your answer and prepare an oral response. Find additional details in the selections that will support your points. If necessary, make notes to guide your response.

Rubric for Evaluating Extended Responses

0	1	2	3	4
Blank paper Foreign language Illegible, incoherent Not enough content to score	Incorrect purpose, mode, audience Brief, vague Unelaborated Rambling Lack of language control Poor organization	Correct purpose, mode, audience Some elaboration Some details Gaps in organization Limited language control	Correct purpose, mode, audience Moderately well elaborated Clear, effective language Organized (perhaps with brief digressions)	Correct purpose, mode, audience Effective elaboration Consistent organization Sense of completeness, fluency

Name _____ Date _____

"To Build a Fire" by Jack London

Open-Book Test

Multiple Choice and Short Answer

Write your answers to all questions in this section on the lines provided.
For multiple-choice questions, circle the letter of the best answer.

1. There are several clues in the first paragraph of "To Build a Fire" that give the reader a sense of problems or dangers that may arise later in the story. Name at least two of them.

    _____

    _____

2. From your reading of "To Build a Fire," what can you infer about London's opinion of the man in his story? Does he respect him? Why or why not? Use at least two details from the page to support your answer.

    _____

    _____

3. London includes an extensive description of the husky's awareness of the intense cold in "To Build a Fire." What might be his purpose in using the dog as part of his account of the weather conditions? Choose the best answer. Explain why you did or did not choose each answer.

    a. London is saying that people should always travel with a companion. _____

    _____

    b. London is giving credit to the many dogs who have served travelers in the Northwestern territories. _____

    _____

    c. London is saying that the dog is cold and seeking shelter. _____

    _____

    d. London is saying that a dog, who is supposed to be less smart than a man, has instincts about the extreme cold. _____

    _____

4. Although the man in "To Build a Fire" seems to have few thoughts, London suggests that he is smarter than one may think. What evidence does London provide that shows the man is somewhat aware of the dangerous conditions, and that he is able to think quickly?

    _____

    _____

    _____

    _____

    _____

5. The man "chuckled at his foolishness" at not having built a fire before he eats lunch. Should the act of laughing at himself be a clue to the reader of coming danger? Why or why not? Select the best answer, and provide the quotation that describes his more appropriate reaction later on the same page.
   a. No, because he is just having a healthy reaction to his mistake.
   b. No, because he is about to build a fire, so the situation will be remedied.
   c. Yes, because his laughter might disturb forest creatures that could find and harm him.
   d. Yes, because his laughter shows a lack of awareness about the danger of his situation—which signifies that the cold may be affecting his brain.

   _____

   _____

6. After the man has built a fire, London goes on to write that "For the moment the cold of space was outwitted." In what way does this sentence define the central conflict that goes on for the length of this story?

   _____

   _____

7. The tree under which the man builds his fire represents part of the conflict he experiences with the natural world. Why does the tree become a problem for the man, and how could he have prevented the problem?

   _____

   _____

8. London refers to the man being out of touch with "the conjectural field of immortality and man's place in the universe." Use context clues from the entire sentence to help you determine the meaning of *conjectural*. Choose the words that define conjectural. Describe what kind of person is *conjectural*, and what type of person is not.
   a. well-known   c. uncertain, based on guessing
   b. having to do with temperature   d. having to do with cold weather clothing

   _____

   _____

9. In "To Build a Fire," the relationship between the man and the dog is confined to their being physically near each other, but not actually traveling as real companions. In general, the man speaks to the dog "peremptorily." Reread the sentence from the text that contains this word. Select the word that represents the best meaning of *peremptorily*. Give context clues from the sentence that suggest the meaning.
   a. loudly, so the dog can hear him   c. quietly, or in a soothing manner
   b. in a commanding or decisive manner d. lovingly and pleasantly

   _____

   _____

10. As "To Build a Fire" progresses, the man feels an increasing realization about the level of dangerous cold he faces. List three examples from the story that are evidence of that danger.

   _____

   _____

   _____

Extended Response

11. Imagine that you are the dog in this story, and that you are able to express your thoughts. Write a short essay describing some of your feelings, hopes, and fears as "To Build a Fire" progresses. Use details from the story to support your writing.

12. Create a story map of "To Build a Fire." You may choose a variety of events that lead to or from the climax. Your opinion about what constitutes the climax may differ from that of other students. However, all of your choices must be based upon details that you find in the story.

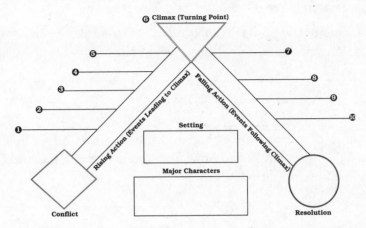

13. Using the above story map as your guide, write a short essay in which you analyze the effectiveness of the way in which London crafted "To Build a Fire." Does he create suspense? Are there details that could have been changed or eliminated for a greater impact? How successful is the story as a tale about humans in conflict with nature?

14. In two or three paragraphs, examine the relationship between the man and the dog in "To Build a Fire." Using details from the story, discuss their level of communication, the dog's needs and desires, and possible conflicts between the man and the dog.

15. London mentions that the man is not a person to "meditate upon his frailty." Using other details from this page or other parts of "To Build a Fire," write an essay that describes London's opinions about what the man should be thinking about.

Oral Response

16. Go back to question 4, 6, 10, 12, or 15 or one assigned by your teacher, and take five to ten minutes to expand your answer and prepare an oral response. If necessary, make notes to guide your response.

Rubric for Evaluating Extended Responses

0	1	2	3	4
Blank paper Foreign language Illegible, incoherent Not enough content to score	Incorrect purpose, mode, audience Brief, vague Unelaborated Rambling Lack of language control Poor organization	Correct purpose, mode, audience Some elaboration Some details Gaps in organization Limited language control	Correct purpose, mode, audience Moderately well elaborated Clear, effective language Organized (perhaps with brief digressions)	Correct purpose, mode, audience Effective elaboration Consistent organization Sense of completeness, fluency

"The Story of an Hour" by Kate Chopin

Open-Book Test

Multiple Choice and Short Answer

Write your answers to all questions in this section on the lines provided.
For multiple-choice questions, circle the letter of the best answer.

1. What is the meaning of the phrase "veiled hints that revealed in half concealing"?
    Explain how this phrase represents a usage of verbal irony.

    _____

    _____

    _____

2. There is an ironic detail about the author's portrayal of how Mrs. Mallard takes the news
    of her husband's death, compared to how other women might react to similar news. How
    does her reaction compare to that of others?

    _____

    _____

3. Mrs. Mallard had a sense of something that was about to happen to her, but it was
    "elusive." Using the context clues from the sentence that contains *elusive*. Determine the
    meaning of this word. Choose the correct answer. Explain the clues that helped you to
    figure out the meaning.
    a. frightening   b. fascinating   c. cheerful   d hard to grasp

    _____

    _____

    _____

4. Often in a scene portraying death, an author will create a detail that seems out of place.
    Reread only the first few paragraphs of the text (pretend you have not read any further in
    the story). Given the seriousness of the news Mrs. Mallard has just heard, which parts of
    the scene where she is sitting in her room seem strange? Select the correct answer.
    Explain your reasoning.
    a. She is sitting in a comfortable chair.
    b. She is pressed into her chair by a sense of overwhelming fatigue.
    c. There are signs of springtime and new life outside her window.
    d. There is a peddler in the street.

    _____

    _____

5. There is an enormous situational irony—an occurrence that is exactly the opposite of
    what the reader would expect—presented by Mrs. Mallard in "The Story of an Hour."
    Reread the paragraph that begins with "When she abandoned herself . . . ," and, on the
    lines below, write the quotation that she says to herself.

    _____

    _____

    _____

6. Josephine expresses a concern to her sister about her welfare, fearing that Louise's bereavement will make her ill. In this passage from "The Story of an Hour," the reader is aware of some information of which the character Josephine remains unaware. Provide the quotation that is an example of this dramatic irony.

_____

_____

7. Reread the following sentence "She arose at length and opened the door to her sister's importunities." What does the word "importunities" mean? Choose the correct answer. Provide the information that is located elsewhere on the same page that provides the contextual meaning for this word.
   a. inappropriate behavior
   b. persistent requests or demands
   c. weeping cries
   d. opportunities

   _____

   _____

8. Imagine that you can envision what is going through Louise's mind, based on the information provided by Chopin in "The Story of an Hour." List thoughts or emotional reactions that the character Louise might have at different points in the story.

   _____

   _____

9. What can the reader conclude to be the assumption of the doctors about Louise when they pronounce her dead? Select, then explain, what Louise is actually feeling when she dies.
   a. They assume that her joy is so intense that it kills her.
   b. They assume that she is completely unaware of what has happened.
   c. They assume that someone already told her that her husband is alive.
   d. They assume that her sister Josephine is actually Mrs. Mallard.

   _____

   _____

10. Chopin titled this story carefully. Does the title, "Story of an Hour," seem appropriate or inappropriate to you? Why or why not?

    _____

    _____

Extended Response

11. Reread the paragraph beginning "She did not stop to ask if it were or were not a monstrous joy that held her." Then, in a short essay, analyze and explain this paragraph. Use details from the rest of the page to help you.

12. Chopin uses this story to express some doubts about the benefits of marriage and the role of women at the time of her writing. In a few paragraphs, use at least three details from "The Story of an Hour" that reflect Chopin's concerns.

13. There are several uses of irony in "The Story of an Hour." Using the chart at the top of the next page, list two examples of verbal irony (words that suggest the opposite of their usual meaning), dramatic irony (where the reader is more aware than the character), and situational irony (where the outcome is not what the reader would expect).

VERBAL IRONY		
DRAMATIC IRONY		
SITUATIONAL IRONY		

Extended Response

14. Although Chopin's story is focused primarily on the character of Louise, there are two significant males in "The Story of an Hour." Who are they, and in what ways are they significant? Write a brief essay, using details from the text to support your ideas.

15. It seems that Josephine and Richards are very much aware of Louise's "heart trouble." Is Chopin using this description of a physical disease in a somewhat ironic manner? Use details from "The Story of an Hour," and, in a short essay, express an opinion about what the use of the term "heart trouble" may imply.

Oral Response

16. Go back to question 1, 6, 8, 11, or 13 or one assigned by your teacher, and take five to ten minutes to expand your answer and prepare an oral response. Find additional details in the story that will support your points. You may wish to write down some notes to guide you.

Rubric for Evaluating Extended Responses

0	1	2	3	4
Blank paper Foreign language Illegible, incoherent Not enough content to score	Incorrect purpose, mode, audience Brief, vague Unelaborated Rambling Lack of language control Poor organization	Correct purpose, mode, audience Some elaboration Some details Gaps in organization Limited language control	Correct purpose, mode, audience Moderately well elaborated Clear, effective language Organized (perhaps with brief digressions)	Correct purpose, mode, audience Effective elaboration Consistent organization Sense of completeness, fluency

"April Showers" by Edith Wharton

Open-Book Test

Multiple Choice and Short Answer

Write your answers to all questions in this section on the lines provided.
For multiple-choice questions, circle the letter of the best answer.

1. What can the reader expect to find out during a story's exposition? Quote the information from the Literary Analysis section of your textbook that gives the answer.

    _____

    _____

    _____

2. What was Theodora thinking about when she chose the pen name Gladys Glyn? What makes you think so?

    _____

    _____

3. What happens at the climax of this story? How do you know this is the climax?

    _____

    _____

4. Theodora and the reader share a sense of anticipation after she takes what action?

    _____

    _____

5. When Theodora finds out why her story wasn't published, the story reaches its _____.
    a. rising action   b. resolution   c. hyperbole   d. motivation
    Explain your answer choice.

    _____

    _____

    _____

6. Who or what is Kathleen Kyd? Cite the passage from the story that supports your answer.

    _____

    _____

    _____

7. When she finds out that her novel is to be published in *Home Circle*, what is the one thing that Theodora enjoys most? Quote the lines from the story that support your answer. To organize your thoughts, complete this diagram by writing details about what happens in Theodora's life after she receives the acceptance letter.

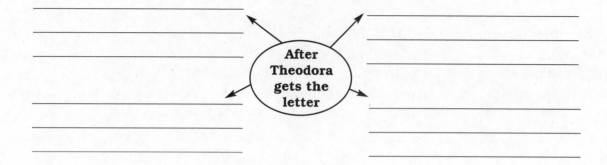

8. What does Theodora do when she believes that the *Home Circle* printed the wrong story? Support your answer with evidence from the story.

9. Explain how the denouement in this story evokes in the reader a feeling of empathy.

10. Define the word *commiseration*, and use it in a sentence of your own.

Extended Response

11. There is an old saying that "April showers bring May flowers." Roughly translated, this means that you have to experience some pain to grow or to appreciate pleasure. Write an essay explaining how this saying applies to Edith Wharton's story. What pain is presented in the story? What growth or appreciation of pleasure do you see? Use evidence from the story to support your answers.

12. Put yourself in Theodora's shoes as she is returning home from Boston on the train. How do you think she feels when she anticipates her father's reaction to what has happened? What information in the story has led you to think she would feel this way? Do you think Theodora is justified in feeling this way? Answer these questions in a brief essay. Use evidence from the story as support.

13. The events of the story make up its plot, which can be divided into the following parts: exposition, conflict, rising action, climax, resolution, and denouement. Write an essay discussing these plot elements in relation to the events of "April Showers." What is the general definition of each element? What events in the story correspond to each element?

14. Even though it is never expressly stated, the story gives the impression that "April Showers" is Theodora's first novel. Write a brief essay explaining why this is a reasonable inference. Use evidence from the story as support.

15. Although writers need self-confidence to work at a difficult craft, too much self-confidence can turn into harmful pride. Write an essay explaining how Theodora's youthful pride in "April Showers" could be considered harmful. How does her pride affect her as a writer? How does it affect those around her? Illustrate your points with examples of Theodora's prideful behavior and attitudes.

Oral Response

16. Choose question 3, 5, 7, 8, or 11 or the question your teacher assigns you. Take a few minutes to look through the story to prepare an oral response to give in class. If necessary, make notes to be clear about the order in which you want to present your answer.

Rubric for Evaluating Extended Responses

0	1	2	3	4
Blank paper Foreign language Illegible, incoherent Not enough content to score	Incorrect purpose, mode, audience Brief, vague Unelaborated Rambling Lack of language control Poor organization	Correct purpose, mode, audience Some elaboration Some details Gaps in organization Limited language control	Correct purpose, mode, audience Moderately well elaborated Clear, effective language Organized (perhaps with brief digressions)	Correct purpose, mode, audience Effective elaboration Consistent organization Sense of completeness, fluency

"Douglass" and **"We Wear the Mask"** by Paul Laurence Dunbar

Open-Book Test

Multiple Choice and Short Answer

Write your answers to all questions in this section on the lines provided.
For multiple-choice questions, circle the letter of the best answer.

1. Dunbar addresses Frederick Douglass in the poem, "Douglass," and begins by saying that the current difficult times are "Such days as thou, not even thou didst know." Since Douglass endured the early part of his life as a slave, what message is Dunbar trying to send to his readers? Use the poem and the background information to help you answer this question.

   _____

   _____

2. Based on your reading of the following line, what can you assume might be one possible purpose that Dunbar had in writing "Douglass"?
   > And all the country heard thee [Douglass] with amaze.

   _____

   _____

3. There is a distinctive use of imagery in "Douglass." Which line provides the reader with the first clear hint of the poem's dominant mental picture? Select the correct answer; then provide an additional line from the poem that adds to this image.
   a. "Ah, Douglass, we have fall'n on evil days"
   b. "When thee, the eyes of that harsh long ago"
   c. "And all the country heard thee with amaze"
   d. "Not ended then, the passionate ebb and flow"

   _____

   _____

4. Reread Dunbar's poem, "Douglass," and concentrate on the main visual images of the poem. Provide several words or phrases that support this imagery, including the vehicle that would be used for safe travel.

   _____

   _____

5. Dunbar writes: "We ride amid a tempest of dispraise." What does the word "tempest" mean? Choose the correct answer. Translate the sentence to show which type of hardship is being endured.
   a. ship   b. storm   c. impoverishment   d. hunger

   _____

   _____

6. Rhyme is a feature of both "Douglass" and "We Wear the Mask." Examine both poems, and fill in the chart below with examples of end rhyme contained in both poems. The first set is provided as an illustration.

TRUE OR END RHYMES	
"DOUGLASS"	**"WE WEAR THE MASK"**
1. days, ways, amaze, dispraise	5.
2.	6.
3.	7.
4.	8.

7. The basic message of "We Wear the Mask" is that people camouflage their feelings to hide them from others. Which feelings are being hidden? Select the best answer; then name the group that is represented by the use of "we."
   a. envy towards others   b. embarrassment   c. despair   d. superiority

8. In "We Wear the Mask," Dunbar suggests that the mask shows happiness. Cite three examples from the poem that support this statement.

   _____

9. In "We Wear the Mask," Dunbar writes: "This debt we pay to human guile." What does the word *guile* mean? Choose the correct answer. Explain what he means by a "debt" in this context.
   a. guilt   b. need   c. posterity   d. craftiness

   _____

   _____

   _____

10. In "Douglass," Dunbar suggests that the struggle for racial equality is not over. Find and write down the lines in the poem that convey this belief.

   _____

   _____

Extended Response

11. In "Douglass," Dunbar's use of imagery suggests a particular type of voyage that African Americans are undertaking. Make a list of words or phrases from the poem that support that imagery and help to draw a more detailed mental picture for the reader. Write a paragraph describing that picture in your own words.

12. In addition to using imagery in "Douglass" that depicts a voyage, Dunbar describes the difficult conditions of that voyage in colorful language. In a brief essay, use phrases from the poem, and describe the ways in which they can be an analogy for the difficulties of African Americans during Dunbar's time. Use background information from the poem to assist you.

13. The poem "Douglass" is addressed to the famous abolitionist; the poem "We Wear the Mask" is addressed to Jesus Christ. Using specific phrases from each poem, construct two paragraphs in which you discuss the kind of help that is being requested from these sources, and how appealing to them adds to the power of his poems.

14. Dunbar clearly reveres Frederick Douglass's work and life. How does the poem "Douglass" honor many attributes of the abolitionist? Use at least four specific details from the poem to discuss which of Douglass's characteristics Dunbar values. You may wish to reread the background information about Frederick Douglass, in order to refresh your knowledge about his life.

15. Dunbar writes in "We Wear the Mask" that the world does not need to be "overwise" to the feelings and thoughts he is discussing. Think about the times during which he is writing. If you need to, refer to the background information in the textbook. In a short essay, discuss the conclusions that a reader can draw about why Dunbar wants other people to be less than "overwise."

Oral Response

16. Go back to question 1, 4, 13, 14, or 15 or one assigned by your teacher, and take five to ten minutes to expand your answer and prepare an oral response. Find additional details in the poems that will support your points. You may wish to write down some notes to guide you.

Rubric for Evaluating Extended Responses

0	1	2	3	4
Blank paper Foreign language Illegible, incoherent Not enough content to score	Incorrect purpose, mode, audience Brief, vague Unelaborated Rambling Lack of language control Poor organization	Correct purpose, mode, audience Some elaboration Some details Gaps in organization Limited language control	Correct purpose, mode, audience Moderately well elaborated Clear, effective language Organized (perhaps with brief digressions)	Correct purpose, mode, audience Effective elaboration Consistent organization Sense of completeness, fluency

"Luke Havergal" and **"Richard Cory"** by Edwin Arlington Robinson
"Lucinda Matlock" and **"Richard Bone"** by Edgar Lee Masters

Open-Book Test

Multiple Choice and Short Answer

Write your answers to all questions in this section on the lines provided.
For multiple-choice questions, circle the letter of the best answer.

1. Reread the first stanza of "Luke Havergal." In it, Robinson refers to "her" and "she." To whom is he probably referring? Select the correct answer, then write a line from the poem to support your choice.
    a. the sun, whom he refers to as a female
    b. the moon, whom he refers to as a female
    c. his lover, who has died
    d. his sister, who is waiting for him near the western gate

    _____

    _____

2. Although it may be difficult to determine the exact identity of the speaker in "Luke Havergal," there are several clues in the poem that suggest it. What is the most likely identity of the speaker who recommends what Luke should do next, and which line or lines imply who it might be?

    _____

    _____

3. As one reads "Richard Cory," in addition to being surprised by the ending, the reader might feel that Robinson is offering a particular moral or philosophical message. On the lines below, explain what Robinson's message might be.

    _____

    _____

4. Reread the first stanza of "Richard Cory." The poem's subject is "clean favored, and imperially slim." What is the meaning of the word *imperially*? Choose the correct answer; then provide the context clues that suggest the meaning of the word.
    a. unusually   b. unhealthily   c. genetically   d. majestically

    _____

5. Cite two lines from "Richard Cory" that suggest that the speaker of the poem admired Richard Cory's character and manners.

    _____

    _____

6. In "Lucinda Matlock," the speaker uses much of the poem to express a particular attitude towards her life. In addition, she also uses the poem to pass on a cautionary message. What is her attitude, and what is her message?

_____

_____

_____

7. Masters has Lucinda Matlock say:
   > At ninety-six I had lived enough, that is all
   > And passed to a sweet repose.

   What is the meaning of "repose"? Select the answer. Explain the meaning of the word in the context of this poem.
   a. state of resting
   b. garden
   c. place away from her home
   d. place for older people

_____

8. Consider that the poem, "Lucinda Matlock," is supposed to represent an epitaph for this character (see background information in the textbook). What is the most important information about Lucinda that one might put into use as a philosophy of life? Cite a line from the poem to answer this question.

_____

_____

9. As the poem's speaker, Richard Bone describes his life and his occupation. What is his occupation? Select the correct answer, and explain who comes to him for assistance.
   a. He is a pastor and sometimes has to deliver eulogies.
   b. He is a funeral director.
   c. He is a stonemason who chisels tombstones.
   d. He is the town historian and often interviews people.

_____

_____

10. In "Richard Bone," the speaker says the following:
    > When I first came to Spoon River
    > I did not know whether what they told me
    > Was true or false.

    Why was he unable to discern the truth of the information given to him? How did this situation change?

_____

_____

Extended Response

11. There are several possible interpretations of the action that the speaker in "Luke Havergal" suggests to Luke. Select one, and, in a short essay, support your choice with details from the poem.

12. For much of "Richard Cory," the speaker wants certain things for himself and others that they do not possess. Summarize some of the speaker's desires in a few paragraphs, using details from the poem.

13. Select a character from one of the two Masters poems. Complete the following diagram by filling in thoughts and feelings he or she may have had during his or her lifetime. Use details from one of the two poems to support your information.

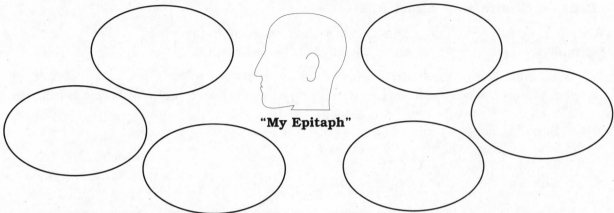

"My Epitaph"

14. Reread the last stanza of "Richard Bone." He acknowledges that "I . . . made myself party to the false chronicles." In the rest of the stanza, do you agree with his picture of the work of a historian? Write a short essay that discusses writing "without knowing the truth" or being "influenced to hide it." Use details from the poem, and your personal knowledge of history, to analyze whether he is correct about how historians act.

15. Choose the person or speaker whom you find most interesting among these four poems. Write a short essay about him or her, and explain why you find the character intriguing. Use evidence from the poem you have selected to support that this person is a character worth discovering.

Oral Response

16. Go back to question 2, 5, 8, 11, or 13 or one assigned by your teacher, and take five to ten minutes to expand your answer and prepare an oral response. Find additional details in the poems that will support your points. You may wish to write down some notes to guide you.

Rubric for Evaluating Extended Responses

0	1	2	3	4
Blank paper Foreign language Illegible, incoherent Not enough content to score	Incorrect purpose, mode, audience Brief, vague Unelaborated Rambling Lack of language control Poor organization	Correct purpose, mode, audience Some elaboration Some details Gaps in organization Limited language control	Correct purpose, mode, audience Moderately well elaborated Clear, effective language Organized (perhaps with brief digressions)	Correct purpose, mode, audience Effective elaboration Consistent organization Sense of completeness, fluency

"A Wagner Matinée" by Willa Cather

Open-Book Test

Multiple Choice and Short Answer

Write your answers to all questions in this section on the lines provided.
For multiple-choice questions, circle the letter of the best answer.

1. What initial impression does the reader receive from the nephew's description of Aunt Georgiana? Choose the correct answer. Support your answer choice with details from the story.
   a. She is a pleasant person with an excellent disposition.
   b. She is someone her nephew is excited to see again.
   c. She brings back wonderful memories for her nephew.
   d. She is a sad and not very presentable individual.

2. What can the reader infer about Aunt Georgiana's feelings about the life she left in Boston, judging from the description of her life in Nebraska? Use a detail or two from the page to support your opinion.

3. The narrator mentions his "reverential affection" for his aunt. What does the word *reverential* mean? Select the correct answer; then cite the phrase from the story that supports your choice.
   a. relevant and important   c. caused by a deep feeling of love or respect
   b. complicated by other emotions   d. shy and hesitant

4. In "A Wagner Matinée," Aunt Georgiana's nephew, Clark, offers a current picture of his aunt, along with memories of her and his years growing up. What impression might the reader receive if Cather had revealed information that concerned only the present time? Support your answer with a detail from the text.

5. The narrator of "A Wagner Matinée" gives an extensive description of the orchestra's appearance. What does his attention to these details tell you about his character, and about how Aunt Georgiana may have contributed to his development?

6. Clark takes great pains to mention the ways in which his Aunt sustained him during his years on the Nebraska farm. In the chart below, list some of his more difficult moments on the farm, along with the memories that helped him to survive emotionally.

PAINFUL MEMORIES	PLEASANT MEMORIES
1.	1.
2.	2.
3.	3.
4.	4.

7. What is the overall impression the reader gets from Clark's portrayal of the women who attend the concert? Cite a quotation from the page that supports your answer choice.
   a. They seem as though they are part of a large picture, rather than being individuals with unique qualities.
   b. They are unable to keep themselves quiet during the concert.
   c. They are dressed for work and have taken an afternoon break to enjoy the concert.
   d. They are people whom Aunt Georgiana hopes she will get to know better.

   _____

   _____

8. In the paragraph that begins with "The first number was . . . ," Clark makes a reference to breaking the "silence" of the last thirty years. Using words from the paragraph, explain the connotation of the word *silence* in the context of Aunt Georgiana's life.

   _____

   _____

9. Clark describes his aunt as appearing somewhat "inert" as they arrive at the concert. Select the correct meaning of the word. Provide the context clues from the sentence containing "inert," and from the sentence in the previous paragraph, that suggest the meaning of the word.
   a. afraid   b. motionless   c. angry   d. focused

   _____

   _____

10. Reread the paragraph that begins, "The second half of the program consisted of. . . . " Clark experiences a sense of confusion, wondering how his aunt is responding to the music she has just heard. What is the source of his confusion? Cite a detail to support your response.

   _____

   _____

Extended Response

11. Clark refers to the many ways in which his Aunt Georgiana has used her hands during her difficult years on the farm. Write a few paragraphs about the physical life she has led including examples of her use of her hands for work or other purposes.

12. As Clark spends time with his aunt, he recalls details of his own life on the farm. What impression does he give to the reader about his time there? Write a short reflective essay as though you are Clark, reminiscing about your earlier years. Use details from the text to strengthen your descriptions, and write about your feelings as a young boy.

13. In "A Wagner Matinée," Clark is trying to repay his Aunt Georgiana for her many years of kindness to him. He believes he is giving her a meaningful gift by taking her to a concert. In a few paragraphs, discuss whether his gift is appropriate. In your essay, consider Aunt Georgiana's state of mind at the beginning and end of the story.

14. Unlike some of her other writings, in this story Cather explores the more painful parts of life on the frontier. In a short essay, explore how those aspects might be alleviated. What judgment might Cather be making about those who went westward as early pioneers? Use one or more details from the text to support your opinion.

15. In reflecting upon Clark's apparent love for music as a young boy, Aunt Georgiana cautions, "Don't love it so well, Clark, or it may be taken from you." In a short essay, explain how music is used as an analogy in the story. Use story details to explain how music represents other aspects of life.

Oral Response

16. Go back to question 5, 7, 8, 14, or 15 or one assigned by your teacher, and take five to ten minutes to expand your answer and prepare an oral response. Find additional details in the story that will support your points. You may wish to write down some notes to guide you.

Rubric for Evaluating Extended Responses

0	1	2	3	4
Blank paper Foreign language Illegible, incoherent Not enough content to score	Incorrect purpose, mode, audience Brief, vague Unelaborated Rambling Lack of language control Poor organization	Correct purpose, mode, audience Some elaboration Some details Gaps in organization Limited language control	Correct purpose, mode, audience Moderately well elaborated Clear, effective language Organized (perhaps with brief digressions)	Correct purpose, mode, audience Effective elaboration Consistent organization Sense of completeness, fluency

"The Love Song of J. Alfred Prufrock" by T. S. Eliot

Open-Book Test

Multiple Choice and Short Answer

Write your answers to all questions in this section on the lines provided.
For multiple-choice questions, circle the letter of the best answer.

1. "The Love Song of J. Alfred Prufrock" is written in the form of a dramatic monologue. What does this tell you about the speaker in the poem? Cite a line from the poem that provides a clue to the form, and explain what the clue is.

   _____

   _____

2. How would you describe the setting of this poem? Cite evidence from the poem as support. To organize your thoughts, complete this chart. In the first column, write clues about the setting. In the second column, write what the clues reveal about the setting.

	CLUES	WHAT CLUES REVEAL
1		
2		
3		

   _____

   _____

3. At the beginning of the poem, how would you describe the mood of the evening? What descriptive words and phrases create this feeling?

   _____

   _____

4. In a dramatic monologue, whom does the speaker address?

   _____

   _____

5. Which musical devices are used in the following lines from "The Love Song of J. Alfred Prufrock"?

   > There will be time, there will be time / To prepare a face to meet the faces that you meet . . .

   Explain how each device contributes to the musicality of the poem.

   _____

   _____

   _____

6. Cite two or three lines from "The Love Song of J. Alfred Prufrock" and explain how musical devices are used. Indicate why you think these devices are, or are not, effective.

    _____

    _____

    _____

7. When Prufrock says: "I have seen the moment of my greatness flicker . . . And, in short I was afraid." What do you think he is afraid of? Explain.

    _____

    _____

8. What best describes the theme of the poem?
    a. the satisfaction of a life well-lived
    b. fear about growing old and uncertainty about expressing love
    c. excitement about new possibilities
    d. regret for hurting someone else

    Cite a line from the poem to support your answer choice.

    _____

    _____

9. Identify how alliteration is used in the following lines, and describe its effect.
    We have lingered in the chambers of the sea / By sea-girls wreathed in seaweed red and brown . . .

    _____

    _____

10. What do the mermaids at the end of the poem represent when Prufrock says, "I do not think that they will sing for me?" Explain.

    _____

    _____

Extended Response

11. Does Prufrock show us that expressing love is easy and uncomplicated, or difficult and confusing? Support your answer with evidence from the poem.

12. Is this poem like any other love songs that you know of? How is it different? Why do you think Eliot chose to call this poem a "love song"? How does it help you to understand and interpret the poem? Use the chart below to organize your notes.

Typical Love Song	"The Love Song of J. Alfred Prufrock"

13. How does the dramatic form of the poem help you to understand the thoughts and feelings of Prufrock the speaker? If the poem were written in another form, such as a dialogue between two people, how would that change the feeling of the poem?

_____

_____

14. In a dramatic monologue, the speaker addresses a silent listener. To whom might Prufrock be speaking in this poem? Is it someone he once loved, or another person like himself who may share his feelings? What message is the author trying to give to the reader of the poem? Use evidence from the poem in your answer.

_____

_____

15. What is Eliot, the author, trying to say about aging and love in this poem? Why would he choose the character of Prufrock to tell this story? If Prufrock is meant to represent the experiences of his generation in history, as some have said he does, do you think his outlook is typical or unusual? Do you think the feelings he describes are still shared by others today? Answer these questions in an essay.

Oral Response

16. Choose question 5, 6, 8, 9, or 12 or the question your teacher assigns you. Take a few minutes to look through the poem to prepare an oral response to give in class. If necessary, make notes to be clear about the order in which you want to present your answer.

Rubric for Evaluating Extended Responses

0	1	2	3	4
Blank paper Foreign language Illegible, incoherent Not enough content to score	Incorrect purpose, mode, audience Brief, vague Unelaborated Rambling Lack of language control Poor organization	Correct purpose, mode, audience Some elaboration Some details Gaps in organization Limited language control	Correct purpose, mode, audience Moderately well elaborated Clear, effective language Organized (perhaps with brief digressions)	Correct purpose, mode, audience Effective elaboration Consistent organization Sense of completeness, fluency

Name _____   Date _____

Imagist Poets

Open-Book Test

Multiple Choice and Short Answer

Write your answers to all questions in this section on the lines provided.
For multiple-choice questions, circle the letter of the best answer.

1. In "A Few Don'ts by an Imagiste," what does Pound warn against when writing
    descriptive verse? Include evidence to support your answer.

    _____

    _____

2. In "The River Merchant's Wife," what images does Pound use to show that the speaker
    is a child?

    _____

    _____

3. How are "petals on a wet, black bough" like transient faces in a crowd in "In a Station
    of the Metro"?

    _____

    _____

4. Why do you think Williams emphasizes color in his poem "The Red Wheelbarrow"? What
    does this emphasis do in the poem?

    _____

    _____

5. Williams never says where "The Great Figure" is going as it moves through the city. How
    can you tell—from the words Williams uses?

    _____

    _____

6. In "This Is Just to Say," Williams suggests that the speaker is sorry but couldn't resist
    the plums. What words add to this feeling? How?

    _____

    _____

7. In "Pear Tree," H. D. presents the tree as something almost unreal. What words create this impression?

   a. flower-tufts thick on the branch

   b. silver dust lifted from the earth

   c. so staunch a white leaf

   d. bring summer and ripe fruits

   Explain your answer choice.

   _____

   _____

8. In "Heat," what does H. D. suggest will happen after the wind has "cut apart the heat"?

   _____

   _____

9. What kinds of things does William Carlos Williams write about in his poems? Explain your answer choice.

   a. biblical themes   c. complex ideas

   b. ordinary things   d. abstract images

   _____

   _____

10. In "A Few Don'ts by an Imagiste," what does Ezra Pound say about the use of rhyme in poetry? Cite a relevant passage to support your answer.

   _____

   _____

Extended Response

11. When appealing to the senses, what techniques does Williams use? Name some of the five senses, and provide examples of wording and images in his poems to support your answer. Use the following chart to organize your notes.

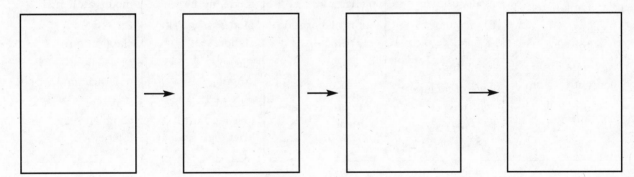

12. For Ezra Pound, an "image" in well-written verse is more than just a picture. How are they different? What does Pound say are the differences? What makes an "image" in verse unique? What can verse express that a picture cannot? Answer these questions in an essay. Cite passages from the text to support your answer.

13. In "The River–Merchant's Wife," what concrete images does the author present to mark the passage of time and changes in the woman's feelings toward her husband? Cite examples to support your answer.

14. In one line, Ezra Pound captures all the activity in a busy, crowded subway station in "In a Station of the Metro." If you had to rewrite "The River–Merchant's Wife" and reduce it from six stanzas to one, what key elements and images would you include to capture all the feelings there? Write a brief essay in which you explain your choices.

15. Wílliam Carlos Williams once said that the goal of Imagism was to create a "divergence from the old" styles of poetry that came before it. It focuses on vivid and sensual descriptions of common objects and things. In an essay, explain whether you think this style is useful for writing about all subjects equally or believe it is better for some things and not others. What would Pound say? Do you agree? Give some examples to support your answer.

Oral Response

16. Choose question 3, 4, 6, 11, or 15 or the question your teacher assigns you. Take a few minutes to look through the poems to prepare an oral response to give in class. If necessary, make notes to be clear about the order in which you want to present your answer.

Rubric for Evaluating Extended Responses

0	1	2	3	4
Blank paper Foreign language Illegible, incoherent Not enough content to score	Incorrect purpose, mode, audience Brief, vague Unelaborated Rambling Lack of language control Poor organization	Correct purpose, mode, audience Some elaboration Some details Gaps in organization Limited language control	Correct purpose, mode, audience Moderately well elaborated Clear, effective language Organized (perhaps with brief digressions)	Correct purpose, mode, audience Effective elaboration Consistent organization Sense of completeness, fluency

Name _____ Date _____

Open-Book Test

Multiple Choice and Short Answer

Write your answers to all questions in this section on the lines provided.
For multiple-choice questions, circle the letter of the best answer.

1. At the beginning of "Winter Dreams," what is Dexter's dream accomplishment? How does it compare to the reality of his summer job?

    _____

    _____

2. Why does Dexter decide that he no longer wants to be a caddy?

    a. he has a better job offer   c. he's afraid of Judy Jones' nurse

    b. he's going away to college   d. he realizes his dream is not coming true

    Cite a detail from the story to support your answer choice.

    _____

    _____

3. As a teenager, why is Dexter particularly fond of the fall? Find the passage in the story that explains this, and include it in your answer. Before you write your answer, organize your thoughts in the cluster diagram by writing words and phrases describing Dexter's reaction to the fall.

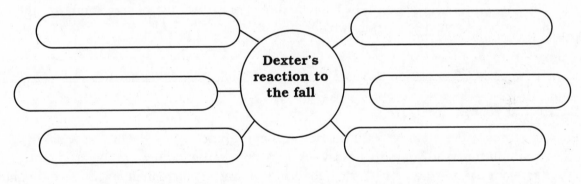

    _____

    _____

4. When she is a young woman, the most important person to Judy Jones is herself. Cite an example from the story to prove this statement.

    _____

    _____

5. When Dexter starts to make money, does he seem surprised or not surprised? To what does he attribute his success?

    _____

    _____

6. At the end of part II, Dexter meets Judy Jones again. The author says, " . . . for the second time, her casual whim gave a new direction to his life." What effect does she have on Dexter and his choices in life? Support your answer with evidence from the story.

   _____

   _____

7. How does Fitzgerald portray Judy as a young woman? We know that Dexter thinks she's beautiful, but what else do we know about her?

   a. She is shy and nervous.

   b. She is considerate and generous.

   c. She is manipulative and desirable.

   d. She is lonely and scared.

   Cite a detail from the story to support your answer choice.

   _____

   _____

8. When Judy asks Dexter to marry her, why doesn't he tell her that he is already engaged to Irene? What does he think will happen if he tells her the truth?

   _____

   _____

9. Why does Dexter Green quit seeing Irene Scheerer? Cite a passage from the story that supports your answer.

   _____

   _____

10. What would a *pugilistic* youth be likely to do? After answering this question, use the word *pugilistic* in a sentence of your own.

    _____

    _____

Extended Response

11. We get many descriptions of Judy's physical appearance, but none of Dexter's. Why do you think this is so? In a brief essay, explain why you think Fitzgerald chose to present them differently. What is he saying about the character's personalities, and what might the author be revealing about his view of relations between men and women?

12. An obsession is a thought, idea, or feeling that fills a person's mind and cannot be driven out. It is often concerned with an unreasonable idea or goal. Some obsessions, such as a drive to succeed in a certain sport or field of study, can be productive and lead to positive results. Other obsessions, such as a preoccupation with an unattainable goal, can lead to very negative results. Consider the obsession Dexter has with Judy and the things she represents. What eventual effect does this obsession have on Dexter's life? Write an essay answering this question. Cite evidence from the story as support.

13. At the end of the story, Dexter learns that Judy may no longer be the beauty she once was. In an essay, explain why Dexter seems upset and depressed. Why is the thought of her changing so troubling to him? What might her beauty mean to Dexter, or to the author?

14. The theme of "Winter Dreams" can be seen as this: Those whose lives are based on the pursuit of illusions are doomed to disappointment. Write a brief essay in which you support this statement. Use evidence from the story as support.

15. At the end of the story, Dexter says, "long ago there was something in me, but now that thing is gone . . ." What thing does he mean? What does this ending suggest about the theme of "Winter Dreams"? Answer these questions in an essay. Use evidence from the story to support your answer.

Oral Response

16. Choose question 2, 3, 4, 9, or 15 or the question your teacher assigns you. Take a few minutes to look through the story to prepare an oral response to give in class. If necessary, make notes to be clear about the order in which you want to present your answer.

Rubric for Evaluating Extended Responses

0	1	2	3	4
Blank paper Foreign language Illegible, incoherent Not enough content to score	Incorrect purpose, mode, audience Brief, vague Unelaborated Rambling Lack of language control Poor organization	Correct purpose, mode, audience Some elaboration Some details Gaps in organization Limited language control	Correct purpose, mode, audience Moderately well elaborated Clear, effective language Organized (perhaps with brief digressions)	Correct purpose, mode, audience Effective elaboration Consistent organization Sense of completeness, fluency

"The Turtle" from ***The Grapes of Wrath*** by John Steinbeck

Open-Book Test

Multiple Choice and Short Answer

Write your answers to all questions in this section on the lines provided.
For multiple-choice questions, circle the letter of the best answer.

1. What did the turtle carry across the road? Quote the passage that supports your answer.

   _____

   _____

2. How does this seemingly small event described in this selection relate to the larger struggles of the Great Depression?

   _____

   _____

3. The persevering turtle is an instrument in a cycle of nature. Cite lines in the first paragraph of the story that explain the cycle.

   _____

   _____

4. How does the following excerpt relate to the theme of the story? Explain the larger implications of this quotation.

   > "And as the turtle crawled on down the embankment, its shell dragged dirt over the seeds."

   _____

   _____

5. Why did the sedan driver swerve when she saw the turtle? Cite the passage that supports your answer.

   _____

   _____

6. What do the wild oats represent?

   _____

   _____

7. How are the obstacles faced by the turtle a good preview of a novel in which the characters are faced with an economic depression and the Dust Bowl conditions of the Southwest in the 1930s?

   _____

   _____

8. What is a tiddly–wink, and why is it a good description of the turtle flying through the air?

   _____

   _____

9. From the phrase, "and the grass heads were heavy with oat beards to catch on a dog's coat, and foxtails to tangle in a horse's fetlocks," you can figure out that a fetlock has something to do with _____. Write a word or phrase that would complete the sentence correctly, and explain your answer.

10. Define the word *protruded*, and use it in a sentence of your own. Then complete this cluster diagram by writing synonyms of the word *protruded* in the ovals.

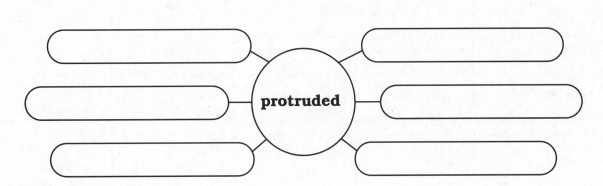

Extended Response

11. To anthropomorphize means to give human form or personality to things that are not human. Write an essay in which you show how Steinbeck anthropomorphizes the turtle. What human characteristics does he give the turtle? What effect does such humanizing have on the reader?

12. The setting of this story could be described as dry. Find evidence in the story to support this statement. Write a brief essay in which you describe the setting more fully.

13. The novels and stories of John Steinbeck often have characters who face hardships. Decide whether "The Turtle" is an example of such a story. Write an essay explaining your position. How would you characterize the events of the turtle's life in the story? Does it matter that the turtle is not human? Support your position with details from the story.

14. Steinbeck describes how the head of wild oats is carried across the highway and finally planted in the ground on the other side. What theme do you think the head of wild oats might represent? Write a brief essay answering this question. Use passages in the story as support.

15. Although this selection from *The Grapes of Wrath* is entitled "The Turtle," it might just as appropriately have been called "The Seeds." Write an essay in which you agree or disagree with this statement. What is the relationship between the turtle and the seeds in the story? What do the seeds represent? Include evidence to support your opinion.

Oral Response

16. Choose question 4, 6, 7, 11, or 13 or the question your teacher assigns you. Take a few minutes to look through the story to prepare an oral response to give in class. If necessary, make notes to be clear about the order in which you want to present your answer.

Rubric for Evaluating Extended Responses

0	1	2	3	4
Blank paper Foreign language Illegible, incoherent Not enough content to score	Incorrect purpose, mode, audience Brief, vague Unelaborated Rambling Lack of language control Poor organization	Correct purpose, mode, audience Some elaboration Some details Gaps in organization Limited language control	Correct purpose, mode, audience Moderately well elaborated Clear, effective language Organized (perhaps with brief digressions)	Correct purpose, mode, audience Effective elaboration Consistent organization Sense of completeness, fluency

126 Open-Book Test

© Prentice-Hall, Inc.

"anyone lived in a pretty how town" and **"old age sticks"**
by E. E. Cummings
"The Unknown Citizen" by W. H. Auden

Open-Book Test

Multiple Choice and Short Answer

Write your answers to all questions in this section on the lines provided.
For multiple-choice questions, circle the letter of the best answer.

1. Reread line 2 of "anyone lived in a pretty how town." Why does Cummings alter normal word order in this line? Give a brief explanation of your answer choice.
    a. to convey a sense of social optimism
    b. to emphasize the number of church bells
    c. to reflect the breakdown of the social order
    d. to imitate the motion of bells ringing

    _____

    _____

2. Identify the theme of "anyone lived in a pretty how town." Cite proof from the poem as support.

    _____

    _____

3. Reread line 7 in "anyone lived in a pretty how town." What group is Cummings satirizing in this line? Use evidence from the poem to support your answer.

    _____

    _____

4. Why does Cummings break the word "growing" in the last two lines of "old age sticks"? Give a brief explanation.
    a. to imitate the faltering speech of old people
    b. to emphasize the grumbly nature of old people
    c. to preserve the sticklike shape of the poem
    d. to emphasize the gradual nature of aging

    _____

    _____

5. What is the theme of "old age sticks"? Cite evidence from the poem as support for your answer.

    _____

    _____

6. What are the youth doing in the last stanza in "old age sticks?"

    _____

    _____

7. In "The Unknown Citizen," Auden directs his satire against what he sees as too great an emphasis on _____.
    a. independence and freedom   c. creativity and initiative
    b. obedience and conformity   d. originality and eccentricity
    Explain your answer choice.

    _____

    _____

8. In "The Unknown Citizen," what does Auden suggest modern society is doing to people? Provide evidence from the poem to support your answer.

    _____

    _____

9. Which passage from "The Unknown Citizen" is the clearest example of satirical writing? Explain your answer choice.
    a. lines 6–7   c. lines 22–23
    b. line 17   d. lines 25

    _____

    _____

10. What does the word *statistics* mean? After defining the word, use it in a sentence of your own.

    _____

    _____

    _____

Extended Response

11. In "The Unknown Citizen," Auden implies that the society treats the citizen as just another statistic. How do you think the citizen would feel about being treated this way? How might he want to be treated instead? Write an essay in which you answer these questions. To organize your thoughts, complete this chart. In column 1, list details showing how the citizen is being treated at different times of his life. In column 2, list details showing how he would probably prefer to be treated.

How the Citizen is Being Treated	How He Would Probably Like to Be Treated

12. In "The Unknown Citizen," what is Auden's attitude toward the modern version or sense of the word *saint*? Do you think Auden would want to meet such a person? What do you

think he might say to such a person if he ever met one? Answer these questions in a brief essay. Cite evidence from the poem to support your points.

13. Poets, through their poems, sometimes reveal their personal concerns about the nature of society. This tells the reader something about the poet—his or her likes, dislikes, beliefs, fears, and hopes. A reader of "The Unknown Citizen" can form a reasonably accurate picture of what the poet dislikes and, by inference, what he admires. Write an essay in which you speculate on the kind of person and the kind of society that Auden respects. Support your opinion with evidence from the poem.

14. In "anyone lived in a pretty how town," Cummings uses lowercase letters to refer to the subject of the poem, a person apparently named anyone. He also describes the women and men in the town as being "(both little and small)." What do these details tell you about Cummings's attitude toward the people he describes in his poem? Write a brief essay in which you answer this question. Support your answer with details from the poem.

15. It has been said that in "anyone lived in a pretty how town," E. E. Cummings focuses on the eternal rhythms of life, the seasons of nature, and the cycle of human rituals that are universally connected with childhood, adulthood, and death. In an essay, discuss Cummings's focus. What elements in the poem support this statement about his focus?

Oral Response

16. Choose question 2, 4, 5, 8, or 13 or the question your teacher assigns you. Take a few minutes to look through the poems to prepare an oral response to give in class. If necessary, make notes to be clear about the order in which you want to present your answer.

Rubric for Evaluating Extended Responses

0	1	2	3	4
Blank paper Foreign language Illegible, incoherent Not enough content to score	Incorrect purpose, mode, audience Brief, vague Unelaborated Rambling Lack of language control Poor organization	Correct purpose, mode, audience Some elaboration Some details Gaps in organization Limited language control	Correct purpose, mode, audience Moderately well elaborated Clear, effective language Organized (perhaps with brief digressions)	Correct purpose, mode, audience Effective elaboration Consistent organization Sense of completeness, fluency

"The Far and the Near" by Thomas Wolfe

Open-Book Test

Multiple Choice and Short Answer

Write your answers to all questions in this section on the lines provided.
For multiple-choice questions, circle the letter of the best answer.

1. Which of the following details from the story best illustrates why the engineer feels happy when he sees the women waving? Explain your choice.
   a. "To one side of the house there was a garden . . ."
   b. "He had seen them in a thousand lights, a hundred weathers."
   c. "[H]e felt that he knew their lives completely, to every hour. . . ."
   d. "The whole place had an air of tidiness, thrift, and modest comfort."

   _____

   _____

2. Why does the engineer want to visit the cottage? Quote the passage from the story that supports your answer.

   _____

   _____

3. The women don't understand why it is important to the engineer to visit them at the end of the story. This ending is _____. Explain your answer choice.

   a. climactic   b. an epigram   c. anticlimactic   d. foreshadowing

   _____

   _____

4. The vision of the little house doesn't change despite the changes in the engineer's life. How does this make him feel? Cite a detail from the story to support your answer.

   _____

   _____

5. Briefly describe the theme of the story.

   _____

   _____

6. When the engineer walks into the streets of the town, what causes his bewilderment? Cite a detail from the story to support your answer.

   _____

   _____

7. Reread the last paragraph of the story. What effect do you think Wolfe is striving for by giving the story this anticlimax—surprise, shock, insight, or laughter? Explain your answer. To organize your thoughts, complete this cluster diagram. In the ovals, write words and phrases from the story that support the effect Wolfe is trying to accomplish.

_____

_____

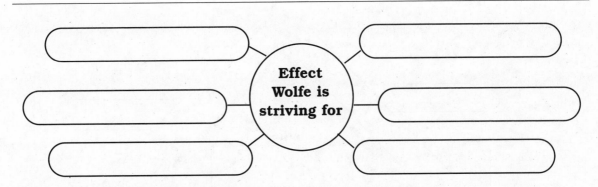

8. Which of the following sentences best explains the meaning of the last paragraph of the story? Give a brief explanation of your answer choice.
   a. The woman's house looked tidy from a distance, but close up, it appears to be run-down and neglected.
   b. The engineer's heart was strong, but now that he is old, it has become weak and sick.
   c. The world that was so near to the engineer geographically turned out to be very far from him personally.
   d. The engineer used to think that the women were nice, but now he has discovered that they are terrible and mean.

_____

_____

9. Explain why the engineer's expectations of the women and their cottages are bound to be disappointing. Cite evidence from the story as support for your answer.

_____

_____

10. If an animal had a very _timorous_ manner, how would it act? Define the word and explain your answer.

_____

_____

Extended Response

11. In an essay, interpret the engineer's feelings and explain why he might have found the women and the house "beautiful and enduring." Use details from the story to explain why they were so important to him.

12. Why does the little house give the engineer such "extraordinary happiness"? Explain your answer in an essay. Use passages from the story to support your points.

13. When the climax of a story is unexpectedly disappointing, ridiculous, or trivial, it is called an anticlimax. In an essay, discuss how the ending of "The Far and the Near" is anticlimactic; include details from the story. To organize your thoughts, complete this story map.

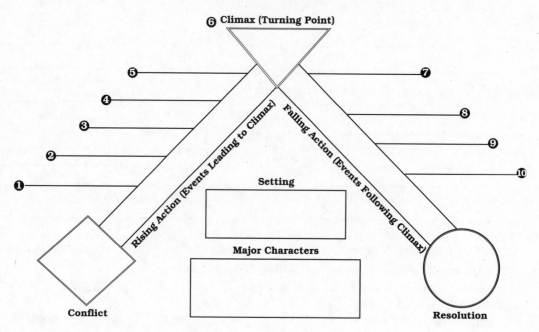

14. In a brief essay, explain the theme of "The Far and the Near". Use details from the story to support your answer.

15. In Wolfe's "The Far and the Near," the railroad engineer realizes, after his retirement, that he is unable to recapture the past. Write an essay in which you interpret the engineer's state of mind at the end of the story. Why does he feel "confusion, doubt and hopelessness"? What has changed for him?

Oral Response

16. Choose question 2, 3, 4, 9, or 14 or the question your teacher assigns you. Take a few minutes to look through the story to prepare an oral response to give in class. If necessary, make notes to be clear about the order in which you want to present your answer.

Rubric for Evaluating Extended Responses

0	1	2	3	4
Blank paper Foreign language Illegible, incoherent Not enough content to score	Incorrect purpose, mode, audience Brief, vague Unelaborated Rambling Lack of language control Poor organization	Correct purpose, mode, audience Some elaboration Some details Gaps in organization Limited language control	Correct purpose, mode, audience Moderately well elaborated Clear, effective language Organized (perhaps with brief digressions)	Correct purpose, mode, audience Effective elaboration Consistent organization Sense of completeness, fluency

"Of Modern Poetry" and **"Anecdote of the Jar"** by Wallace Stevens
"Ars Poetica" by Archibald MacLeish
"Poetry" by Marianne Moore

Open-Book Test

Multiple Choice and Short Answer

Write your answers to all questions in this section on the lines provided.
For multiple-choice questions, circle the letter of the best answer.

1. What is the theme of "Of Modern Poetry"? Cite passages from the poem to support your answer.

    _____

    _____

2. In "Anecdote of the Jar," what does the jar symbolize? Explain your answer.
    a. the ambivalence that many people feel toward the wilderness
    b. the order that nature imposes on herself
    c. the carelessness of humans in dealing with nature
    d. the power that human civilization holds over nature

    _____

    _____

3. The following excerpt is a _____. Explain your answer.
    "A poem should be wordless / As the flight of birds."

    a. climax   b. simile   c. legend   d. paradox

    _____

    _____

4. Does the theme of "Ars Poetica" suggest that a poem should appeal more to the senses or more to the intellect? Cite evidence from the poem to support your answer.

    _____

    _____

5. Cite a simile from "Ars Poetica" that appeals primarily to the sense of sight. Give a brief explanation of your answer.

    _____

    _____

6. Cite an example of concreteness in "Ars Poetica." Give a brief explanation.

    _____

    _____

7. What does Moore suggest about poetry by the line "imaginary gardens with real toads in them"? Explain your answer.

8. Reread lines 2–3 of "Poetry," beginning with "Reading it, however . . ." and ending with "geniune," and paraphrase what Moore is saying in these lines.

9. Reread lines 15–17 of "Poetry," beginning with "nor is it valid" and ending with "schoolbooks." Paraphrase these lines.

10. Define the word *slovenly*, and use it in a sentence of your own.

Extended Response

11. Poems are sometimes remembered for an unforgettable line or image. Marianne Moore's "Poetry," for example, contains the often quoted portrayal of good poetry: "imaginary gardens with real toads in them." Write an essay in which you identify and discuss memorable lines or images from at least one other poem in this grouping. Include a discussion of Moore's "imaginary gardens" image, analyzing its effectiveness. To organize your thoughts, complete this diagram. Write the name of one of the poems in the circle. On the lines, write memorable images from that poem.

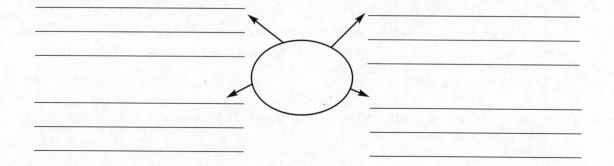

12. One of the themes of "Anecdote of the Jar" can be seen as this: Humans have the power either to enhance or to destroy the beauty of nature. Write a brief essay in which you respond to this statement. Cite evidence from the poem to support the statement.

13. In "Ars Poetica," Archibald MacLeish writes several short couplets that give examples, ultimately supporting the idea that "A poem should not mean / But be." Which do you think is more effective in making the author's point to the audience: using examples, as in "Ars Poetica," or using a more direct approach, as in Wallace Stevens's "Of Modern Poetry"? Give details from the two poems to support your choice.

14. Write an essay in which you agree or disagree with this statement: The message of "Poetry" is that poets should avoid obscuring the meaning in their poems. Cite passages from the poem to support your points.

15. Wallace Stevens wrote that poetry "touches the sense of reality, it enhances the sense of reality, heightens it, intensifies it." Yet some readers feel that Stevens's poems convey a sense of unreality. Write an essay in which you state and support your opinion on whether Stevens's "Anecdote of the Jar" touches and enhances the reader's sense of reality. Cite evidence from the poem to support your position.

Oral Response

16. Choose question 2, 4, 6, 8, or 12 or the question your teacher assigns you. Take a few minutes to look through the poems to prepare an oral response to give in class. If necessary, make notes to be clear about the order in which you want to present your answer.

Rubric for Evaluating Extended Responses

0	1	2	3	4
Blank paper Foreign language Illegible, incoherent Not enough content to score	Incorrect purpose, mode, audience Brief, vague Unelaborated Rambling Lack of language control Poor organization	Correct purpose, mode, audience Some elaboration Some details Gaps in organization Limited language control	Correct purpose, mode, audience Moderately well elaborated Clear, effective language Organized (perhaps with brief digressions)	Correct purpose, mode, audience Effective elaboration Consistent organization Sense of completeness, fluency

"In Another Country" by Ernest Hemingway
"The Corn Planting" by Sherwood Anderson
"A Worn Path" by Eudora Welty

Open-Book Test

Multiple Choice and Short Answer

Write your answers to all questions in this section on the lines provided.
For multiple-choice questions, circle the letter of the best answer.

1. Why does the narrator in "In Another Country" feel separated from the three Italian soldiers who had won medals? Quote the line from the story that proves your point.

   _____

   _____

   _____

2. Why does the major in "In Another Country" never miss a day with the machines? Explain your answer.

   _____

   _____

3. How would you describe the major's attitude toward the doctor in "In Another Country"? Cite details from the story.

   _____

   _____

   _____

4. Explain how you know that "The Corn Planting" is told from a first-person point of view.

   _____

   _____

5. Explain how you would know when a story is told from the third-person limited point of view.

   _____

   _____

6. Find a detail in "A Worn Path" that supports the interpretation that Phoenix's grandson is still alive.

   _____

   _____

   _____

7. Find a detail in "A Worn Path" that supports the interpretation that Phoenix's grandson is dead.

   _____

   _____

   _____

8. Phoenix shows cunning and resolve in her interaction with the hunter. Cite one or two examples from the story that support this statement.

_____

_____

9. In "A Worn Path," what literary technique is most instrumental in conveying Phoenix's character? Cite a detail to support your answer choice.
   a. first-person narration
   b. metaphor
   c. foreshadowing
   d. indirect characterization

_____

_____

10. Complete this Analysis Map for the word *limber*. In the box labeled "Compare to," write synonyms of the word. In the box labeled "Contrast with," write antonyms of the word. In the box labeled "Examples," write two sentences using the word.

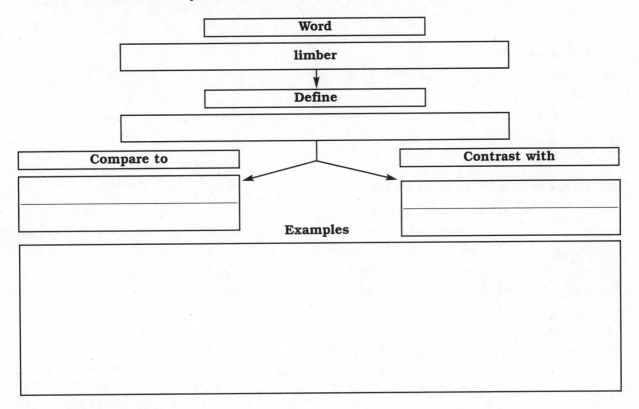

Extended Response

11. Fiction writers may reveal the nature of a character mainly through his or her involvement with other characters. Hal in "The Corn Planting" is such a character. Write an essay describing Hal's character. What can you tell about his character from his involvement in the lives of the Hutchensons? What do we know about him outside of this involvement? Support your answer with details from the story.

12. In "A Worn Path," Phoenix encounters many obstacles along the path. What can you infer about her personality based on her reactions to these obstacles? Answer this question in a brief essay. Use details from the story to support your answer.

13. Sometimes characters who are different on the surface and live quite different lives share similar outlooks and character traits. Write an essay comparing the major in "In Another Country" to Phoenix Jackson in "A Worn Path." How are their approaches to life similar? How are they different? Use examples from the stories to make your points.

14. In an essay, explain why the theme of "In Another Country" might be that life is full of loneliness and loss. Think about what each character has suffered and will suffer. How does each character's situation contribute to the theme? Include details from the story as support for your answer.

15. In stories told from a first-person point of view, the reader learns only about the narrator's experiences and thoughts. How much the reader finds out depends on how closely involved the narrator is with the events of the story. Write an essay discussing the role of the first-person narrator in "In Another Country" and in "The Corn Planting." How do the narrators of these stories differ in their involvement? Why do you think the author of each story chose to tell it using a first-person narrator? Give evidence from the stories to support your answers.

Oral Response

16. Choose question 1, 6, 7, 11, or 13 or the question your teacher assigns you. Take a few minutes to look through the stories to prepare an oral response to give in class. If necessary, make notes to be clear about the order in which you want to present your answer.

Rubric for Evaluating Extended Responses

0	1	2	3	4
Blank paper Foreign language Illegible, incoherent Not enough content to score	Incorrect purpose, mode, audience Brief, vague Unelaborated Rambling Lack of language control Poor organization	Correct purpose, mode, audience Some elaboration Some details Gaps in organization Limited language control	Correct purpose, mode, audience Moderately well elaborated Clear, effective language Organized (perhaps with brief digressions)	Correct purpose, mode, audience Effective elaboration Consistent organization Sense of completeness, fluency

Name _____ Date _____

Open-Book Test

Multiple Choice and Short Answer

Write your answers to all questions in this section on the lines provided.
For multiple-choice questions, circle the letter of the best answer.

1. Reread the first five lines of "Chicago." What is the function of the passage? Explain
    your answer.

    _____

    _____

2. "And they tell me you are crooked and I answer: Yes, it is true" is an example of

    a. alliteration   b. allusion   c. anecdote   d. apostrophe

    Explain your answer choice.

    _____

    _____

3. What does the narrator of "Chicago" mean when he says that the young man has "a
    terrible burden of destiny" and that he laughs "even as an ignorant fighter laughs who
    has never lost a battle"?

    _____

    _____

4. Which line from "Chicago" appeals to the sense of hearing? Select the correct answer, and
    give a brief explanation of your choice.
    a. "I have seen your painted women under the gas lamps"
    b. "Flinging magnetic curses amid the toil of piling job on job"
    c. "here is a tall bold slugger set vivid against the little soft cities"
    d. "under his wrist is the pulse, and under his ribs the heart of the people"

    _____

    _____

5. Complete the diagram by citing other images from the poem to which a reader would
    respond with the sense of hearing.

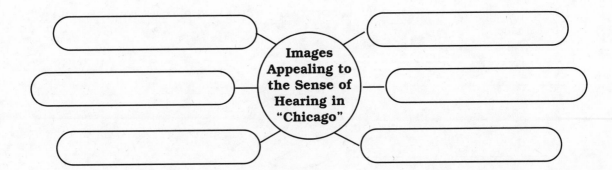

6. Which line from "Chicago" appeals to the sense of touch? Select the correct answer, and give a brief explanation of your choice.
    a. "I have seen your painted women under the gas lamps"
    b. "Flinging magnetic curses amid the toil of piling job on job"
    c. "here is a tall bold slugger set vivid against the little soft cities"
    d. "under his wrist is the pulse, and under his ribs the heart of the people"

    _____

    _____

7. Reread lines 7–9 of "Grass." What is Sandburg trying to create with these lines? Explain your answer.

    _____

    _____

8. Who or what is the speaker in "Grass"? Quote a passage that supports your answer.

    _____

    _____

9. Why do you think Sandburg write his poem from the point of view of the grass? Use evidence from the poem to support your answer.

    _____

    _____

10. Define the word *cunning* and use it in a sentence of your own.

    _____

    _____

Extended Response

11. In "Chicago," the speaker of the poem acts as a judge, arbitrating a dispute between the city and its critics. Write an essay discussing the charges of the critics against Chicago, and the speaker's verdict. Why does the speaker reach this verdict and not another one? Use details from the poem to support your answer.

12. The theme of "Chicago" can be seen as this: Like people, cities grow up with their own personalities and have both good and bad traits. Write a short essay in which you support this interpretation of the poem. Use details from the poem in your answer.

13. "Chicago" describes the city by using images of violence, brutality, and suffering. In an essay, describe another image that you could use to portray this city. Explain your choice. To organize your thoughts, complete this diagram by writing your image in the circle and then, in the surrounding lines, write words and phrases you associate with that image.

14. What do you think the theme of "Grass" is? Write a brief essay in which you state a possible theme and explain what you mean. Use details from the poem as support for your answer.

15. "Grass" could be understood as a reflection on the statement "Time heals all wounds." However, it could also be understood as a reflection on the pointlessness of fighting a war that may barely be remembered by future generations. In an essay, explain which interpretation you think is more appropriate. Why do you think so? Use details from the poem to support your answer.

Oral Response

16. Choose question 2, 4, 6, 7, or 15 or the question your teacher assigns you. Take a few minutes to look through the poems to prepare an oral response to give in class. If necessary, make notes to be clear about the order in which you want to present your answer.

Rubric for Evaluating Extended Responses

0	1	2	3	4
Blank paper	Incorrect purpose, mode, audience	Correct purpose, mode, audience	Correct purpose, mode, audience	Correct purpose, mode, audience
Foreign language	Brief, vague	Some elaboration	Moderately well elaborated	Effective elaboration
Illegible, incoherent	Unelaborated	Some details	Clear, effective language	Consistent organization
Not enough content to score	Rambling	Gaps in organization	Organized (perhaps with brief digressions)	Sense of completeness, fluency
	Lack of language control	Limited language control		
	Poor organization			

"The Jilting of Granny Weatherall" by Katherine Anne Porter

Open-Book Test

Multiple Choice and Short Answer

Write your answers to all questions in this section on the lines provided.
For multiple-choice questions, circle the letter of the best answer.

1. At the beginning of the story, what disturbs Granny Weatherall most about Doctor Harry's presence? Support your answer with a quote from the story.

    _____

    _____

2. John Weatherall would probably remember Ellen Weatherall as _____.
    Explain this statement by citing evidence from the story.

    _____

    _____

3. Strength and industriousness are the predominant character traits revealed by Granny's thoughts. Explain this statement by citing details from the story.

    _____

    _____

4. In stream-of-consciousness writing, how does the author present the character's thoughts? Explain your answer.

    _____

    _____

5. What do you learn about Granny's husband through the use of flashbacks? Quote the passage from the story that supports your answer.

    _____

    _____

6. Why is Father Connolly in the room? Cite a passage from the story to support your answer.

    _____

    _____

7. Which character trait does Granny seem to value most? Back up your answer with a passage from the story.

    _____

    _____

8. Which of the following moments takes place in the story's present? Briefly explain your answer choice.
    a. Granny wants to give Cornelia the amethyst set.
    b. Granny faces the priest alone.
    c. Granny gathers the children around her as she lights the lamps.
    d. Granny dusts the bronze clock with the lion on top.

    To organize your thoughts, complete this diagram. In the top half, write events that took place in the story's past. In the bottom half, write events that take place in the story's present.

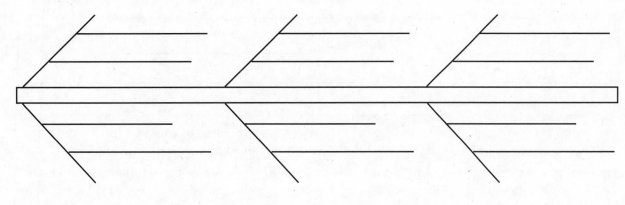

_____

_____

9. In what way does Granny Weatherall associate Father Connolly's presence with her jilting? Use evidence from the story as support.

_____

_____

10. What is _dyspepsia_? Write a sentence in which you use the word.

_____

_____

Extended Response

11. Katherine Anne Porter chose to call this story "The Jilting of Granny Weatherall." Write an essay stating why you think this title was chosen to represent this fictional work. What do you think this title signifies in the story? Use events from the story to back up your opinion.

12. Benjamin Disraeli, a British statesman, is credited with the statement, "Youth is a blunder; [adult]hood a struggle; old age a regret." Do you think Granny Weatherall would agree or disagree with this statement? State your position in an essay. Support your position with details from the selection.

13. We learn about Granny Weatherall's life through a series of flashbacks. What do these flashbacks reveal about her relationships with her children? Write a short essay discussing this question. Use details from the story as support. To organize your thoughts, complete this chart.

Flashback	What It Reveals

14. What do you think the theme (the central or dominating idea) of this story is? Write an essay answering this question. Use details from the story to support your opinion.

15. Katherine Anne Porter uses the narrative technique of stream-of-consciousness to present Granny's thoughts and to indicate how close she is to death. Write a brief essay discussing Porter's use of this technique. How would you describe stream-of-consciousness? How well does it indicate how close Granny is to death? Include details from the selection that illustrate the technique.

Oral Response

16. Choose question 3, 7, 8, 9, or 14 or the question your teacher assigns you. Take a few minutes to look through the story to prepare an oral response to give in class. If necessary, make notes to be clear about the order in which you want to present your answer.

Rubric for Evaluating Extended Responses

0	1	2	3	4
Blank paper Foreign language Illegible, incoherent Not enough content to score	Incorrect purpose, mode, audience Brief, vague Unelaborated Rambling Lack of language control Poor organization	Correct purpose, mode, audience Some elaboration Some details Gaps in organization Limited language control	Correct purpose, mode, audience Moderately well elaborated Clear, effective language Organized (perhaps with brief digressions)	Correct purpose, mode, audience Effective elaboration Consistent organization Sense of completeness, fluency

"Race at Morning" and **"Nobel Prize Acceptance Speech"**
by William Faulkner

Open-Book Test

Multiple Choice and Short Answer

Write your answers to all questions in this section on the lines provided.
For multiple-choice questions, circle the letter of the best answer.

1. In "Race at Morning," why doesn't Mister Ernest shoot the buck when he has a chance? Cite the passage from the story that supports your answer.

    _____

    _____

    _____

2. Cite an example of dialect in "Race at Morning." Give a brief explanation.

    _____

    _____

    _____

3. Reread the paragraph beginning with "Because he had . . ." In that paragraph, where does the action take place? How do you know?

    _____

    _____

4. Cite details that tell how the narrator came to live with Mister Ernest.

    _____

    _____

    _____

5. What word does Mister Ernest in "Race at Morning" believe gives people hope in the future? Give details from the story to support your answer.

    _____

    _____

6. Using standard English, rewrite the following line from "Race at Morning." Explain why you made the changes you did.

    Because me and Mister Ernest was going to git him.

    _____

    _____

7. Complete this chart by writing five other examples of speech in dialect from the story, and then writing them in standard English.

Example of Dialectical Speech from Story	Standard English

8. Explain why Faulkner says that young writers today have forgotten the "problems of the human heart in conflict with itself."

_____

_____

9. Cite details from Faulkner's "Nobel Prize Acceptance Speech" that indicate he believes that most writers write about superficial topics rather than subjects that really matter.

_____

_____

10. What is a *bayou*? Use the word in a sentence of your own.

_____

_____

Extended Response

11. Apart from the narrator and Mister Ernest, the most important characters in "Race at Morning" are the animals Dan, Eagle, and the buck. Although minor characters, they are developed with individual personalities and placed in situations in which they must make critical decisions. In an essay, describe the character traits of these animals and assess their importance to the plot. How fully are their personalities developed? Which of these characters is most important to the development of the story?

12. In the paragraph beginning with, "So at least one of us . . . ," what does the narrator in "Race at Morning" mean when he says that hunting and farming are "jest the other side of each other"? Answer this question in a short essay, using passages from the story as support.

13. The narrator of "Race at Morning" is uneducated—he can't even write his own name—but is he intelligent? Write an essay in which you assess the narrator's intelligence. Give examples to support your conclusion. What does the narrator's use of language tell you about his intelligence? Is he simply Mister Ernest's ears, or does he help in other ways, too? Is he able to think through complex issues and arrive at valid conclusions?

14. Write a brief essay in which you explain what Faulkner's main point is in his "Nobel Prize Acceptance Speech." Quote passages from the essay as support.

15. In his "Nobel Prize Acceptance Speech," Faulkner says that writing about "the human heart in conflict with itself" is what makes writing worthwhile. Write an essay in which you explain how Faulkner investigated this conflict within the hearts of the narrator and Mister Ernest in his story "Race at Morning." What events or situations demonstrate that Mister Ernest and the narrator have internal conflicts? Does either character resolve any conflicts?

Oral Response

16. Choose question 1, 7, 8, 9, or 13 or the question your teacher assigns you. Take a few minutes to look through the selections to prepare an oral response to give in class. If necessary, make notes to be clear about the order in which you want to present your answer.

Rubric for Evaluating Extended Responses

0	1	2	3	4
Blank paper Foreign language Illegible, incoherent Not enough content to score	Incorrect purpose, mode, audience Brief, vague Unelaborated Rambling Lack of language control Poor organization	Correct purpose, mode, audience Some elaboration Some details Gaps in organization Limited language control	Correct purpose, mode, audience Moderately well elaborated Clear, effective language Organized (perhaps with brief digressions)	Correct purpose, mode, audience Effective elaboration Consistent organization Sense of completeness, fluency

Robert Frost's Poetry

Open-Book Test

Multiple Choice and Short Answer

Write your answers to all questions in this section on the lines provided.
For multiple-choice questions, circle the letter of the best answer.

1. For the speaker of "Mending Wall," what does the wall itself most clearly symbolize? Cite evidence from the poem as support for your answer.

   _____

   _____

2. The neighbor in "Mending Wall" tells the speaker of the poem that good fences make good neighbors. What does he mean by this? Explain your answer.

   _____

   _____

3. Reread the last three and a half lines of " 'Out, Out—,' " beginning with "They listened . . ." What do these lines tell you about the farm family in the poem?

   _____

   _____

4. For the speaker of "Acquainted With the Night," what does night itself most likely symbolize? Explain your answer, citing evidence from the poem.

   _____

   _____

5. What is an *iamb*? Give an example of a line from a Robert Frost poem that has four iambs in a row.

   _____

   _____

   _____

6. What is the form of blank verse? Give an example of a line from a Robert Frost poem that is written in blank verse.

   _____

   _____

   _____

7. Verse that captures the rhythm of human speech in unrhymed iambic pentameter is called _____.

   a. alliteration   b. blank verse   c. sonnet   d. ode

8. Give two possible meanings of the last two lines of "Stopping by Woods on a Snowy Evening."

   _____

   _____

9. Cite one detail from "Stopping by Woods on a Snowy Evening" that give the poem its quiet, thoughtful mood.

_____

_____

10. Complete this Analysis Map based on the word *rueful*. In the "Compare to" section, write synonyms for the word. In the "Contrast with" section, write antonyms for the word. In the "Examples" box, write two sentences using the word.

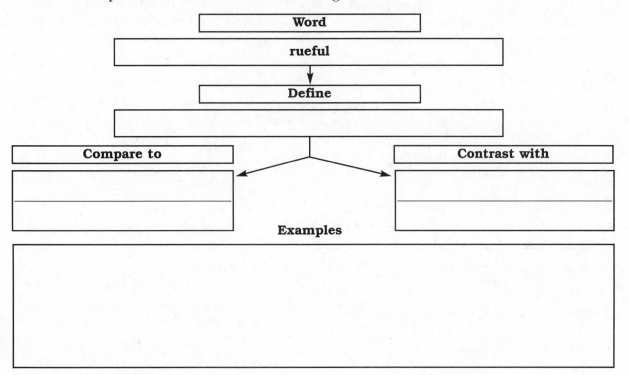

Extended Response

11. As you read Frost's poems, you probably noted that they are often tinged with a feeling of regret. Many of Frost's poems contain a sense of rueful longing for lost childhood or for a bygone way of life. In an essay, discuss specific examples from the poems concerning this theme of loss of innocence, the death of childhood, and the longing for a simpler way of life. Use quotations from the poems to illustrate your points. Why do you think such themes hold such mass appeal?

12. What do you think is the theme, or central idea, of "Stopping by Woods on a Snowy Evening"? Think about what the speaker is doing and what he seems to want to do. What stops him from doing what he wants to do? Is there a conflict in the speaker's mind? Answer these questions in a brief essay, using evidence from the poem as support.

13. Robert Frost is famous for having written poems that seem simple but actually operate on a number of different emotional and intellectual levels. For example, in "Mending Wall," Frost depicts two neighbors with very different attitudes toward the fence line that divides their property. One, the speaker, proclaims that "Something there is that doesn't love a wall, that wants it down." The other, the speaker's neighbor, insists that "Good fences make good neighbors." Consider the two statements, and write an essay about the merits of each point of view. In what situations might the neighbor's unyielding stance about the necessity of defined boundaries cause problems? Discuss how these statements might be said to illustrate two common American points of view.

14. For the speaker in "Birches," what does swinging on birch trees most clearly symbolize? Answer this question in a brief essay, and use lines from the poem to support your answer.

15. Most poets are known for more than one or two poems. Robert Frost wrote perhaps the greatest number of poems that are familiar to American readers. Of them, Frost called "Stopping by Woods on a Snowy Evening" his "best bid for remembrance." The poem excels in the three parts that Frost regarded as essential: the point or idea; the details that develop it; and the technique with which it is crafted. Write an essay in which you analyze Frost's "Stopping by Woods on a Snowy Evening," exploring each of these three parts. Be as specific as possible.

Oral Response

16. Choose question 1, 2, 4, 11, or 12 or the question your teacher assigns you. Take a few minutes to look through the poems to prepare an oral response to give in class. If necessary, make notes to be clear about the order in which you want to present your answer.

Rubric for Evaluating Extended Responses

0	1	2	3	4
Blank paper Foreign language Illegible, incoherent Not enough content to score	Incorrect purpose, mode, audience Brief, vague Unelaborated Rambling Lack of language control Poor organization	Correct purpose, mode, audience Some elaboration Some details Gaps in organization Limited language control	Correct purpose, mode, audience Moderately well elaborated Clear, effective language Organized (perhaps with brief digressions)	Correct purpose, mode, audience Effective elaboration Consistent organization Sense of completeness, fluency

Name _____ Date _____

"The Night the Ghost Got In" by James Thurber
from *Here Is New York* by E. B. White

Open-Book Test

Multiple Choice and Short Answer

Write your answers to all questions in this section on the lines provided.
For multiple-choice questions, circle the letter of the best answer.

1. In "The Night the Ghost Got In," Thurber notes that his "grandfather was in the attic, in the old walnut bed which, as you will remember, once fell on my father." How does this detail contribute to the essay's humor? Explain your answer.

    _____

    _____

2. Reread the paragraph beginning with "It was now two o'clock. . . ." Which aspect of the interaction between Thurber's mother and Mr. Bodwell is an example of hyperbole? Cite the passage in which you find the answer. To organize your thoughts, complete this chart. In the first column, write one aspect of the interaction between Thurber's mother and Mr. Bodwell. In the second column, write yes or no to indicate whether it is an example of hyperbole.

Aspect of Interaction	Example of Hyperbole?

    _____

3. What does the cop mean to say when he tells his colleagues that the mother seems "historical"? Explain your answer.

    _____

    _____

4. How would you summarize the theme, or central idea, of "The Night the Ghost Got In"? Use evidence from the essay to support your answer.

    _____

    _____

5. In "The Night the Ghost Got In," which detail is a digression that has little purpose other than comic effect? Circle the letter of the correct answer, and give a brief explanation on the lines provided.
    a. the footsteps
    b. the narrator's towel
    c. the shoe
    d. the zither

    _____

    _____

6. Cite an example of hyperbole from "Here Is New York." Then explain it briefly.

_____

_____

7. Look at the paragraph beginning with "The oft-quoted. . . ." Read the second sentence in that paragraph, beginning with, "I have an idea . . ." What characteristic of the informal essay does this sentence from _Here Is New York_ exemplify? Explain your answer.

_____

_____

8. E.B. White believes that New York City is a majestic city of which all Americans can be proud. Give a brief explanation supporting this statement, citing evidence from the essay.

_____

_____

9. The excerpt from _Here Is New York_ may be described as an informal essay. Cite one or two lines from the selection that support this statement.

_____

_____

10. If a person who suffered from _claustrophobia_ got into an elevator, would he or she be comfortable? Explain your answer.

_____

_____

Extended Response

11. Eccentric characters are one of the traditional features of humorous writing. Usually these characters act in ways that stretch the bounds of credibility without becoming completely preposterous. In Thurber's "The Night the Ghost Got In," the narrator's mother and grandfather fit this description. Write an essay in which you describe the personalities and actions of the narrator's mother and grandfather. Comment on their believability. To organize your thoughts, complete these diagrams based on each character. In the ovals, write words and phrases that describe the personalities and actions of the characters.

12. Writers often create humor by depicting serious events in a comic light. Think about the events that Thurber recounts in "The Night the Ghost Got In." Try to imagine a more factual reporting of those events. Then answer this question in a short essay: Which aspects of the essay would not be amusing without Thurber's embellishment? Explain your answer.

13. One critic said of E. B. White, "His interests are broad—nothing, it seems, that is human is alien to him. His eye and intelligence see what lies beneath the surface." In an essay, discuss how *Here Is New York* supports these points, citing specific examples from the text. What does "nothing . . . human is alien to him" imply?

14. In *Here Is New York*, E. B. White says, "Each area is a city within a city within a city." What do you think he means by this? Write a brief essay in which you answer this question. Cite passages in the essay that support your answer.

15. Humor is often based on the depiction of other people's behavior. Sometimes this sort of humor is used at the expense of its subjects and is unkind. Write an essay in which you explain what determines the line between humor and unkindness and apply it to *Here Is New York* and Thurber's essay. Is there humor in these pieces that crosses the line? Use examples from the essays to support your ideas.

Oral Response

16. Choose question 4, 6, 8, 11, or 14 or the question your teacher assigns you. Take a few minutes to look through the selections to prepare an oral response to give in class. If necessary, make notes to be clear about the order in which you want to present your answer.

Rubric for Evaluating Extended Responses

0	1	2	3	4
Blank paper Foreign language Illegible, incoherent Not enough content to score	Incorrect purpose, mode, audience Brief, vague Unelaborated Rambling Lack of language control Poor organization	Correct purpose, mode, audience Some elaboration Some details Gaps in organization Limited language control	Correct purpose, mode, audience Moderately well elaborated Clear, effective language Organized (perhaps with brief digressions)	Correct purpose, mode, audience Effective elaboration Consistent organization Sense of completeness, fluency

from *Dust Tracks on a Road* by Zora Neale Hurston

Open-Book Test

Multiple Choice and Short Answer

Write your answers to all questions in this section on the lines provided.
For multiple-choice questions, circle the letter of the best answer.

1. In the excerpt from *Dust Tracks on a Road*, Hurston relates that she regarded the white people passing by with curiosity. Explain the reason for her curiosity and cite a detail from the text that supports your answer.

    _____

    _____

2. Hurston explains that her grandmother worried very much about Hurston's "forward ways." Explain why she was so worried. What detail in the text supports this view?

    _____

    _____

3. What do you think the dust tracks in the title symbolize? Explain your answer.

    _____

    _____

4. The Negro school was a curiosity to visitors because there was little contact between races at the time the writer describes. Cite details from the text that show the attitude of the white visitors at the school.

    _____

    _____

5. Why were the ladies so impressed with Hurston? Explain your answer, citing evidence from the autobiography as support. To organize your thoughts, complete this chart. In column 1, write things Zora did or said when the ladies visited the classroom. In column 2, write yes or no to indicate whether this was unusual behavior and explain your response.

What Zora Did or Said	Was the Behavior Unusual?

_____

_____

6. Hurston presents her critical feelings about school to show that being educated is not dependent on loving school. Support or refute this view, citing details from the text.

_____

_____

7. List two things that Zora Neale Hurston portrays about her social context in writing her autobiography.

_____

_____

8. Hurston discovered the Bible in an unusual way. Explain how she came to read the Bible. What parts did she like the most?

_____

_____

9. What can you infer about Hurston's taste in literature as a child? Explain your answer, citing details from the text.
    a. She preferred stories with a clear moral.
    b. She preferred stories about gods and goddesses.
    c. She preferred the New Testament to the Old Testament.
    d. She preferred stories with adventure and excitement.

_____

_____

10. Define *brazenness* and give an example of Zora's brazen behavior.

_____

_____

Extended Response

11. In her later life, Hurston became a folklorist and writer. Reread the details about her career in Prepare to Read. Then fill in the chart below, listing aspects of Hurston's character which you can infer from reading the excerpt from Dust Tracks on a Road. Cite details from the text that support your listings. Write an essay about the aspects of Hurston's character evident in the excerpt which may have helped her in her later career. How would these characteristics have aided, or hindered, her?

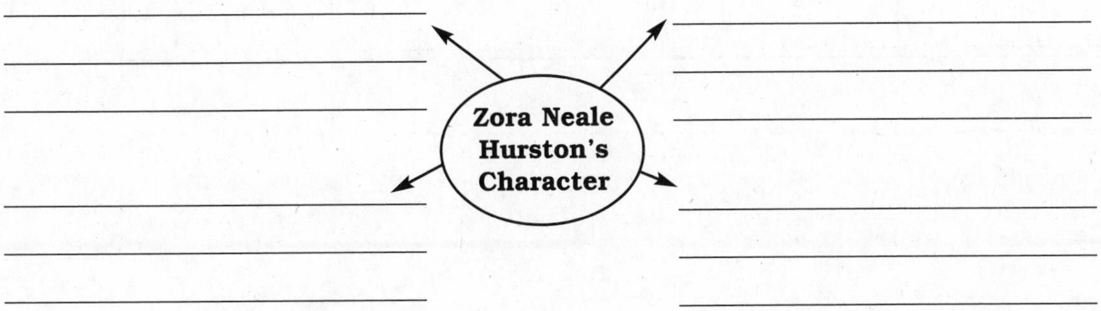

```
_____              ↖        ↗              _____
_____                                      _____
_____          ( Zora Neale                _____
                                 Hurston's
                                 Character )
_____              ↙        ↘              _____
_____                                      _____
_____                                      _____
```

12. Why did the schoolchildren feel threatened when the visitors came to observe them? Do you think they felt more threatened by the visitors or by their own teachers? Answer these questions in a short essay, using evidence from the autobiography as support.

13. Write an essay in which you discuss what the excerpt from *Dust Tracks on a Road* reveals about race relations of that time. What attitudes and feelings can you infer from the incidents related? How did the blacks feel about the whites, and the whites about the blacks? Cite evidence from the selection to support your response.

14. Hurston carefully describes her reading likes and dislikes, mentioning Greek, Roman, and Norse mythology, *Gulliver's Travels, Grimm's Fairy Tales, Dick Whittington,* and the *Jungle Book,* among others. Why do you think she does this? Answer this question in an essay. As you write, you might want to consider what she has in common with the characters she admires and how she is different from the characters she does not admire.

15. One critic said of *Dust Tracks on the Road* that with it "Zora had found a recipe for success—entertain but don't blame." Write an essay discussing this view of Zora's purpose. In what sense does the selection support the critic's view? In what sense does it not? Cite examples from the text to support your ideas.

Oral Response

16. Choose question 1, 3, 8, 11, or 14 or the question your teacher assigns you. Take a few minutes to look through the selection to prepare an oral response to give in class. If necessary, make notes to be clear about the order in which you want to present your answer.

Rubric for Evaluating Extended Responses

0	1	2	3	4
Blank paper	Incorrect purpose, mode, audience	Correct purpose, mode, audience	Correct purpose, mode, audience	Correct purpose, mode, audience
Foreign language	Brief, vague	Some elaboration	Moderately well elaborated	Effective elaboration
Illegible, incoherent	Unelaborated	Some details	Clear, effective language	Consistent organization
Not enough content to score	Rambling	Gaps in organization	Organized (perhaps with brief digressions)	Sense of completeness, fluency
	Lack of language control	Limited language control		
	Poor organization			

Name _____ Date _____

"Refugee in America," "Ardella," "The Negro Speaks of Rivers," and "Dream Variations" by Langston Hughes
"The Tropics in New York" by Claude McKay

Open-Book Test

Multiple Choice and Short Answer

Write your answers to all questions in this section on the lines provided.
For multiple-choice questions, circle the letter of the best answer.

1. Who is the speaker in "Refugee in America"? Select the answer that provides a clue, and give a brief explanation.
   a. "On my heart-strings freedom sings"   c. "There are words like Liberty"
   b. "All day everyday."   d. "You would know why."

   _____

   _____

2. In "Ardella," the speaker compares Ardella to "a night without stars/Were it not for your eyes." Explain briefly what he means by this metaphor.

   _____

   _____

3. In "Ardella," what can you infer about the speaker's feelings for Ardella? Explain your answer.

   _____

   _____

4. It could be said that the theme, or central idea, of "The Negro Speaks of Rivers" is the long history of the black race. What evidence from the poem supports this view?

   _____

   _____

5. The tone of a piece of writing is defined as the author's attitude toward his or her subject. Which word best describes the tone in "The Negro Speaks of Rivers"? Briefly explain your answer choice.
   a. arrogant   c. proud
   b. humble   d. self-deprecating

   _____

   _____

6. In "Dream Variations," how does the speaker view the daytime? What does he think should be done during the day? Support your answer with a line from the poem.

   _____

   _____

7. What can the reader infer about the appearance of the speaker in "Dream Variations"? Cite the lines from the poem that support your answer.

   _____

   _____

8. In the first stanza of "The Tropics in New York," the speaker describes the fruit in great detail. What effect does the fruit have on him? Explain your answer.

    a. The fruit makes him hungry.

    b. The fruit reminds him that he is seeking employment.

    c. The fruit reminds him that he is broke.

    d. The fruit reminds him of his native land.

    _____

    _____

9. Suppose you were reading "The Tropics in New York," but the title was missing from the copy you had. How would you know that the speaker is not in the tropics when the poem is written? Cite details from the poem to support your answer.

    _____

    _____

10. Complete this Analysis Map based on the word *dusky*. In the box labeled "Compare to," write synonyms of the word. In the box labeled "Contrast with," write antonyms of the word. In the box labeled "Examples," write two sentences in which you use the word.

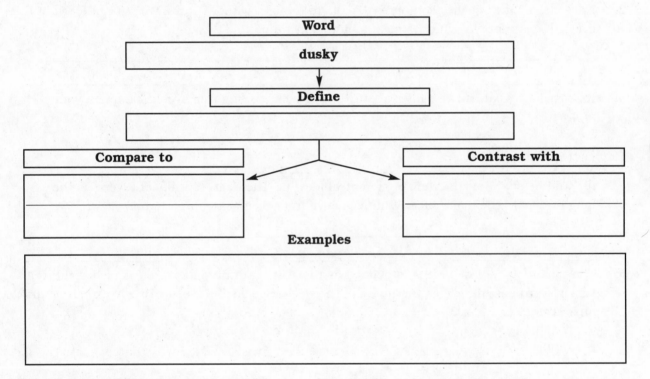

Extended Response

11. Langston Hughes's poem, "The Negro Speaks of Rivers," created a powerful impression when it was first published in 1921. African American readers recognized it immediately as a great poem about their heritage. Critics in general praised it lavishly. Write an essay in which you analyze how the poem achieves its effectiveness.

12. In a short essay, defend the following statement, using evidence from the poem: The theme of "Refugee in America" is that liberty means a great deal when you know what it is like to live without it.

13. What effect does the use of the first person *I* have on the reader in "Refugee in America," "The Negro Speaks of Rivers," and "The Tropics in New York"? Complete the chart below to help organize your thoughts. Then write an essay comparing and contrasting the speakers in these three poems.

Name of Poem	Whom Does the I Represent?	Effect on Reader
"Refugee in America"		
"The Negro Speaks of Rivers"		
"The Tropics in New York"		

14. How does the speaker of "Dream Variations" portray night? Does he see it as a positive or a negative time? Write a brief essay explaining your answer. Use evidence from the poem as support.

15. In three of the four poems by Hughes in this group, words and images of darkness appear. An example is the last three lines of "The Negro Speaks of Rivers." Write an essay discussing these lines and other words and images from his poems containing images of darkness. What is the significance of these images? What point do you think Hughes is trying to make by using them? Use details from the poems to support your answers.

Oral Response

16. Choose question 3, 4, 5, 6, or 11 or the question your teacher assigns you. Take a few minutes to look through the poems to prepare an oral response to give in class. If necessary, make notes to be clear about the order in which you want to present your answer.

Rubric for Evaluating Extended Responses

0	1	2	3	4
Blank paper Foreign language Illegible, incoherent Not enough content to score	Incorrect purpose, mode, audience Brief, vague Unelaborated Rambling Lack of language control Poor organization	Correct purpose, mode, audience Some elaboration Some details Gaps in organization Limited language control	Correct purpose, mode, audience Moderately well elaborated Clear, effective language Organized (perhaps with brief digressions)	Correct purpose, mode, audience Effective elaboration Consistent organization Sense of completeness, fluency

Name _____   Date _____

"From the Dark Tower" by Countee Cullen
"A Black Man Talks of Reaping" by Arna Bontemps
"Storm Ending" by Jean Toomer

Open-Book Test

Multiple Choice and Short Answer

Write your answers to all questions in this section on the lines provided.
For multiple-choice questions, circle the letter of the best answer.

1. In "From the Dark Tower," what is suggested by the last line? Support your answer with other lines from the poem.

    _____

    _____

2. Explain the references to slavery in the excerpt "From the Dark Tower." Cite specific details from the text.

    _____

    _____

3. In your own words, paraphrase lines 9–10 in "From the Dark Tower." In what way do these lines give evidence of black pride at the time of the Harlem Renaissance writers?

    _____

    _____

4. Which of the following best describes the use of poetic devices in "A Black Man Talks of Reaping"? Explain why you think this is the best choice.
    a. a series of brief metaphors comparing the stages of a man's life to the seasons of the agricultural year and his feelings to a farmer's tasks
    b. a single extended metaphor comparing the black race to a family of farmers trying to survive off the land in different parts of the world
    c. a single extended metaphor comparing the work of the black race to one man's planting and harvest for a single year
    d. three brief metaphors comparing a man's life to a season's planting, his death to a harvest, and his children's life to bitter fruit

    _____

    _____

5. Explain the metaphor of sowing in "A Black Man Talks of Reaping." What does sowing represent? Explain your answer.

    _____

    _____

6. What does "reaping" represent in "A Black Man Talks of Reaping"? Give a brief explanation citing details from the text.

    _____

    _____

7. What is the theme, or main idea, of "Storm Ending"? Support your answer with evidence from the poem.

_____

8. In "Storm Ending," how does Toomer characterize thunder? Does he describe it as beautiful, destructive, frightening, or invigorating? Defend your choice with evidence from the poem. To organize your thoughts, complete this cluster diagram. In the ovals, write words that Toomer uses to describe the thunder. Add some more ovals if necessary.

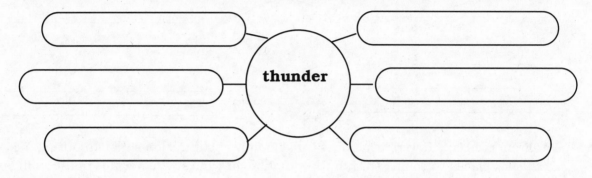

_____

9. How does Toomer employ metaphor in "Storm Ending"? Choose the correct answer, and explain your choice.
    a. A brief metaphor compares the thunder to a flower, and then an extended metaphor compares it to a bell.
    b. In an extended metaphor comparing thunder to a bell, Toomer also compares it to a flower.
    c. The poem comprises several brief metaphors comparing thunder to various different kinds of flowers.
    d. In an extended metaphor comparing thunder to a flower, Toomer also compares it to a bell and a person.

_____

10. What feeling does the last line of "Storm Ending" leave the reader with? Explain your answer.

_____

Extended Response

11. Choose a word or phrase that you feel describes the mood of the poem, "A Black Man Talks of Reaping." In an essay, discuss your choice and why you made it. How does your word or phrase capture the mood of the poem? Support your choice with details from the poem.

12. One way to determine the theme of a poem is to paraphrase it, or restate it in your own words, and then to ask yourself what various images might symbolize. Follow this process with "A Black Man Tells of Reaping." Then write a brief essay explaining what you think the theme, or central idea, of the poem is.

13. All three of the poems in this section make use of metaphors to convey their meaning. Select one poem and write an essay explaining how it uses metaphors. What kinds of feelings do the metaphors evoke? Use examples from the poem to clarify your points. To organize your thoughts, complete this diagram. In the circle, write the title of the poem you choose. Then, on the lines, describe the metaphors in the poem and describe the feelings evoked by those metaphors.

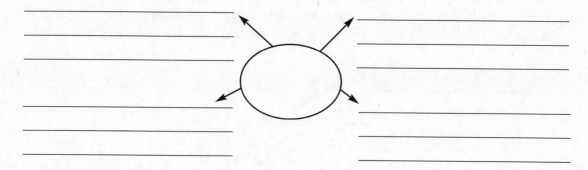

14. In "From the Dark Tower," what does Cullen imply about the job situation during the 1920s for blacks as compared with the situation for whites? Answer this question in an essay, citing details from the poem as support.

15. Some critics think Jean Toomer intended to write about the African American experience in his poem "Storm Ending." Write an essay agreeing or disagreeing with this view of the poem. How do you think this poem relates to the general purposes of the Harlem Renaissance writers? Support your position with specific examples.

Oral Response

16. Choose question 4, 5, 6, 9, or 12 or the question your teacher assigns you. Take a few minutes to look through the poems to prepare an oral response to give in class. If necessary, make notes to be clear about the order in which you want to present your answer.

Rubric for Evaluating Extended Responses

0	1	2	3	4
Blank paper Foreign language Illegible, incoherent Not enough content to score	Incorrect purpose, mode, audience Brief, vague Unelaborated Rambling Lack of language control Poor organization	Correct purpose, mode, audience Some elaboration Some details Gaps in organization Limited language control	Correct purpose, mode, audience Moderately well elaborated Clear, effective language Organized (perhaps with brief digressions)	Correct purpose, mode, audience Effective elaboration Consistent organization Sense of completeness, fluency

"The Life You Save May Be Your Own" by Flannery O'Connor

Open-Book Test

Multiple Choice and Short Answer

Write your answers to all questions in this section on the lines provided.
For multiple-choice questions, circle the letter of the best answer.

1. Which sentence best explains why Mr. Shiftlet stops at the Crater's house?
   Explain your answer choice.
   a. He is tired of walking down the road.
   b. He wants a place where he can enjoy the sunset.
   c. He wants to help the old woman and her daughter.
   d. He notices their car and wants it.

   _____

   _____

2. Use a Character Web to analyze the character traits of Mr. Shiftlet. Then write a brief
   description of him as a grotesque character.

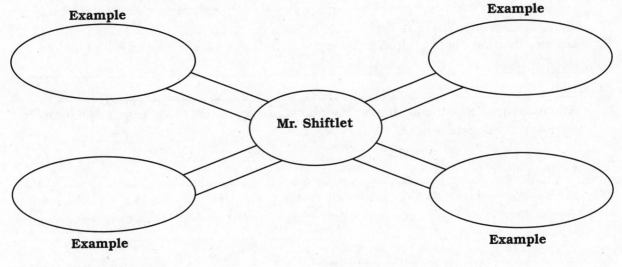

   _____

3. Reread Mr. Shiftlet's comments to the old woman toward the middle of the selection. How
   do these comments about lying help you predict what will happen in the story?

   _____

   _____

4. When Mr. Shiftlet speaks of lying, he uses an ominous tone. Explain the effect he is
   trying to achieve with this tone of voice, and note whether he is successful.

   _____

   _____

   _____

5. Which aspects of the old woman's actions make her a grotesque character? Explain your answer choice.

    I. She is obsessed with finding a husband for her daughter.

    II. She makes her daughter work hard around the house.

    III. She makes her deaf daughter speak to strangers.

    IV. She often exaggerates her daughter's good qualities.

    a. I and II   b. I and III   c. I and IV   d. II and III

_____

_____

6. On the lines provided, briefly explain why the younger Lucynell can be classified as a grotesque character.

_____

_____

7. When Mr. Shiftlet finally agrees to marry the younger Lucynell, you can infer that he wants _____.

    a. to make young Lucynell happy   c. to get money from the old woman

    b. to help the old woman take care of her house   d. to have a place to live in winter

Review the discussion between Mr. Shiftlet and the old woman in your textbook. Cite an example from the story to support your answer.

_____

_____

8. Explain what Mr. Shiftlet thinks will happen to Lucynell after he leaves her in the diner.

_____

_____

9. O'Connor writes that the mother is "ravenous for a son-in-law." What predictions can you make from that statement?

_____

_____

10. Think of any predictions you made while reading "The Life You Save May Be Your Own." Were your predictions correct or incorrect? Explain your answer using examples from the text.

_____

_____

Extended Response

11. Consider the characters in the story. What if one of them had exhibited more "normal" traits? How would it have affected the story and its outcome? Write an essay in which you speculate about the differences in the story had one of the characters been different.

12. What new information do you learn about Mr. Shiftlet when he picks up the hitchhiker at the end of the story? In an essay, discuss how this information does or does not fit with what you have previously learned about the character of Mr. Shiftlet. Cite details and quotations from the story to support your points.

13. Use a Venn diagram to compare and contrast the grotesque character traits of the three characters in "The Life You Save May Be Your Own." Then write an essay in which you describe the use and effect of grotesque characters in fiction.

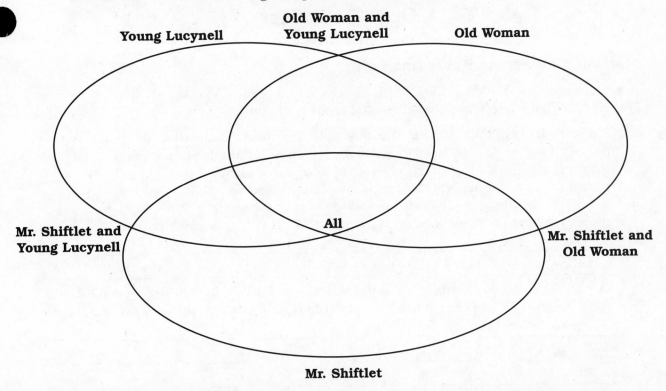

14. Think about Mr. Shiftlet's description of the doctors in Atlanta examining the human heart. Write an essay in which you discuss the significance of this anecdote in relation to Mr. Shiftlet's actions and his comments throughout the story.

15. Write an essay in which you explore Mr. Shiftlet's motivation for baiting the hitchhiker at the end of the story. Why does he make the comments he does? What causes his reaction?

Oral Response

16. Go back to question 2, 5, 12, 13, or 14 or one assigned by your teacher, and take five to ten minutes to prepare an oral response. Find additional details in the story that will support your points. You may wish to write down some notes to guide your response.

Rubric for Evaluating Extended Responses

0	1	2	3	4
Blank paper Foreign language Illegible, incoherent Not enough content to score	Incorrect purpose, mode, audience Brief, vague Unelaborated Rambling Lack of language control Poor organization	Correct purpose, mode, audience Some elaboration Some details Gaps in organization Limited language control	Correct purpose, mode, audience Moderately well elaborated Clear, effective language Organized (perhaps with brief digressions)	Correct purpose, mode, audience Effective elaboration Consistent organization Sense of completeness, fluency

"The First Seven Years" by Bernard Malamud

Open-Book Test

Multiple Choice and Short Answer

Write your answers to all questions in this section on the lines provided.
For multiple-choice questions, circle the letter of the best answer.

1. Circle the letter of the statement that best describes the epiphany that Feld has at the
   end of "The First Seven Years." Explain why the answer you selected is correct.
   a. Feld realizes that Max is not the right suitor for his daughter.
   b. Feld realizes that marrying Miriam is Sobel's life objective.
   c. Feld realizes that Miriam does not want a college education.
   d. Feld realizes that reading books is more valuable than a college education.

   _____
   _____

2. Briefly describe Feld's relationship with his daughter Miriam. In your description include
   the changes that take place in their relationship throughout the course of the story.

   _____
   _____
   _____

3. Identify with the characters of Miriam and Sobel. Explain how their own relationship
   differs from their relationships with the other characters in the story.

   _____
   _____
   _____

4. Why does Feld want Max to meet his daughter? Explain how Max responds to Sobel's
   suggestion that he call Miriam for a date.

   _____
   _____
   _____

5. Describe Sobel's performance as Feld's assistant. How is Sobel different than another
   assistant might be in the same position?

   _____
   _____

6. Why isn't Feld's matchmaking between Max and Miriam successful? Explain your
   answer choice.
   a. Miriam is more interested in Sobel.
   b. Max does not want to marry.
   c. Sobel interrupts Feld's conversation with Max.
   d. Feld's wife does not approve of Max.

   _____
   _____

7. Complete this chart to examine Feld's relationships with each of the story's main characters. In the middle column, write a phrase or short description of how Feld relates to Miriam, Sobel, and Max. In the right column, describe what Feld comes to understand about each of these characters.

Feld	Relationship	Epiphany
Miriam		
Sobel		
Max		

8. Which word best completes this sentence? To _____ the meaning of a short story, you must read it carefully and think about the characters' actions.
   a. specify   b. prove   c. discern   d. modify
   Explain your answer choice.

   _____

   _____

9. Which answer best explains why Sobel works in Feld's shoemaking store? Explain your answer, citing details from the story.
   I. Sobel wants to be near Miriam.
   II. Sobel is indebted to Feld for teaching him the shoe business.
   III. Feld cannot hire a better assistant.
   IV. Feld feels sorry for Sobel.
   a. I and II   b. II and III   c. I and III   d. III and IV

   _____

   _____

10. Why does Feld relent and agree to Sobel's eventual marriage to Miriam? Provide details from the story to support your answer.

   _____

   _____

Extended Response

11. Use this Venn diagram to compare and contrast Feld's and Miriam's ideas about how Miriam should lead her life. Then, in an essay, discuss their different wishes, and explain the conflict that exists because of the differences.

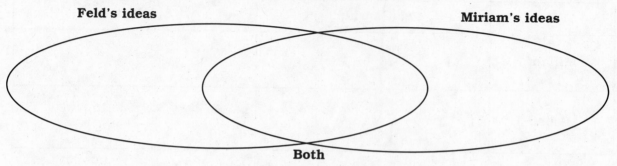

Feld's ideas   Miriam's ideas

Both

12. Feld wants the best for his daughter; yet, he considers his own desires for how she should live her life to be more important than hers. In an essay, discuss how Feld comes to change his mind about the way that Miriam should lead her life.

13. Examine Sobel's interest in Miriam. Why does he give Miriam books to read? Why is he willing to continue working for Feld at a low wage? Why does he want to marry Miriam? Respond to these questions in an essay.

14. In an essay, describe the character of Miriam. Discuss why you think she makes the choices she does. Explain how you do or do not relate to her character. Do you admire her? Do you question her choices and decisions? Would you want to meet her? Use examples of her actions and her relationships with the other characters to support your points.

15. Write an essay about the outcome of the conflicts in "The First Seven Years." To begin your essay, briefly describe each of the conflicts, and the characters involved. Then summarize how each of the conflicts is resolved.

Oral Response

16. Go back to question 1, 6, 7, 11, or 13 or one assigned by your teacher, and take five to ten minutes to expand your answer and prepare an oral response. Find additional details in the story that will support your points. You may wish to write down some notes to guide you.

Rubric for Evaluating Extended Responses

0	1	2	3	4
Blank paper	Incorrect purpose, mode, audience	Correct purpose, mode, audience	Correct purpose, mode, audience	Correct purpose, mode, audience
Foreign language				
Illegible, incoherent	Brief, vague	Some elaboration	Moderately well elaborated	Effective elaboration
Not enough content to score	Unelaborated	Some details	Clear, effective language	Consistent organization
	Rambling	Gaps in organization	Organized (perhaps with brief digressions)	Sense of completeness, fluency
	Lack of language control	Limited language control		
	Poor organization			

"The Brown Chest" by John Updike

Open-Book Test

Multiple Choice and Short Answer

Write your answers to all questions in this section on the lines provided.
For multiple-choice questions, circle the letter of the best answer.

1. Which sentence best describes the brown chest in Updike's story? Explain why the answer you selected is correct.
    a. The brown chest is an ugly piece of furniture that is hidden away.
    b. The brown chest holds papers and books that detail the main character's family history.
    c. The brown chest frightens the main character.
    d. The brown chest holds keys to the main character's family history.

    _____

    _____

2. Review the beginning of the story through the paragraph beginning with "Then everything moved. . . ." Briefly describe that atmosphere in this opening description.

    _____

    _____

    _____

3. When the main character's family moves, what does he discover in the brown chest? Explain the meaning of this discovery.
    a. more lace tablecloths
    b. more photograph albums
    c. his own drawings, report cards, and photographs
    d. his mother's wedding dress and his baby shoes

    _____

    _____

4. The main character finds the task of emptying and packing the U-Haul van to be _____.
    a. exhausting and overwhelming   c. an enjoyable experience with his son
    b. a time for reminiscing   d. depressing and sad
    Cite details from the story to support your answer choice.

    _____

    _____

5. Briefly describe the atmosphere of the attic as the main character and his son sort the contents for packing and disposal.

    _____

    _____

    _____

6. Use this chart to compare and contrast how the main character's attitude toward the brown chest affects the atmosphere at the beginning of the story, and how it affects the atmosphere at the end of the story.

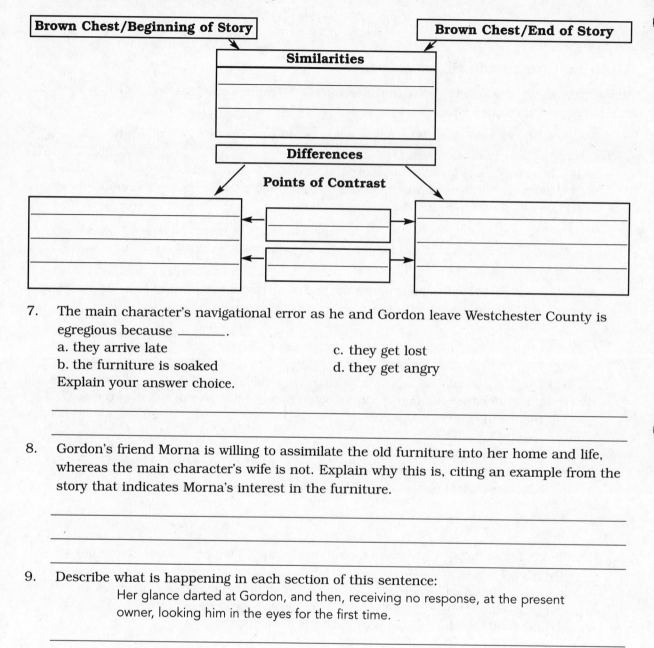

Brown Chest/Beginning of Story

Brown Chest/End of Story

Similarities

Differences

Points of Contrast

7. The main character's navigational error as he and Gordon leave Westchester County is egregious because _____.
   a. they arrive late
   b. the furniture is soaked
   c. they get lost
   d. they get angry
   Explain your answer choice.

   _____

   _____

8. Gordon's friend Morna is willing to assimilate the old furniture into her home and life, whereas the main character's wife is not. Explain why this is, citing an example from the story that indicates Morna's interest in the furniture.

   _____

   _____

   _____

9. Describe what is happening in each section of this sentence:
   Her glance darted at Gordon, and then, receiving no response, at the present owner, looking him in the eyes for the first time.

   _____

   _____

   _____

10. Explain how Morna's interest in the brown chest reaffirms the main character's attitude toward the chest at the end of the story.

    _____

    _____

    _____

Extended Response

11. Use this sunburst diagram to organize the main character's impressions and feelings about the brown chest. Then write one or two paragraphs in which you summarize the narrator's attitude toward the brown chest.

Main character's impressions and feelings

12. In an essay, discuss the importance of the brown chest in the main character's life. Cite details and quotations from the story to support your interpretation.

13. When Morna asks what is in the brown chest, the main character replies, "I forget, actually." This is not the first time in the story that the main character has been vague about the chest's contents. In an essay, explain why the main character never really knows exactly what is in the brown chest.

14. Gordon and his father share two experiences in "The Brown Chest"—when they empty and pack the house, and when Gordon and Morna come to look at the furniture in the barn. Write an essay in which you compare and contrast Gordon and the main character. Explain each character's feelings toward the brown chest.

15. Write an essay in which you speculate about what will happen to the brown chest after Morna has discovered it at the end of the story. As you write, consider how Morna's feelings toward the contents of the brown chest may be the same as or different from the feelings of the main character.

Oral Response

16. Go back to question 1, 5, 11, 13, or 15 or one assigned by your teacher, and take five to ten minutes to expand your answer and prepare an oral response. Find additional details in the story that will support your points. You may wish to write down some notes to guide your response.

Rubric for Evaluating Extended Responses

0	1	2	3	4
Blank paper	Incorrect purpose, mode, audience	Correct purpose, mode, audience	Correct purpose, mode, audience	Correct purpose, mode, audience
Foreign language	Brief, vague	Some elaboration	Moderately well elaborated	Effective elaboration
Illegible, incoherent	Unelaborated	Some details	Clear, effective language	Consistent organization
Not enough content to score	Rambling	Gaps in organization	Organized (perhaps with brief digressions)	Sense of completeness, fluency
	Lack of language control	Limited language control		
	Poor organization			

"Hawthorne" by Robert Lowell
"Gold Glade" by Robert Penn Warren
"The Light Comes Brighter" and **"The Adamant"**
by Theodore Roethke
"Traveling Through the Dark" by William Stafford

Open-Book Test

Multiple Choice and Short Answer

Write your answers to all questions in this section on the lines provided.
For multiple-choice questions, circle the letter of the best answer.

1. The repetition and alliteration in lines 32–42 of "Hawthorne" best describes Hawthorne's
_____.

   a. insignificance   b. inspiration   c. meditation   d. depression
   Explain your answer.

   _____

   _____

2. If you glance furtively at something you are not supposed to see, you are looking at it in
   an _____ way.
   a. peaceful; complacent   c. exposed; open
   b. resigned; submissive   d. sneaky; stealthy
   Explain why the answer you selected is correct.

   _____

   _____

3. In your own words, describe the speaker's impression of the glade in Robert Penn
   Warren's "Gold Glade."

   _____

   _____

   _____

4. Use the five points of a star to identify sensory words Warren uses in "Gold Glade."

Sights:

_____

Sounds:

_____

_____

Smells:

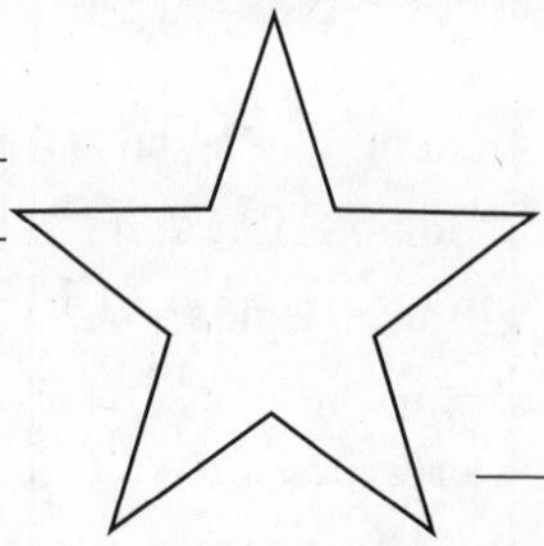

_____

Tastes:

_____

Physical Sensations:

_____

5. Which phrase best describes the subject of "The Light Comes Brighter"? Cite a detail from the poem to support your answer choice.
    a. the change in the sky's light as morning turns to afternoon
    b. the change in the sky's light as the sun rises
    c. the change in seasons from winter to spring
    d. the change in seasons from fall to winter

    _____
    _____

6. Paraphrase the last stanza of "The Light Comes Brighter" (lines 17–20).

    _____
    _____

7. What are the subject and theme of "The Adament" as revealed in the first stanza of the poem?

    _____
    _____

8. In "The Adamant," why is the core sealed (line 12)? Explain why the poet might have chosen these words for the last line of the poem.

    _____
    _____

9. Briefly describe the event that takes place in "Traveling Through the Dark."

    _____
    _____
    _____

10. Circle the letter of the phrase that best describes Stafford's style in "Traveling Through the Dark." Explain your answer choice.
    a. a descriptive, conversational tone   c. an allusion to another poet's work
    b. figurative language   d. repetition and structure

    _____
    _____

Extended Response

11. Use this chart to compare and contrast Theodore Roethke's poems "The Light Comes Brighter" and "The Adamant." Then write two paragraphs about the poems. In the first paragraph, describe the poems' similarities and differences. In the second paragraph, explain why you think the poet chose the approaches he used for each poem.

	The Light Comes Brighter	The Adamant
Subject:		
Theme:		
Style and Diction:		

12. Select one of the poems that you read—"Hawthorne," "Gold Glade," "The Light Comes Brighter," "The Adamant," or "Traveling Through the Dark." Write an essay in which you explore how the poet's style and diction affect readers' impressions of the subject of the poem.

13. Write an essay in which you briefly discuss how each of the poems, "Hawthorne," "Gold Glade," "The Light Comes Brighter," "The Adamant," or "Traveling Through the Dark" demonstrates a sense of emerging identity.

14. In an essay, explain which of the poems, "Hawthorne," "Gold Glade," "The Light Comes Brighter," "The Adamant," or "Traveling Through the Dark," you think has the most powerful effect on readers. Use examples of the poet's diction, style, subject, and theme to support your opinion and include details from the poem to elaborate on your ideas.

15. Choose two of the poems that you read, "Hawthorne," "Gold Glade," "The Light Comes Brighter," "The Adamant," or "Traveling Through the Dark," and write an essay in which you explain how the title relates to the overall effect of the poems.

Oral Response

16. Go back to question 3, 9, 12, 14, or 15 or one assigned by your teacher, and take five to ten minutes to expand your answer and prepare an oral response. Find additional details in the poem(s) that will support your points. You may wish to write down some notes to guide your response.

Rubric for Evaluating Extended Responses

0	1	2	3	4
Blank paper Foreign language Illegible, incoherent Not enough content to score	Incorrect purpose, mode, audience Brief, vague Unelaborated Rambling Lack of language control Poor organization	Correct purpose, mode, audience Some elaboration Some details Gaps in organization Limited language control	Correct purpose, mode, audience Moderately well elaborated Clear, effective language Organized (perhaps with brief digressions)	Correct purpose, mode, audience Effective elaboration Consistent organization Sense of completeness, fluency

Name _____ Date _____

"**Average Waves in Unprotected Waters**" by Anne Tyler

Open-Book Test

Multiple Choice and Short Answer

Write your answers to all questions in this section on the lines provided.
For multiple-choice questions, circle the letter of the best answer.

1. Where is Bet taking Arnold? Explain why she is taking him there.
    a. to visit Mrs. Puckett in the hospital
    b. to visit his grandparents in Salt Spray, Maryland
    c. to see the boats in Salt Spray, Maryland
    d. to the Parkins State hospital

    _____

    _____

    _____

2. Review the first paragraph of the story. Briefly explain how the sentence, "He could tell that something was up" hints at what will occur later in the story.

    _____

    _____

3. Use this sequence-of-events timeline to trace the story's events. On the left-hand side of the timeline, list the events that are happening as the story is told. On the right-hand side of the timeline, list the flashbacks.

Current Events	Flashbacks

4. The description of Arnold's red duffel coat is an example of _____ (text page 926).
    a. chronology   b. flashback   c. foreshadowing   d. imagery
    Explain your answer.

    _____

    _____

5. Cite two quotations from the story that indicate how Mrs. Puckett feels about Arnold and the trip he is taking.

    _____

    _____

    _____

6. Reread the paragraph beginning with "When the train . . ." through the paragraph beginning with "She'd married Avery. . . ." What does this flashback suggest about Bet's future?

    _____

    _____

    _____

7. The woman on the train calls the conductor a "viper" because she is indicating that he is trying to _____ her.
    a. manhandle   b. assault   c. malign   d. assist
    Explain your answer.

    _____

    _____

8. Bet's and Arnold's cab ride from the Parkinsville Railroad Station to the Parkins State Hospital is described in the paragraph beginning with "From the Parkinsville Railroad Station . . . ." What clues does this description offer as to how Bet will feel when she leaves Arnold?

    _____

    _____

    _____

9. Circle the letter of the word that best describes Bet's reaction to leaving Arnold. Give an example from the story to support your answer.
    a. relieved   b. grieving   c. revived   d. desperate

    _____

10. Briefly describe what happens to Bet when she gets back to the train station. Explain why she reacts the way that she does.

    _____

    _____

    _____

    _____

Extended Response

11. Use a Sequence-of-Events organizer to list the six main events of "Average Waves in Unprotected Waters." You may wish to make notes about the story's events before you put them in order in the organizer. Then write the earliest event in the left-hand box, and continue listing the events, in chronological order. Write a summary of the story's events in chronological order.

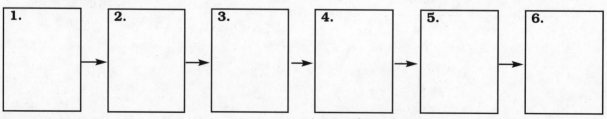

1. → 2. → 3. → 4. → 5. → 6.

12. In an essay, describe the effect of flashbacks in "Average Waves in Unprotected Waters." Cite specific examples from the story and explain how they interrupt the chronological order of the story's events.

13. Write an essay in which you explain Bet's experiences at the train station after she leaves Arnold. In your essay, explain why she reacts the way she does.

14. In an essay, explore Anne Tyler's use of foreshadowing in "Average Waves in Unprotected Waters." Cite specific examples from the story and discuss how they affect the reader's impressions of the story's events.

15. Write an essay about what may happen to the character of Bet after she gets back home. Use the flashback as a basis for logical actions that the character may take. Speculate about how Bet's life will change when she no longer is faced with the difficulties of caring for Arnold.

Oral Response

16. Go back to question 3, 8, 10, 14, or 15 or one assigned by your teacher, and take five to ten minutes to expand your answer and prepare an oral response. Find additional details in the story that will support your points. If necessary, make notes to guide your response.

Rubric for Evaluating Extended Responses

0	1	2	3	4
Blank paper Foreign language Illegible, incoherent Not enough content to score	Incorrect purpose, mode, audience Brief, vague Unelaborated Rambling Lack of language control Poor organization	Correct purpose, mode, audience Some elaboration Some details Gaps in organization Limited language control	Correct purpose, mode, audience Moderately well elaborated Clear, effective language Organized (perhaps with brief digressions)	Correct purpose, mode, audience Effective elaboration Consistent organization Sense of completeness, fluency

from *The Names* by N. Scott Momaday
"Mint Snowball" by Naomi Shihab Nye
"Suspended" by Joy Harjo

Open-Book Test

Multiple Choice and Short Answer

Write your answers to all questions in this section on the lines provided.
For multiple-choice questions, circle the letter of the best answer.

1. Which sentence best describes the point Momaday is making in his anecdote about receiving a horse when he was thirteen years old? Explain your answer.
   a. Horses are an important part of his Kiowa heritage.
   b. He explains why he named the horse Pecos.
   c. He had wanted a horse for a very long time.
   d. Kiowas owned more horses than any other tribe on the Great Plains.

   _____

   _____

2. How does Momaday feel as he begins his journey? Cite details from the essay to support your answer.

   _____

   _____

   _____

3. Write a brief summary of Momaday's journey.

   _____

   _____

   _____

4. "And through the hard hooves, the slender limbs, the supple shoulders, the fluent back of my horse I felt the earth under me." Choose the best synonym for the word *supple* in this context. Explain why the answer you selected is correct and the other answers are incorrect.
   a. compliant   b. sloping   c. flexible   d. straight

   _____

   _____

5. Which word best describes the experience related in the opening paragraph of "Mint Snowball"? Explain your answer.
   a. pleasurable   b. funny   c. tempting   d. melancholy

   _____

   _____

6. Use an Idea Web to organize Nye's thoughts, feelings, associations, and impressions of the Mint Snowball.

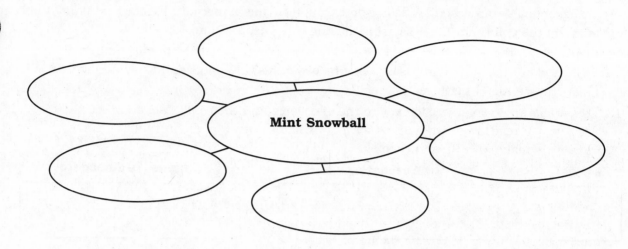

Mint Snowball

7. Explain what happened to the Mint Snowball recipe. Describe how Nye feels about the loss.

_____

_____

_____

8. Choose the best description of Harjo's "rite of passage into the world of humanity." Cite details from the essay that support your answer.
   a. she finds out who Miles Davis is
   b. she takes a ride with her father
   c. she hears jazz
   d. she speaks her first words

_____

_____

9. What does Harjo learn about communication from listening to the music of the jazz trumpeter?

_____

_____

_____

10. Explain how the anecdote in Harjo's essay differs from the anecdotes that Momaday and Nye relate in their essays.

_____

_____

_____

Extended Response

11. Select one of the essays—Momaday's from *The Names*, Nye's "Mint Snowball," or Harjo's "Suspended"—and describe an anecdote from it in one paragraph. In a second paragraph, explain the point that the essayist is making with the anecdote.

12. Throughout the essay from *The Names*, Momaday uses anecdotes to make different points about his life. In an essay, describe two of his anecdotes and explain how they relate to his Kiowa heritage.

13. Use the graphic organizer to explore the anecdotes and their purposes from the three essays you read. Then write an essay that explains a universal truth that all three essayists make with their anecdotes.

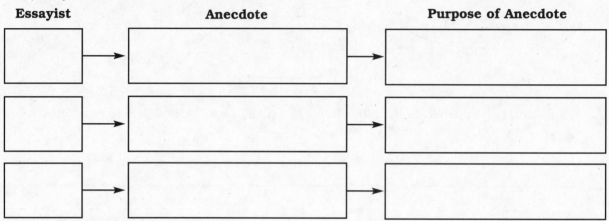

| Essayist | Anecdote | Purpose of Anecdote |

14. Describe an experience of your own that allows you to relate to one of the anecdotes in these essays. Write an essay in which you describe why the essayist's experience inspired you to make your own connections to the ideas of his or her anecdote.

15. An animal, a soda fountain treat, and a piece of recorded music take on significance in these three essays. Write an essay in which you explore the symbolism in the essays. Use the conclusions drawn and generalizations made by the essayists to explain the symbolism.

Oral Response

16. Go back to question 1, 6, 9, 13, or 14 or one assigned by your teacher, and take five to ten minutes to expand your answer and prepare an oral response. Find additional details in the essays that will support your points. If necessary, make notes to guide you in your response.

Rubric for Evaluating Extended Responses

0	1	2	3	4
Blank paper Foreign language Illegible, incoherent Not enough content to score	Incorrect purpose, mode, audience Brief, vague Unelaborated Rambling Lack of language control Poor organization	Correct purpose, mode, audience Some elaboration Some details Gaps in organization Limited language control	Correct purpose, mode, audience Moderately well elaborated Clear, effective language Organized (perhaps with brief digressions)	Correct purpose, mode, audience Effective elaboration Consistent organization Sense of completeness, fluency

"Everyday Use" by Alice Walker

Open-Book Test

Multiple Choice and Short Answer

Write your answers to all questions in this section on the lines provided.
For multiple-choice questions, circle the letter of the best answer.

1. "Everyday Use" is a story that illustrates the impact of _____. Explain your answer.
   a. a tragic fire   c. relatives that move away
   b. conflicts among cultures   d. living in the South

   _____

   _____

2. Why has Dee come to visit her mother and sister? Cite a quotation from the story that explains the motivation for her visit.

   _____

   _____

   _____

3. Use a contrast chart to analyze the contrasts between Maggie and Dee. Then summarize these contrasting characters.

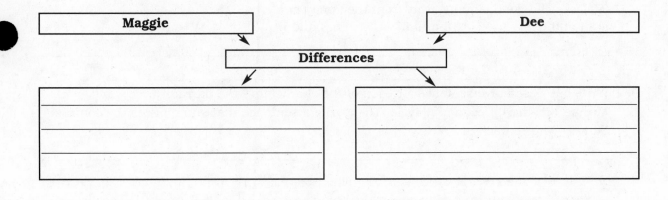

   _____

4. The best description of Maggie's motivation for her timid and insecure behavior is _____. Explain your answer.
   a. Maggie is younger than Dee and feels that her older sister hates her.
   b. Maggie is scarred by a fire that burnt down the family's house.
   c. Maggie's mother is overbearing and intimidates her daughter.
   d. Maggie feels ashamed because of the family's poverty.

   _____

   _____

5. The narrator's reaction to Dee's hair and clothing suggests that Dee (Wangero) has changed since the last time her mother and sister saw her. Briefly describe what has brought about this change in Dee.

_____

_____

_____

6. The first and last paragraphs of the story reveal that, unlike Dee, the narrator and Maggie are not oppressed because _____. Explain your answer.
   a. they seem to enjoy their lives   c. they can make their own quilts
   b. they are not as educated as Dee   d. they were not named after an aunt

_____

_____

7. Briefly describe how Maggie would use the quilts as opposed to how Dee would use them. Then explain the contrast in what the quilts mean to each of the sisters.

_____

_____

_____

8. Choose the answer that best explains why the narrator insists that Dee cannot take the quilts that she wants. Then explain your response, using evidence from the story.
   I. She has promised them to Maggie.
   II. Maggie understands how and why the quilts are made.
   III. Dee has always gotten everything she wants.
   IV. Dee will take the quilts away from the family home.
   a. III and IV   b. II and III   c. I and II   d. IV and I

_____

_____

9. Write one descriptive sentence for each of the characters—the narrator (Dee's and Maggie's mother), Dee, and Maggie. Then write a sentence that summarizes the contrasts between the characters.

_____

_____

_____

_____

10. Explain Walker's title of her story "Everyday Use." Provide a detail or quotation from the story to support your answer.

_____

_____

_____

Extended Response

11. Dee objects to Maggie's having the quilts because "Maggie can't appreciate these quilts! She'd probably be backward enough to put them to everyday use." Write an essay in which you explain why Dee considers it backward to use the quilts for everyday use.

© Prentice-Hall, Inc.

12. Use a herringbone diagram to explore the difference in Dee's motivations when she was growing up and the motivations she has as an adult. Think about the descriptions of Dee when she was younger and briefly summarize them in the top half of the diagram. Write about the descriptions of actions and words as Dee visits her family home in the bottom half of the diagram. Then write one or two paragraphs to describe the character of Dee, including any changes that have occurred since she left home.

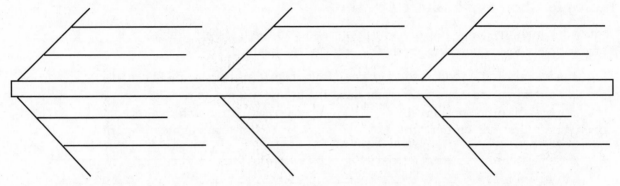

13. As Dee enjoys the food and admires the family benches and butter churn, the narrator sees them with new perspective. Write an essay in which you discuss the perspectives from which Dee and the narrator view everyday parts of life. Does everyday use hold a similar place in both characters' personal histories? Do the two characters appreciate the everyday parts of life in the same manner?

14. In reference to her cultural heritage, Dee states that she has rejected the name her mother gave her because "I couldn't bear it any longer, being named after the people who oppress me." In an essay, explain whether Dee has also been kept down by her family. Include examples from the story to support your opinion.

15. Review the narrator's dream in which she and Dee are brought together on a TV program. In an essay, discuss what this dream reveals about the narrator's feelings toward her oldest daughter.

Oral Response

16. Go back to question 1, 3, 10, 12, or 14 or one assigned by your teacher, and take five to ten minutes to expand your answer and prepare an oral response. Find additional details in the story that will support your points. If necessary, make notes to guide your response.

Rubric for Evaluating Extended Responses

0	1	2	3	4
Blank paper

Foreign language

Illegible, incoherent

Not enough content to score | Incorrect purpose, mode, audience

Brief, vague

Unelaborated

Rambling

Lack of language control

Poor organization | Correct purpose, mode, audience

Some elaboration

Some details

Gaps in organization

Limited language control | Correct purpose, mode, audience

Moderately well elaborated

Clear, effective language

Organized (perhaps with brief digressions) | Correct purpose, mode, audience

Effective elaboration

Consistent organization

Sense of completeness, fluency |

Name _____ Date _____

from _The Woman Warrior_ by Maxine Hong Kingston

Open-Book Test

Multiple Choice and Short Answer

Write your answers to all questions in this section on the lines provided.
For multiple-choice questions, circle the letter of the best answer.

1. This excerpt from _The Woman Warrior_ can be classified as a memoir because _____.
    Explain why it does not fit the standard definition of a memoir.
    a. it is a third-person narrative   c. it recounts a historical event
    b. it is a first-person narrative   d. it recounts a significant event

    _____

    _____

2. Briefly explain why Brave Orchid is anxious and excited about her sister's arrival.

    _____

    _____

    _____

3. Use a sunburst diagram to identify aspects of the character of Brave Orchid. Use the
    surrounding boxes to organize behavior, traits, beliefs, and interactions with other
    characters.

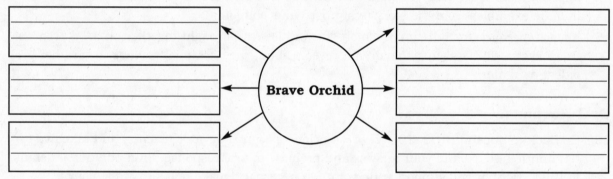

Brave Orchid

4. "Immigration Ghosts were stamping papers." "Ghosts" are referred to several times in this
    excerpt from _The Woman Warrior_. Use the information in Background for Understanding
    to explain who the ghosts are.

    _____

    _____

    _____

5. Briefly describe the differences between Brave Orchid's children and her niece. Use
    details or quotations from the story to support your response.

    _____

    _____

    _____

6. Her daughter could not hear what Moon Orchid said because the glass wall made her words inaudible. Choose the best definition of *inaudible*. Explain the word's use in the context of this sentence.
    a. unable to be heard
    b. unable to be understood
    c. unable to be translated
    d. unable to be absorbed

7. Brave Orchid has not seen her sister, Moon Orchid, for thirty years; her niece has not seen her mother for five years. Explain why Moon Orchid's arrival is a significant event for each of them.

8. Why does Brave Orchid want to take care of Moon Orchid as she goes through Customs? Cite one or two details from the memoir to support your answer.
    a. She thinks that her sister will have brought too many gifts.
    b. She is afraid that her sister will not be allowed through immigration.
    c. She is concerned that her sister will not be fashionably dressed.
    d. She doesn't think her sister will be able to communicate with the Customs officer.

9. Briefly describe Brave Orchid's and Moon Orchid's responses to each other when they finally come face to face.

10. Which reason best describes why this excerpt is an atypical memoir? Explain your answer.
    a. The narrative focuses on six people's experiences.
    b. The narrative focuses on the experiences of someone other than the writer.
    c. The narrative focuses on details of a personal experience.
    d. The narrative focuses on more than one culture.

Extended Response

11. Use this chart to analyze Brave Orchid's preparations for her sister's arrival. In the first column, list the details of her actions and thoughts. In the second column, identify whether Brave Orchid's preparations are indicative of her Chinese culture or are universal kinds of behavior associated with the arrival of a relative. Then write one or two paragraphs to summarize Brave Orchid's preparations.

Brave Orchid's Preparations	Cultural? or Universal?

12. In an essay, discuss the cultural attitudes of Brave Orchid's children as compared to the cultural attitude of her niece. Use examples from the memoir to explain the differences in their perspectives.

13. Consider Brave Orchid's attitude toward American culture. Does she understand it? Appreciate it? Like it? Dislike it? Write an essay that explores Brave Orchid's beliefs, thoughts, feelings, and actions in relation to American culture.

14. Review footnotes 1, 8, and 12. Then write an essay in which you explain how background information can increase readers' understanding and appreciation of the characters and events in the excerpt from *The Woman Warrior*.

15. Many Chinese immigrants came to the United States during the mid-twentieth century to escape the politics and war in their homeland. In an essay, discuss the significance of the references to Vietnam in Kingston's memoir.

Oral Response

16. Go back to question 3, 5, 7, 13, or 14 or one assigned by your teacher, and take five to ten minutes to expand your answer and prepare an oral response. Find additional details in the story that will support your points. If necessary, make notes to guide your response.

Rubric for Evaluating Extended Responses

0	1	2	3	4
Blank paper	Incorrect purpose, mode, audience	Correct purpose, mode, audience	Correct purpose, mode, audience	Correct purpose, mode, audience
Foreign language	Brief, vague	Some elaboration	Moderately well elaborated	Effective elaboration
Illegible, incoherent	Unelaborated	Some details	Clear, effective language	Consistent organization
Not enough content to score	Rambling	Gaps in organization	Organized (perhaps with brief digressions)	Sense of completeness, fluency
	Lack of language control	Limited language control		
	Poor organization			

"Antojos" by Julia Alvarez

Open-Book Test

Multiple Choice and Short Answer

Write your answers to all questions in this section on the lines provided.
For multiple-choice questions, circle the letter of the best answer.

1. Choose the answer that best describes Yolanda's reason for taking her trip. Explain your answer.
   a. She wants to travel by herself.
   b. She wants to go to the beach.
   c. She is looking for ripe guavas.
   d. She is rebelling against her aunts.

   _____

   _____

2. On the lines provided, explain what *antojos* are. Give an example of your own *antojos*.

   _____

   _____

   _____

3. The point where the men with the machetes show up might be called the _____ of the story. Select the correct answer and explain why it is correct.
   a. exposition   b. denoument   c. plot   d. climax

   _____

   _____

4. Use an Idea Web to organize Yolanda's thoughts, feelings, experiences, and associations in relation to guavas. Then on the lines provided below, explain what guavas mean to her.

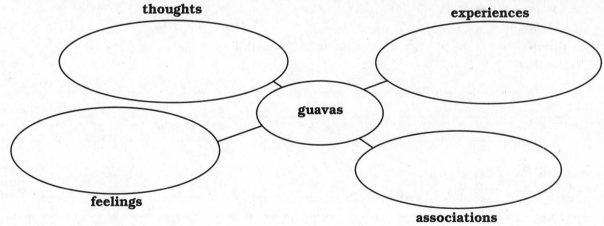

   _____

   _____

5. Do you agree or disagree that the resolution of the plot comes when the men explain themselves to Yolanda? Support your opinion by giving examples from the story.

   _____

   _____

6. Select the best explanation for Yolanda's intense fear of the men with machetes. Explain how the aunts' cautions have heightened Yolanda's reaction.
   a. Because she has spent most of her life in the United States, she has never seen machetes.
   b. The men are making threats with their machetes.
   c. The men are speaking in a language that she does not understand.
   d. Yolanda is aware of the civil unrest in the Dominican Republic.

   _____

   _____

7. "*Directo, directo,*' he enunciated the words carefully." Explain why the man enunciates these words carefully.

   _____

   _____

8. Why does Yolanda decide to speak English rather than Spanish with the men? Briefly explain how her decision affects the situation with the flat tire.

   _____

   _____

   _____

9. At the end of the story Yolanda, once more, notices the "Palmolive woman" poster as she drives away. Why is this image important to the story?

   _____

   _____

   _____

10. In addition to finding ripe guavas, what else has Yolanda discovered on her trip? Which phrase best describes Yolanda's discovery? Explain your answer using evidence from the story.
    a. a part of her Caribbean heritage
    b. how to change a tire on a compact car
    c. where the best guavas are in the Dominican Republic
    d. the dangers of her trip

    _____

    _____

    _____

Extended Response

11. Think about Yolanda's experiences on her trip. What has motivated her to drive north? What events have resulted because of her decision? What has she learned? How has she grown? Write one or two paragraphs in which you discuss the changes Yolanda notices in herself after she returns to the Dominican capital to visit her aunts—and later to the United States.

12. Consider Yolanda's interactions with the other characters in the story. Organize your ideas in the space below. Then write an essay in which you explore the character of Yolanda, as reflected in her relationships with the other characters.

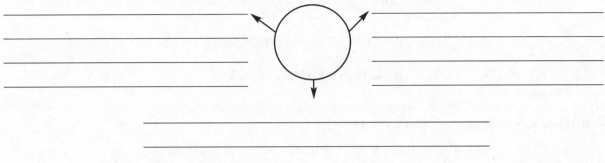

_____   _____
_____   _____
_____   _____
_____   _____

_____
_____
_____

13. The flashback scene in which Yolanda remembers her aunt's concerns and warnings sets up the scene of the story's main conflict when Yolanda is stranded and needs help. Write an essay that discusses the relationship between these two parts of the story. Include details from the story that explain how the two scenes are related.

14. Write an essay in which you explain the significance of the title, "Antojos." In your essay, discuss what *antojos* means, why guavas are Yolanda's *antojos* and how *antojos* lead her to the experiences she has in the story.

15. Yolanda offers to pay Jose to go for help with the flat tire and she also offers to pay the men who change the tire for her. Review the men's and Jose's responses to the offers of money. In an essay, discuss the cultural and age differences that become apparent because of Yolanda's offers of money.

Oral Response

16. Go back to question 2, 4, 6, 10, or 12 or one assigned by your teacher, and take five to ten minutes to expand your answer and prepare an oral response. Find additional details in "Antojos" that will support your points. If necessary, make notes to guide your response.

Rubric for Evaluating Extended Responses

0	1	2	3	4
Blank paper Foreign language Illegible, incoherent Not enough content to score	Incorrect purpose, mode, audience Brief, vague Unelaborated Rambling Lack of language control Poor organization	Correct purpose, mode, audience Some elaboration Some details Gaps in organization Limited language control	Correct purpose, mode, audience Moderately well elaborated Clear, effective language Organized (perhaps with brief digressions)	Correct purpose, mode, audience Effective elaboration Consistent organization Sense of completeness, fluency

"Freeway 280" by Lorna Dee Cervantes
"Who Burns for the Perfection of Paper" by Martín Espada
"Hunger in New York City" by Simon Ortiz
"Most Satisfied by Snow" by Diana Chang
"What For" by Garrett Hongo

Open-Book Test

Multiple Choice and Short Answer

Write your answers to all questions in this section on the lines provided.
For multiple-choice questions, circle the letter of the best answer.

1. Describe the setting of "Freeway 280." Include details from the poem that indicate specific aspects of the setting.

    _____

    _____

    _____

2. Which factors contribute to the poet's voice in "Freeway 280"? Write one or two sentences that describe the poet's voice.
    I. use of Spanish words and phrases
    II. use of rhyme
    III. use of word patterns
    IV. visual imagery
    a. I, II, and III   b. I, III, and IV   c. II, III, and IV   d. I, II, III, and IV

    _____

    _____

3. Review lines 1–2 and 22–23 of "Who Burns for the Perfection of Paper." How has the speaker's attitude toward legal pads changed in ten years? How has it remained the same?

    _____

    _____

    _____

4. Which word best describes Espada's voice in "Who Burns for the Perfection of Paper"? Explain why the answer you selected is correct and the others answers are not.
    a. rambling   b. elaborate   c. insincere   d. straightforward

    _____

    _____

    _____

5. Use this graphic organizer to gather, restate, and summarize the poet's ideas in "Hunger in New York City."

Hunger in New York City

Beginning	Middle	End

Summary

6. Briefly explain the hunger that the speaker describes in "Hunger in New York City."

_____

_____

_____

7. In a sentence or two, summarize "Most Satisfied by Snow." Then write another sentence that describes Diana Chang's voice in this poem.

_____

_____

_____

8. If fog and heavy rain pervade the area, they are _____.
   a. about to arrive   b. scattered here and there
   c. spread throughout   d. on the edges
   Explain why the answer you chose is correct.

_____

_____

9. Choose the best description of the speaker's attitude toward his father in "What For."
   List details from the poem that support your answer.
   a. He would like to lighten his father's workload.
   b. He is angry at his father for not spending more time at home.
   c. He doesn't understand why his father is away for so much of the time.
   d. He is confused by his father's job and workload.

_____

_____

10. The figurative language of "What For" helps convey the speaker's distinctive voice. Cite one or two examples of figurative language in the poem, explaining how these words establish the poet's voice.

_____

_____

_____

Extended Response

11. Select one of the poems that you read—"Freeway 280," "Who Burns for the Perfection of Paper," "Hunger in New York City," "Most Satisfied by Snow" or "What For"—and write an essay in which you summarize the poet's main points.

12. Select two of the poems and write an essay in which you discuss how the poems reflect the cultural roots of the poets. In your essay, include specific examples from the poems, explaining what part of the poet's culture is being portrayed.

13. Use a chart to identify the voice of the poets. Then think about a universal truth that is conveyed by the poems. Write an essay in which you explain what the poems have in common.

POEM	VOICE
Freeway 280	
Who Burns for the Perfection of Paper	
Hunger in New York City	
Most Satisfied by Snow	
What For	

14. Each of the poems addresses a significant part of life, such as work, where one lives, or the importance of self. Write an essay in which you explore two of the poems' themes. You may wish to use two poems that have similar themes or you may use two poems with contrasting themes. As you write, think about the poets' voices in relation to how the poems' themes are conveyed.

15. Consider the titles that the poets chose for their poems. Choose two of the poems, and in an essay, discuss why the poets titled their poems as they did. Discuss how the poems' titles contribute to your understanding and appreciation of the poets' voices.

Oral Response

16. Go back to question 2, 5, 11, 12, or 15 or one assigned by your teacher, and take five to ten minutes to expand your answer and prepare an oral response. Find additional details in the poems that will support your points. If necessary, make notes to guide your response.

Rubric for Evaluating Extended Responses

0	1	2	3	4
Blank paper	Incorrect purpose, mode, audience	Correct purpose, mode, audience	Correct purpose, mode, audience	Correct purpose, mode, audience
Foreign language	Brief, vague	Some elaboration	Moderately well elaborated	Effective elaboration
Illegible, incoherent	Unelaborated	Some details	Clear, effective language	Consistent organization
Not enough content to score	Rambling	Gaps in organization	Organized (perhaps with brief digressions)	Sense of completeness, fluency
	Lack of language control	Limited language control		
	Poor organization			

from *The Mortgaged Heart* by Carson McCullers
"Onomatopoeia" by William Safire
"Coyote v. Acme" by Ian Frazier

Open-Book Test

Multiple Choice and Short Answer

Write your answers to all questions in this section on the lines provided.
For multiple-choice questions, circle the letter of the best answer.

1. Choose the word that best describes McCullers's topic in the excerpt from *The Mortgaged Heart*. Cite examples from the essay to support your answer choice.
   a. dreariness   b. closeness   c. fondness   d. loneliness

   _____

   _____

2. What type of essay is McCullers's excerpt from *The Mortgaged Heart*? Explain your answer.
   a. satirical   b. analytical   c. expository   d. descriptive

   _____

   _____

3. Briefly explain what McCullers thinks is the cause of loneliness in America. Provide details from the essay that support her opinion.

   _____

   _____

   _____

4. List three examples of Safire's explanation of the origin, meaning, and usage of onomatopoeia in his expository essay, "Onomatopoeia."

   _____

   _____

5. Using information from Safire's essay, "Onomatopoeia," explain why *yakking, pooh-pooh,* and *murmur* are examples of onomatopoeia.

   _____

   _____

   _____

6. Use this graphic organizer to identify Safire's line of reasoning in "Onomatopoeia." Jot down the main points of Safire's essay. Note the reasons, facts, and examples that Safire uses to back up his points. You will not have to fill in every box in the chart.

MAIN POINT:	REASONS:	FACTS:	EXAMPLES:

_____

_____

_____

7. Legal cases attempt to prove an argument. The argument that Frazier presents in "Coyote v. Acme" is that the Acme products Coyote uses in his attempts to capture the Road Runner have _____. Choose the correct answer, and cite evidence from the essay to support your answer.
   a. caused injury to the plaintiff due to defects in manufacture or improper cautionary labeling
   b. cost the plaintiff excess expenditure in relation to the benefits of their use
   c. provided an unfair advantage to the plaintiff's prey in his profession of predator
   d. consistently been constructed of inferior quality materials

_____

_____

8. Explain why "Coyote v. Acme" is a satirical essay. Provide an example from the essay to demonstrate its satire.

_____

_____

9. If you hear a *precipitate* sound, you may be _____. Select the best answer, and explain your answer choice.
   a. relieved   b. soothed   c. startled   d. angry

_____

_____

10. Identify Frazier's line of reasoning in "Coyote v. Acme."

_____

_____

Extended Response

11. Carson McCullers analyzes American loneliness in the excerpt from *The Mortgaged Heart.* Write one or two paragraphs about her essay. Explain her main points and discuss the effectiveness of her essay.

12. Examine the lines of reasoning that McCullers, Safire, and Frazier use in their essays. In a short essay, explain which essayist uses the most effective line of reasoning. Include examples from the essay to support your opinion.

13. Compare and contrast the essay form used in two of the three essays. Explain how the different essay styles are effective in making the authors' points.

14. In an essay, explore the relationship between the Warner Brothers cartoon "Road Runner and Coyote" and Frazier's essay "Coyote v. Acme." Discuss the parallels that may exist between the cartoon and the essay, the confrontational nature of each, and any other similarities you may notice.

15. How would you address the issue of the validity of product liability lawsuits? Write an essay in which you suggest an alternative approach. Would your essay be analytical, expository, or—like Frazier's—satirical? As you write, consider whether you would be addressing the same audience that Frazier addresses.

Oral Response

16. Go back to question 2, 4, 10, 11, or 14 or one assigned by your teacher, and take five to ten minutes to expand your answer and prepare an oral response. Find additional details in the essays that will support your points. If necessay, make notes to guide your response.

Rubric for Evaluating Extended Responses

0	1	2	3	4
Blank paper Foreign language Illegible, incoherent Not enough content to score	Incorrect purpose, mode, audience Brief, vague Unelaborated Rambling Lack of language control Poor organization	Correct purpose, mode, audience Some elaboration Some details Gaps in organization Limited language control	Correct purpose, mode, audience Moderately well elaborated Clear, effective language Organized (perhaps with brief digressions)	Correct purpose, mode, audience Effective elaboration Consistent organization Sense of completeness, fluency

Name _____ Date _____

"Straw Into Gold" by Sandra Cisneros
"For the Love of Books" by Rita Dove
"Mother Tongue" by Amy Tan

Open-Book Test

Multiple Choice and Short Answer

Write your answers to all questions in this section on the lines provided.
For multiple-choice questions, circle the letter of the best answer.

1. In the opening paragraphs of "Straw Into Gold," what personal experience does Cisneros compare to the experience of being ordered to spin straw into gold? Select the correct answer and explain the comparison.
    a. moving into a new house
    b. making corn tortillas
    c. reading library books
    d. learning to garden

    _____

2. In "Straw Into Gold," Cisneros states, "Didn't think I could do it. But I did." Briefly explain how she accomplished something she thought she could not do.

    _____

    _____

3. Cite an example of "straw" that Cisneros remembers from her childhood. What gold did she spin from that straw?

    _____

    _____

4. Describe Rita Dove's passion for books. Explain why she "even loved to gaze at a closed book . . ."

    _____

    _____

    _____

5. In "For the Love of Books," Rita Dove realizes that writers are real people. Which statement best describes this experience? Explain her understanding of the realization that writers are real people.
    a. She reads Louis Untermeyer's *Treasury of Best Loved Poems*.
    b. She finds a fascinating story in a science fiction magazine.
    c. She meets John Ciardi at a book-signing.
    d. She samples Shakespeare's works.

    _____

    _____

6. Why did Rita Dove's English teacher, Miss Oechsner, take her to the book-signing? Explain the effect of the book-signing on Dove.

_____

_____

7. If you rely on empirical evidence to hypothesize, you _____. Choose the answer that best completes this sentence and explain your answer.
   a. research a topic on the Internet
   b. use data derived from a survey
   c. use information derived from observation or experiment
   d. speculate about all of the possible scenarios

_____

_____

8. Use a chart to analyze the different "Englishes" that Amy Tan describes in "Mother Tongue." In the left-hand column, identify the different kinds of English; in the right-hand column briefly explain how Tan uses them in her life and in her writing. On the lines provided below, explain why Tan uses different kinds of English.

Kinds of English	Its Use

_____

_____

9. Which sentence best describes Amy Tan's realization about her mother's English? Explain your answer.
   a. Tan's mother's math skills are much better than her language skills.
   b. The English that Tan uses with her mother prevents them from understanding analogies.
   c. Tan's mother relies on her daughter to help her communicate.
   d. Despite her "limited" English, Tan's mother communicates well.

_____

_____

10. Identify the message of Tan's essay, "Mother Tongue." Then evaluate her message. Do you think her idea is valid?

_____

_____

_____

Extended Response

11. Select one of the essays that you read—"Straw Into Gold," "For the Love of Books," or "Mother Tongue." In one or two paragraphs, describe the personal experience that the writer had, and the understanding she gained through her reflection about the experience.

12. Write an essay in which you identify and explain Rita Dove's message in her essay "For the Love of Books." In your essay, evaluate Dove's message. Is it valid? Do you agree or disagree with it?

13. Use the following space to organize and examine the ideas about communication that Cisneros, Dove, and Tan present in their essays. Then write an essay that summarizes the writers' messages.

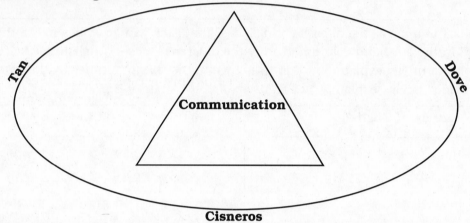

14. In an essay, explore the significance of the titles of the three essays—"Straw Into Gold," "For the Love of Books," or "Mother Tongue." Discuss how the titles indicate the writers' messages and whether you think the titles are appropriate for the essays.

15. Use Tan's ideas about different kinds of English as a basis to consider the kinds of English you encounter every day. Then write an essay in which you explain the use of English in your life and communications.

Oral Response

16. Go back to question 3, 4, 8, 12, or 15 or one assigned by your teacher, and take five to ten minutes to expand your answer and prepare an oral response. Find additional details in the essays that will support your points. If necessary, make notes to guide your response.

Rubric for Evaluating Extended Responses

0	1	2	3	4
Blank paper Foreign language Illegible, incoherent Not enough content to score	Incorrect purpose, mode, audience Brief, vague Unelaborated Rambling Lack of language control Poor organization	Correct purpose, mode, audience Some elaboration Some details Gaps in organization Limited language control	Correct purpose, mode, audience Moderately well elaborated Clear, effective language Organized (perhaps with brief digressions)	Correct purpose, mode, audience Effective elaboration Consistent organization Sense of completeness, fluency

Name _____   Date _____

"The Rockpile" by James Baldwin

Open-Book Test

Multiple Choice and Short Answer

Write your answers to all questions in this section on the lines provided.
For multiple-choice questions, circle the letter of the best answer.

1. Briefly describe the setting of "The Rockpile." Use details and images from the story in your description.

   _____

   _____

   _____

2. Roy and John have been forbidden to go to the rockpile because _____. Select the phrase that best completes this sentence. Cite evidence from the story to support your answer.
   a. it is too far away from home   c. a neighborhood boy got hurt there
   b. it is a dangerous place to play   d. it is a sinful place

   _____

   _____

3. Compare and contrast the characters of John and Roy by filling in the chart below. In each character column, write a word or phrase that describes each character for the category listed in the left-hand column. Then write a brief description of the similarities and differences of the two characters.

	John	Roy
family role		
temperament		
attitude toward rockpile		
relationship with Elizabeth		
relationship with Gabriel		

   _____

   _____

   _____

4. Describe what the boys see from the fire escape. What clues to the story's setting are found in their observations?

     _____

     _____

     _____

5. If you greet people decorously, you might _____. Choose the phrase that best completes the sentence and explain your answer.
     a. shake their hands   c. barely acknowledge them
     b. shout at them   d. offer them a stick of gum

     _____

     _____

6. Explain why Roy disobeys his parents and goes to the rockpile. Provide at least two examples of dialogue that indicate that he knows he is disobeying.

     _____

     _____

     _____

7. Describe the setting of the confrontation between the family members. Explain how the setting affects the characters' actions.

     _____

     _____

     _____

8. Which sentence best describes what has caused the heated argument between Gabriel and Elizabeth? Cite evidence from the story to support your answer.
     a. Each of them feels differently about Roy and John.
     b. They disagree about how to punish Roy.
     c. John will not accept the blame for the accident.
     d. Delilah's crying has made them tense and argumentative.

     _____

     _____

9. Everyone is upset about what has happened to Roy. However, Elizabeth and Gabriel are arguing about far more than Roy's accident. Choose the sentence that best describes the nature of their disagreement. Provide at least two details from the story that illustrate the tension between Elizabeth and Gabriel.
     a. Gabriel distrusts John and Elizabeth distrusts Roy.
     b. They have always hated each other.
     c. Each of them has different feelings toward the children.
     d. Sister McCandless has meddled in their family business.

     _____

     _____

10. Explain how the tense situation resolves at the end of the story.

     _____

     _____

     _____

Extended Response

11. "The Rockpile" details a chain of related events that are based on cause and effect. Trace the story's events. Start with Gabriel and Elizabeth forbidding the boys to go to the rockpile, which results in the rockpile taking on "such mysterious importance that Roy felt it to be his right, not to say his duty, to play there." Write one or two paragraphs to summarize the cause-and-effect pattern that evolves from the story's events.

12. Write an essay in which you discuss the effect the rockpile incident will have on the family in the future. In your essay, discuss how the characters may react to the situation the following day, a month later, or a year later.

13. The situation that arises from Roy's injuries is painfully portrayed by the family's confrontation. In an essay, discuss whether you think the problem is unique to the situation, to the family, or whether the issues exist for people in general.

14. Write an essay in which you explore how the setting of the story affects the events that occur. Would boys in a suburb be apt to play on a rockpile? Would boys in a setting 75 years later want to play on a rockpile? As you write, answer these questions that relate to the time and place in which the story's events occur.

15. In an essay, examine the deeper meaning of the rockpile. What does it symbolize? How does it affect the characters? Do you think James Baldwin played on a rockpile when he was a boy?

Oral Response

16. Go back to question 3, 9, 11, 13, or 15 or one assigned by your teacher, and take five to ten minutes to expand your answer and prepare an oral response. Find additional details in "The Rockpile" that will support your points. If necessary, make notes to guide your response.

Rubric for Evaluating Extended Responses

0	1	2	3	4
Blank paper Foreign language Illegible, incoherent Not enough content to score	Incorrect purpose, mode, audience Brief, vague Unelaborated Rambling Lack of language control Poor organization	Correct purpose, mode, audience Some elaboration Some details Gaps in organization Limited language control	Correct purpose, mode, audience Moderately well elaborated Clear, effective language Organized (perhaps with brief digressions)	Correct purpose, mode, audience Effective elaboration Consistent organization Sense of completeness, fluency

Name _____   Date _____

from *Hiroshima* by John Hersey
"Losses" and "The Death of the Ball Turret Gunner"
by Randall Jarrell

Open-Book Test

Multiple Choice and Short Answer

Write your answers to all questions in this section on the lines provided.
For multiple-choice questions, circle the letter of the best answer.

1. Select the phrase that best describes the mood of the people in Hiroshima during the
    time before the bomb drops. Cite evidence from the story to support your answer.
    a. angry at the military
    b. constantly worried about spies
    c. anxious for the hot weather to break
    d. uneasy about the threat of an air raid

    _____

    _____

2. Mr. Tanimoto was 3,500 yards from the center of the explosion; Mrs. Nakamura was
    1,350 yards away. Why does Hersey specifically state where each person was in relation
    to the explosion of the bomb that dropped on Hiroshima?

    _____

    _____

3. Use the graphic organizer to help you make inferences about the theme of the excerpt
    from *Hiroshima*. In the left-hand column of boxes, list details, events, characters, and
    literary devices that carry importance in Hersey's writing. Then in the middle column
    make inferences about them. Use the inferences you draw to state the implied theme.

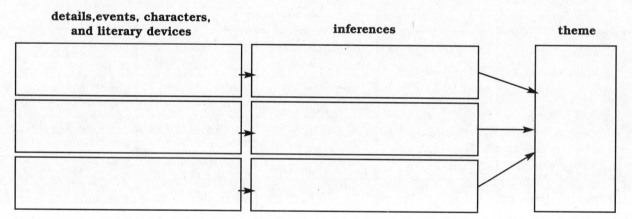

details, events, characters,   **inferences**   **theme**
and literary devices

4. Hersey spent a great deal of time in East Asia. What effect do you think his time with the
    people had on his writing about the effects of the bomb in Hiroshima?

    _____

    _____

5. Hersey was assigned to write articles for news publications but he wrote *Hiroshima* on his own volition. What is the meaning of *volition?* Explain your answer choice.
   a. act of rebellion
   b. act of using the will
   c. act of compliance
   d. act of preference

6. What is the best interpretation of the first two lines of "Losses"? Explain your answer.
   a. The pilots' deaths are regarded as normal occurrences ("everybody died") or routine events ("we had died before").
   b. The pilots never die ("it was not dying").
   c. The pilots always die ("everybody died").
   d. The pilots' deaths are regarded as accidents or mistakes ("it was not dying") instead of war casualties.

7. The pilots are trained to fly planes and drop bombs in places that strategically advance the war effort. Keeping this fact in mind, explain the significance of line 25 of "Losses."

8. The theme of "Losses" is that war is violent, senseless, and impersonal. Explain how the poem reveals this theme.

9. Choose the sentence that best describes what happens in "The Death of the Ball Turret Gunner." Explain your answer.
   a. The gunner falls asleep in his position in the ball turret.
   b. The gunner is hit by enemy fire and dies in his position in the ball turret.
   c. The gunner is hit by enemy fire and receives a medal for his bravery.
   d. The gunner freezes to death in the ball turret.

10. What does the main character of "The Death of the Ball Turret Gunner" reveal about the central idea that Jarrell presents in his poem?

Extended Response

11 Jarrell's poems, "Losses," and "The Ball Turret Gunner," have themes about war. Write two paragraphs: in the first state and describe the implied theme of each poem; in the second paragraph, explain why Jarrell wrote two different poems with similar themes.

12. The excerpt from *Hiroshima* and the poems "Losses" and "The Death of the Ball Turret Gunner" all have themes relating to war. Use the graphic organizer to jot down the ideas about war that are presented in each selection. Then write an essay in which you explore the writers' themes.

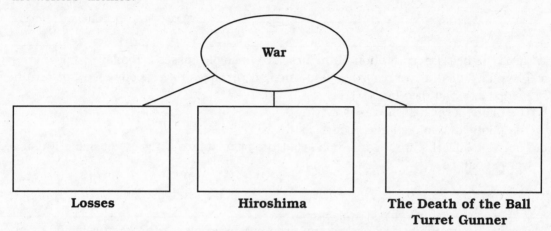

Losses   **Hiroshima**   **The Death of the Ball Turret Gunner**

13. The excerpt from *Hiroshima* and the poems "Losses" and "The Death of the Ball Turret Gunner" address death as a result of war. Write an essay in which you discuss the impact of wartime death. As you write, consider Jarrell's line in "Losses," " . . . the people we had killed and never seen." Use details from the selections to support the ideas.

14. In an essay, discuss the effect of Hersey's specific details about the routine activities of the people in the days and hours before the bomb dropped in Hiroshima. Would a more general description have had the same impact?

15. The excerpt from *Hiroshima* and the poems "Losses" and "The Death of the Ball Turret Gunner" were written in response to World War II. Write an essay in which you discuss the selections' relevance to other wars throughout history.

Oral Response

16. Go back to question 3, 8, 11, 13, or 15 or one assigned by your teacher, and take five to ten minutes to expand your answer and prepare an oral response. Find additional details in the selections that will support your points. If necessary, make notes to guide your response.

Rubric for Evaluating Extended Responses

0	1	2	3	4
Blank paper Foreign language Illegible, incoherent Not enough content to score	Incorrect purpose, mode, audience Brief, vague Unelaborated Rambling Lack of language control Poor organization	Correct purpose, mode, audience Some elaboration Some details Gaps in organization Limited language control	Correct purpose, mode, audience Moderately well elaborated Clear, effective language Organized (perhaps with brief digressions)	Correct purpose, mode, audience Effective elaboration Consistent organization Sense of completeness, fluency

"Mirror" by Sylvia Plath
"In a Classroom" by Adrienne Rich
"The Explorer" by Gwendolyn Brooks
"Frederick Douglass" and **"Runagate Runagate"**
by Robert Hayden

Open-Book Test

Multiple Choice and Short Answer

Write your answers to all questions in this section on the lines provided.
For multiple-choice questions, circle the letter of the best answer.

1. The mirror in "The Mirror" symbolizes _____. Choose the answer that best completes this sentence, and explain your answer.
   a. vanity   b. self-reflection   c. opposites   d. smoothness

   _____

   _____

2. If you meditate on a painting in an art gallery, you _____ about it. Select the best meaning for *meditate* in this sentence, and explain your answer.
   a. think deeply   c. express ideas
   b. take notes   d. form a quick opinion

   _____

   _____

3. Explain the theme of "In a Classroom." Use details from the poem to support your answer.

   _____

   _____

   _____

4. Reread lines 6–10 of "In a Classroom." Explain Jude's response to the poetry being read and discussed.

   _____

   _____

5. Gwendolyn Brooks grew up in an urban setting. This information helps you determine that the setting of "The Explorer" is _____. Cite details from the poem to support your answer choice and explain them in the context of Brooks's background.
   a. an empty classroom   c. a crowded apartment building
   b. a busy city street   d. a shopping mall after hours

   _____

   _____

6. Describe what the speaker of "The Explorer" is looking for. In your description, use details from the poems to explain whether he does or does not find it.

   _____

   _____

7. Use the sunburst diagram to record and organize the words and images of "Frederick Douglass." Then interpret the poet's message by looking at the underlying meaning of these words and images.

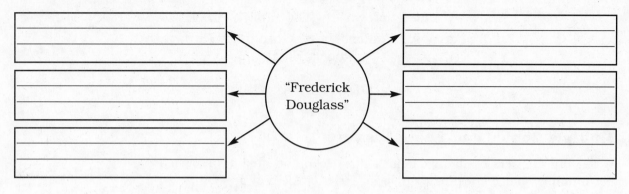

8. Review the biographical information about Robert Hayden. Then think about the details of "Frederick Douglass" in the context of Hayden's African American culture. Briefly explain the context and theme of the poem.

9. Which sentence best explains why Hayden refers to writers such as Ralph Waldo Emerson and Henry David Thoreau when he lists abolitionists such as Thomas Garrett and John Brown (lines 50–53) ? Explain your answer.
   a. They were also abolitionists.
   c. They wrote about abolitionists.
   b. They wrote about independence.
   d. They wrote about American history.

10. Explain how the indentations in the text of "Runagate Runagate" contribute to the poem's message and the feelings conveyed about the message.

Extended Response

11. Select one of the poems and use historical context or the author's background information to write an essay in which you explain the connection between the context and the theme of the poem.

12. In "The Mirror," the speaker is unhappy and agitated about seeing her aging reflection in the mirror. In an essay, discuss how the context of society's attitudes toward aging connect to the theme of Plath's poem.

13. Use the historical context to connect the ideas of "Frederick Douglass" and "Runagate Runagate" to the poems' themes. In the top space of the graphic organizer, list facts and information you know about abolitionists and the Underground Railroad; in the bottom boxes, list characters, details, and events from the poems. Then write an essay in which you explain the themes of Hayden's poems.

Abolitionists and the Underground Railroad

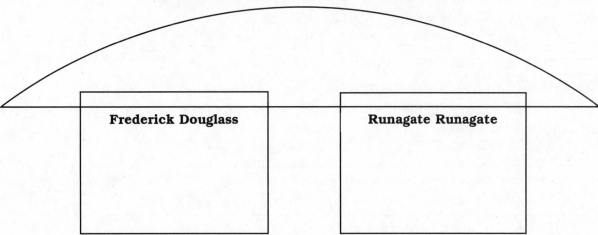

| **Frederick Douglass** | **Runagate Runagate** |

14. In an essay, explore the speaker's attitude and feelings in "The Explorer." Is he looking for a quiet place to relax, or is he trying to escape? Reread the poem carefully and look for clues to the speaker's state of mind. Use the clues in your essay.

15. Write an essay in which you discuss the freedom that Hayden describes in "Frederick Douglass." Use the context of the Hayden's life and other writings to amplify the ideas that are found in the poem. Connect these ideas to Hayden's message.

Oral Response

16. Go back to question 3, 6, 11, 12, or 14 or one assigned by your teacher, and take five to ten minutes to expand your answer and prepare an oral response. Find additional details in the poems that will support your points. If necessary, make notes to guide your response.

Rubric for Evaluating Extended Responses

0	1	2	3	4
Blank paper	Incorrect purpose, mode, audience	Correct purpose, mode, audience	Correct purpose, mode, audience	Correct purpose, mode, audience
Foreign language	Brief, vague	Some elaboration	Moderately well elaborated	Effective elaboration
Illegible, incoherent	Unelaborated	Some details	Clear, effective language	Consistent organization
Not enough content to score	Rambling	Gaps in organization	Organized (perhaps with brief digressions)	Sense of completeness, fluency
	Lack of language control	Limited language control		
	Poor organization			

Name _____ Date _____

Open-Book Test

Multiple Choice and Short Answer

Write your answers to all questions in this section on the lines provided.
For multiple-choice questions, circle the letter of the best answer.

1. In "For My Children," the tales that the speaker has for her children are from _____.
   Choose the answer that best completes this sentence and cite evidence from the poem to
   support your answer.
   a. the United States   c. northern Africa
   b. a Caribbean island   d. southern Africa

   _____

   _____

2. Briefly explain why "For My Children" can be classified as a lyric poem. Support your
   answer with examples from the poem.

   _____

   _____

   _____

3. Write the third stanza of "For My Children" on the lines below, as sentences. Place a
   slash mark [/] between each sentence. Identify how many sentences make up the
   stanza.

   _____

   _____

   _____

4. The speaker of "For My Children" is using the poem to educate her children about their
   heritage. Define the word *heritage*. Explain why heritage is important to the speaker and
   why she feels her children should learn about their heritage.

   _____

   _____

   _____

5. Reread the fifth and sixth stanzas of "For My Children." Explain what connection the
   speaker is making between her children and their heritage in these lines.

   _____

   _____

   _____

6. Select the phrase that best describes who the Bidwell Ghost is. Explain your answer.
   a. the ancestor of a woman named Bidwell   c. a child who died in a fire
   b. a woman who has suffered a terrible tragedy d. the speaker's grandmother

   _____

   _____

7. Use the graphic organizer to explore the main character in "Bidwell Ghost." In the outer circle, write examples of her current behavior; in the inner circle briefly describe what happened to cause her to act the way she does.

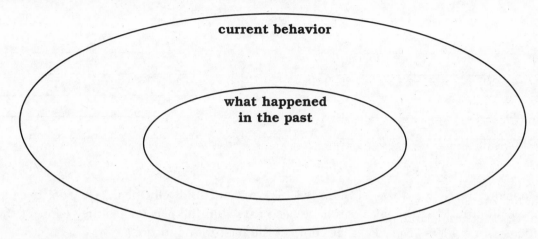

8. Besides the woman, _____ survived the fire that burnt down her home in "Bidwell Ghost." Choose the correct answer, and explain the connection of the woman to the other "survivor."
    a. the woman's white dress   c. the apple trees
    b. the family car   d. nothing

    _____

9. Which phrase best describes the single, unified effect of "Bidwell Ghost"? Identify lines or details from the poet that contribute to the lyric effect.
    a. a mother's legacy for her children   c. a historical account of a tragedy
    b. the sorrowful portrayal of a tragic figure d. a reverie on an apple orchard

    _____

    _____

10. Briefly describe the mood that Louise Erdrich creates in her lyric poem "Bidwell Ghost." Identify aspects of lyric poetry that contribute to the mood.

    _____

    _____

Extended Response

11. In "For My Children," the speaker has educated herself about her heritage and now she is passing what she has learned on to her children. Write an essay in which you discuss the results of learning about one's heritage. Where does the information come from? Why is it important to share the information? Use ideas from "For My Children" to elaborate the points you make in your essay.

12. Write an essay in which you compare and contrast the lyric qualities of "For My Children" and "Bidwell Ghost." In your essay, explain how the poets' use of lyricism helps communicate the message of their poems.

13. Select either "For My Children" or "Bidwell Ghost," and use the open mind organizer to explore the effects of the poem. Then use the ideas that you generated to write one or two paragraphs in which you explain the single, unified effect that makes it a lyric poem.

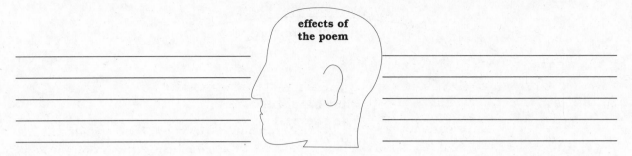

effects of the poem

14. Consider the final stanzas of "For My Children" and "Bidwell Ghost." How do these last lines sum up what the speakers have been saying in the poems? Do they connect the themes to readers' lives? Do they connect the past to the future?

15. In an essay, explain the use of figurative language in "For My Children" and "Bidwell Ghost." Write about the effect of figurative language on the subjects, lyric qualities, and intended audiences of the poems.

Oral Response

16. Go back to question 2, 7, 11, 12, or 15 or one assigned by your teacher, and take five to ten minutes to expand your answer and prepare an oral response. Find additional details in the poems that will support your points. If necessary, make notes to guide your response.

Rubric for Evaluating Extended Responses

0	1	2	3	4
Blank paper Foreign language Illegible, incoherent Not enough content to score	Incorrect purpose, mode, audience Brief, vague Unelaborated Rambling Lack of language control Poor organization	Correct purpose, mode, audience Some elaboration Some details Gaps in organization Limited language control	Correct purpose, mode, audience Moderately well elaborated Clear, effective language Organized (perhaps with brief digressions)	Correct purpose, mode, audience Effective elaboration Consistent organization Sense of completeness, fluency

"The Writer in the Family" by E.L. Doctorow

Open-Book Test

Multiple Choice and Short Answer

Write your answers to all questions in this section on the lines provided.
For multiple-choice questions, circle the letter of the best answer.

1. The issues that the characters of "The Writer in the Family" face are based on the _____
    of the narrator's father. Choose the answer that best completes this sentence, and explain
    your answer.
    a. profession   b. background   c. death   d. favorite pastime

    _____

    _____

2. Why do the aunts decide not to tell the grandmother what has happened to Jack?
    Describe the outcome of this decision.

    _____

    _____

    _____

3. The narrator's aunt asks him to write letters to his grandmother. Briefly explain why this
    is an unusual request.

    _____

    _____

    _____

4. Use a chart to trace the narrator's thoughts and actions throughout the story. Jot down
    words or phrases that describe what the narrator is thinking and doing at the beginning,
    in the middle, and at the end of the story. Explain whether he is a static or dynamic
    character.

Narrator at the beginning of the story	Narrator in the middle of the story	Narrator at the end of the story

_____

_____

_____

5. The conflict between the narrator's mother and Aunt Frances contributes to each of these characters being _____. Explain your answer using examples from the story.
   a. flat   b. static   c. minor   d. dynamic

   _____

   _____

6. Which answer contains Aunt Frances's remarks that belong in the family anthology of unforgivable remarks? Explain why the remarks are unforgivable.
   I. "You're so right, he [the narrator's father] loved to go places, he loved life, he loved everything."
   II. "You're [the narrator] a very talented young man. I just want to tell you what a blessing your letter was."
   III. "Tell her [the narrator's mother] not to worry, a poor old lady who has never wished anything but the best for her will soon die."
   IV. "Your mother has very bitter feelings and now I see she has poisoned you with them."
   a. I and II   b. II and III   c. III and IV   d. I and IV

   _____

   _____

7. Skim back through the story and review the attitudes and behavior of the narrator's brother. Explain whether he is a static or dynamic character.

   _____

   _____

   _____

8. Choose the sentence that best describes the discovery the narrator makes about his father toward the end of the story. Explain the narrator's reaction to what he learns.
   a. His father served in the Great War.   c. His father served in the Navy.
   b. His father served in the Army.   d. His father served in Vietnam.

   _____

   _____

9. There is a relationship between the letters the narrator is being asked to write, his covering up the activity, and the dream he is having. Relate these three aspects of the story.

   _____

   _____

   _____

10. Reread the narrator's conversation with Aunt Frances and the last letter he writes, and judge his actions. Is his last letter morally defensible? Briefly explain what standards you are using to make your judgment.

   _____

   _____

   _____

Extended Response

11. The narrator has been given a tremendous responsibility by being asked to write the letters to his grandmother. In an essay, discuss why he has been asked to write the letters, the fairness of the request, and the effect it has on him.

12. The narrator states, "We began to try to organize our lives." Write an essay in which you examine the difficulties the family faces after the narrator's father dies. Include examples of complications that are introduced by the story's events, such as the stonecutters' going on strike.

13. Use the chart to organize your ideas about what might have happened if the narrator had continued to write the letters, and what will happen now that he has put an end to the letters. Then write an essay in which you compare and contrast the outcomes of the two scenarios. In your essay, evaluate the character's decision to stop writing the letters.

narrator continues to write letters	narrator puts and end to the letters

14. Write an essay in which you discuss the family dynamics portrayed in the story. Consider the interaction between the aunts and the mother, the two brothers, and all of the characters in relationship to the father. Use examples from the story to support your thoughts and ideas.

15. Explore the impact that the narrator's discovery of his father's interest in the sea has on his feelings about deciding to stop writing the letters. In an essay, explain how this knowledge about his father causes or supports his shift in attitude about the letters.

Oral Response

16. Go back to question 4, 10, 11, 12, or 14 or one assigned by your teacher, and take five to ten minutes to expand your answer and prepare an oral response. Find additional details in the story that will support your points. If necessary, make notes to guide your response.

Rubric for Evaluating Extended Responses

0	1	2	3	4
Blank paper Foreign language Illegible, incoherent Not enough content to score	Incorrect purpose, mode, audience Brief, vague Unelaborated Rambling Lack of language control Poor organization	Correct purpose, mode, audience Some elaboration Some details Gaps in organization Limited language control	Correct purpose, mode, audience Moderately well elaborated Clear, effective language Organized (perhaps with brief digressions)	Correct purpose, mode, audience Effective elaboration Consistent organization Sense of completeness, fluency

"Camouflaging the Chimera" by Yusef Komunyakaa
"Ambush" by Tim O'Brien

Open-Book Test

Multiple Choice and Short Answer

Write your answers to all questions in this section on the lines provided.
For multiple-choice questions, circle the letter of the best answer.

1. Choose the sentence that best states the experience described in "Camouflaging the
    Chimera." Give examples from the poem to support your answer.
    a. The men are waiting for reinforcement troops.
    b. The men are waiting for the approach of enemy soldiers.
    c. The men are ambushing enemy soldiers.
    d. The men are being ambushed by enemy soldiers.

    _____

    _____

2. Review the details in the first two stanzas of "Camouflaging the Chimera" and use them
    to envision the action. Summarize the action described in these stanzas.

    _____

    _____

    _____

3. "Chameleons crawled our spines, . . ." "But we waited till the moon touched metal, till
    something almost broke inside us." These lines from "Camouflaging the Chimera" show
    that the poem is told in the first person. Briefly explain how the first-person point of view
    helps readers understand what is happening.

    _____

    _____

4. Reread the footnote that explains what the chimera is. The title, "Camouflaging the
    Chimera," indicates that the soldiers are being compared to a _____. Explain the
    comparison.
    a. serpent's tail   c. lion's head
    b. Greek monster   d. science fiction monster

    _____

    _____

5. Is the jungle described in "Camouflaging the Chimera" a refuge for the soldiers? Explain
    your answer.

    _____

    _____

    _____

6. "Ambush" is a war story that is a _____ of a soldier's experience in Vietnam. Circle the letter of the phrase that best completes this sentence. Give examples from the story that support your answer.

a. news report
b. buddy's perspective

c. personal account
d. historical account

_____

_____

7. Use the space in the boxes to organize ideas about the narrator's and Kiowa's attitudes toward the killing at the time it happened, as described in "Ambush." Summarize how those attitudes fit in with the attitude that the narrator has about the killing many years later.

Narrator's Attitude	Kiowa's Attitude

Narrator's Attitude Years Later

8. "I had already thrown the grenade before telling myself to throw it." O'Brien includes this line in "Ambush" to illustrate that throwing the grenade was _____. Which phrase best completes this sentence? Cite evidence from the story to support your answer.

a. a conscious act based on his training
b. a conscious act because he hated the enemy
c. a reflex act based on fear
d. a careless act because he wasn't paying attention

_____

_____

9. The last paragraph of "Ambush" sums up the narrator's feelings about killing a man in Vietnam. Has he resolved his feelings? Explain how his first-person perspective communicates his feelings.

_____

_____

_____

10. Review the first paragraph of "Ambush." Explain why the narrator thinks his daughter must be a grown-up to hear about his experience with killing in Vietnam.

_____

_____

_____

Extended Response

11. Select "Camouflaging the Chimera" or "Ambush," and write an essay in which you explain how the first-person point of view enables readers to better appreciate and understand the experience that is being described. Use examples from the selection to support your thoughts and ideas, and include your personal response to the selection in your essay.

12. "Camouflaging the Chimera" and "Ambush" are based on the writers' experiences of fighting in Vietnam. Use the Venn diagram to compare and contrast their experiences. Then write an essay in which you summarize the two men's experiences.

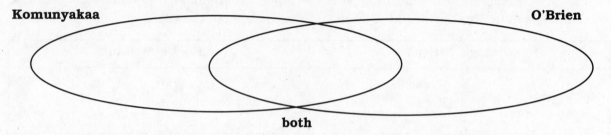

Komunyakaa   **O'Brien**

both

13. "Camouflaging the Chimera" and "Ambush" represent many soldiers' experiences in Vietnam. Write an essay in which you explore the impact of the Vietnam War. Use examples from these two selections to explain the response to the war from the perspective of those who fought in Vietnam.

14. Komunyakaa served as an information specialist in the Vietnam War, working on news reports about the war. In an essay, explain his choice of poetry as a medium to write about the war after he returned home. You may wish to refer to Komunyakaa's biographical information in your textbook for facts and ideas to support your explanation.

15. Write an essay in which you explore the authors' choices of titles for "Camouflaging the Chimera" and "Ambush." What do the titles reveal about the selections' topics? What do the titles reveal about the authors' feelings toward their topics? In your essay, explain your personal response to the titles.

Oral Response

16. Go back to question 1, 3, 7, 12, or 15 or one assigned by your teacher, and take five to ten minutes to expand your answer and prepare an oral response. Find additional details in the selections that will support your points. If necessary, make notes to guide your response.

Rubric for Evaluating Extended Responses

0	1	2	3	4
Blank paper Foreign language Illegible, incoherent Not enough content to score	Incorrect purpose, mode, audience Brief, vague Unelaborated Rambling Lack of language control Poor organization	Correct purpose, mode, audience Some elaboration Some details Gaps in organization Limited language control	Correct purpose, mode, audience Moderately well elaborated Clear, effective language Organized (perhaps with brief digressions)	Correct purpose, mode, audience Effective elaboration Consistent organization Sense of completeness, fluency

Name _____ Date _____

The Crucible, **Act I,** by Arthur Miller

Open-Book Test

Multiple Choice and Short Answer

Write your answers to all questions in this section on the lines provided.
For multiple-choice questions, circle the letter of the best answer.

1. At the beginning of Act I, what is wrong with Betty? Select the phrase that best describes her condition. Describe the other characters' response to Betty's condition.
   a. She is upset and doesn't want to get out of bed.
   b. She has typhoid fever and there is no cure for it.
   c. She is ill and the doctor doesn't know what is wrong with her.
   d. She is overcome with exhaustion because she has worked too hard.

   _____

   _____

2. Explain why Abigail and Parris are concerned about the rumors of witchcraft.

   _____

   _____

3. Describe what the girls have done in the woods to arouse Parris's suspicions and cause the rumor of witchcraft.

   _____

   _____

4. Review the stage directions concerning the characters of Thomas Putnam and John Proctor. Briefly describe each character.

   _____

   _____

5. Because John Proctor is open and direct, he is marked for calumny, and others want to bring him down. Choose the phrase that best defines "calumny." Explain your response.
   a. great accomplishments   c. respectful honor
   b. false accusation   d. dismal failure

   _____

   _____

6. Circle the letter of the phrase that best describes the relationship that Abigail has had with the Proctors. Cite an example of dialogue that explains the relationship.
   a. Abigail has taken care of the Proctors' children; been accused of stealing; been dismissed by John Proctor.
   b. Abigail has been friends with the Proctors; accused Goody Proctor of witchcraft; been dismissed by John Proctor.
   c. Abigail has been friends with Goody Proctor; had an affair with John Proctor; been accused of witchcraft by the Proctors.
   d. Abigail has worked as a servant for the Proctors; had an affair with John Proctor; been dismissed by Goody Proctor.

   _____

   _____

7. Reverend John Hale is described in detail in the stage directions. Use the character web to organize the information about him. Then, briefly summarize the character of Reverend John Hale.

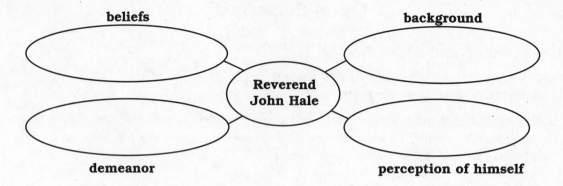

beliefs

background

Reverend John Hale

demeanor

perception of himself

_____

_____

8. When Hale examines Betty, the story of what has happened with the group of girls in the woods begins to come out. Describe Abigail's reaction to what is being said.

_____

9. Tituba's entrance is a turning point in Act I because _____. Select the answer that best completes this sentence. Cite evidence from the play to support your answer.
   a. she corroborates Abigail's story about what happened in the woods.
   b. Abigail diverts the blame for Betty's condition to Tituba.
   c. she accuses Abigail of witchcraft.
   d. Abigail tells the truth because she respects Tituba.

_____

_____

10. Describe Tituba's response to the accusations of compacting with the Devil. How does Tituba's cultural background and position in the household motivate her response?

_____

_____

_____

Extended Response

11. In an essay, summarize the events that have been discovered and those that have subsequently occurred in Act I of *The Crucible*. As you write, explain which characters are key to the controversy over the possibility that there are witches in Salem.

12. In an essay, explore the dynamics of the community of Salem. Using Miller's background information about the characters and conditions, as well as the characters interaction in Act I of *The Crucible*, consider how community dynamics affect the events taking place.

13. Write an essay in which you speculate about where the accusations of witchcraft will lead for the people of Salem. Will others be accused? Will more lies be told? Use the information about the characters in Act I to suggest what their behavior will be in the future.

14. Use the graphic organizer to analyze Abigail Williams's relationships with the other characters in *The Crucible*, as presented in Act I. Then write an essay in which you explore how she is affecting the growing controversy over witchcraft in Salem.

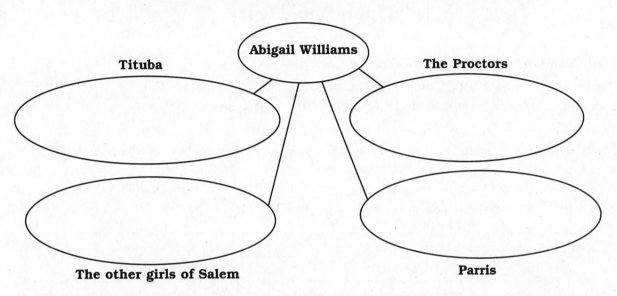

15. The episode that has taken place in the woods with Abigail, Betty, Tituba and the other girls was the catalyst for the events that are now taking place for the people of Salem. Write an essay in which you piece together what has happened, what Parris saw when he came across the girls in the woods, and why their activity was cause for disapproval.

Oral Response

16. Go back to question 3, 11, 12, or 15 or one assigned by your teacher, and take five to ten minutes to expand your answer and prepare an oral response. Find additional details in the play that will support your points. If necessary, make notes to guide your response.

Rubric for Evaluating Extended Responses

0	1	2	3	4
Blank paper Foreign language Illegible, incoherent Not enough content to score	Incorrect purpose, mode, audience Brief, vague Unelaborated Rambling Lack of language control Poor organization	Correct purpose, mode, audience Some elaboration Some details Gaps in organization Limited language control	Correct purpose, mode, audience Moderately well elaborated Clear, effective language Organized (perhaps with brief digressions)	Correct purpose, mode, audience Effective elaboration Consistent organization Sense of completeness, fluency

Name _____ Date _____

The Crucible, Act II, by Arthur Miller

Open-Book Test

Multiple Choice and Short Answer

Write your answers to all questions in this section on the lines provided.
For multiple-choice questions, circle the letter of the best answer.

1. The stage directions at the beginning of Act II indicate the setting of the interaction that takes place between _____. Choose the correct combination of characters. Describe the scene between these two characters.
    a. John Proctor and Abigail
    b. John and Elizabeth Proctor
    c. Elizabeth Proctor and Mary Warren
    d. Abigail and Mary Warren

    _____

    _____

    _____

2. John Proctor is angry with Mary Warren for disobeying him. Explain where she has been and why he has forbidden her to go there.

    _____

    _____

    _____

3. Describe the news that the Proctors learn from Mary Warren about what is happening in Salem. Cite examples of their discussion in your description.

    _____

    _____

    _____

4. The references to The Commandments are an allusion to _____. Select the correct answer and explain why this allusion are important to the events that are taking place in *The Crucible.*
    a. Salem's charter
    b. Salem's laws
    c. the Bible
    d. a play by Shakespeare

    _____

    _____

5. Explain why tricking a friend or loved one would be considered a base act.

    _____

    _____

    _____

6. Hale has been called to Salem to determine whether the Devil is among the people. As Act II progresses, his opinion as to whether the Devil is present is being tempered by his observations of the people of Salem. Use the graphic organizer to trace Hale's observations. Summarize the conclusion he is reaching.

Hale's purpose in Salem		Hale's initial observations in Salem during Act I		Hale's new observations in Salem during Act II

_____

_____

_____

7. When Hale visits the Proctors, he discusses the Gospel with them. This allusion to the Bible indicates _____. Choose the correct answer and explain why Miller has included this dialogue in the play.
    a. their belief in the teachings of Jesus
    b. their belief in the teachings of Hale
    c. their belief in the teachings of Parris
    d. their belief in the teachings of philosophers

_____

_____

8. John Proctor believes the reason that Elizabeth has been accused of witchcraft is _____. Choose the word that best completes this sentence and explain Proctor's line of thinking.
    a. hate   b. hysteria   c. revenge   d. contempt

_____

_____

9. Those that are accused of witchcraft can save themselves by which of the following means? Choose the correct answer and explain why this is so.
    a. proving that they are innocent of being a witch
    b. confessing to being a witch
    c. accusing others of witchcraft
    d. calling friends as character witnesses

_____

_____

10. Explain why the Bible is referred to frequently in The Crucible.

_____

_____

_____

Extended Response

11. The Proctor's worst fears about Abigail's accusations toward Elizabeth are confirmed when Cheever finds the poppet and says that it is hard evidence. Write an essay in which you describe and explain John Proctor's response to his wife's arrest. What does he say? What does he do? Does he understand it?

12. Use the graphic organizer to explore the significance of the "poppet" that Mary Warren gives to Elizabeth Proctor. Then write an essay in which you discuss the poppet and its affect on the characters of the play.

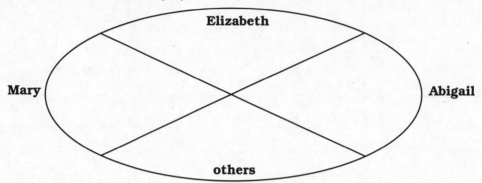

13. Mary Warren plays an important role in Act II. In an essay discuss why she is not important until the second act, the impression that her character makes, what motivates her actions, how she affects the other characters, and how her actions affect plot developments.

14. Write an essay in which you explain the presence of Abigail Williams in Act II. Does she actually appear in the act? How does her character affect the action and dialogue of the other characters? As you write, consider Abigail's motivations for her actions that are affecting the other characters.

15. In an essay, describe the state of life in Salem at the end of Act II. Are people happy or unhappy? Is the situation getting better or worse? Who has had the most influence on the lives of the people of Salem? Cite evidence from the act to support your description.

Oral Response

16. Go back to question 1, 3, 8, 12, or 15 or one assigned by your teacher, and take five to ten minutes to expand your answer and prepare an oral response. Find additional details in the play that will support your points. If necessary, make notes to guide your response.

Rubric for Evaluating Extended Responses

0	1	2	3	4
Blank paper Foreign language Illegible, incoherent Not enough content to score	Incorrect purpose, mode, audience Brief, vague Unelaborated Rambling Lack of language control Poor organization	Correct purpose, mode, audience Some elaboration Some details Gaps in organization Limited language control	Correct purpose, mode, audience Moderately well elaborated Clear, effective language Organized (perhaps with brief digressions)	Correct purpose, mode, audience Effective elaboration Consistent organization Sense of completeness, fluency

The Crucible, Act III, by Arthur Miller

Open-Book Test

Multiple Choice and Short Answer

Write your answers to all questions in this section on the lines provided.
For multiple-choice questions, circle the letter of the best answer.

1. Which sentence best describes what is demonstrated by the questioning of Martha Corey that is heard at the opening of Act III? Explain the dramatic irony of this examination.
    a. Anyone accused of witchcraft will be hanged.
    b. Anyone accused of witchcraft is expected to have relatives who are also witches.
    c. Anyone accused of witchcraft is expected to have proof of their innocence.
    d. Anyone accused of witchcraft is presumed to be guilty.

    _____

    _____

2. By the beginning of Act III, the characters of *The Crucible* are falling into two main categories: those who are driving the witch hunt and those who are trying to stop it. It is still not clear, however, in which category some of the characters belong. Use the following chart to categorize John Proctor, Giles Corey, Thomas Putnam, Reverend Hale, Deputy Governor Danforth, Mary Warren, and Abigail Williams. Explain why each character fits into the category in which you placed them.

For the witch hunt	Against the witch hunt

Undecided

    _____

    _____

3. Explain what Hale means with his statement ". . . I dare not take a life without there be a proof so immaculate no slightest qualm of conscience may doubt it."

    _____

    _____

4. Describe Parris's behavior and attitude during the court proceedings and the conversations that take place in Act III.

    _____

    _____

5. John Proctor speaks during the court proceedings: "It will keep if it is kept, but Mary Warren swears she never saw no poppets in my house, nor anyone else." and "There might also be a dragon with five legs in my house, but no one has ever seen it." Which one of these speeches is an example of verbal irony? Explain your answer.

_____

_____

6. The employee was contentious with his boss about the unpleasant work assignment. Choose the best synonym for *contentious* in the context of this sentence. Explain your answer.
   a. gratified   b. contented   c. argumentative   d. acquiescent

_____

_____

7. The witness agreed to give a statement on the condition of anonymity. Choose the phrase that best completes this sentence and explain why it is correct.
   a. being asked no questions   c. being paid for the information
   b. being unknown or unacknowledged   d. being given a press conference

_____

_____

8. John Proctor has stated that his wife will never lie. Describe the dramatic irony of Elizabeth's response to Danforth's questioning.

_____

_____

9. Describe Mary Warren's words and actions at the end of Act III. Why is her behavior significant?

_____

_____

10. Proctor and Hale both make strong statements at the end of Act III. Explain their motivations on the lines provided.

_____

_____

Extended Response

11. Use a chart to categorize the major characters of The Crucible as leaders or followers. Then write an essay in which you explain why each character exhibits the qualities that he or she does.

Leader	Follower

12. Changes in the behavior and attitudes of Reverend Hale and Mary Warren become apparent in Act III. Write an essay in which you discuss their changing roles and the impact of the changes on the events transpiring, as well as their impact on the other characters in the play.

13. At the close of Act III, which character or characters do you think has the most influence over what is happening in Salem? Write an essay in which you explain your response, using examples from the first three acts of the play to support your thoughts and ideas.

14. Write an essay in which you discuss the contributions of Hathorne and Danforth to the general hysteria about witchcraft that is growing in Salem. Are they showing good leadership skills? Are they acting as good judges? Do you think all judges would have behaved as they do at the time that the play takes place?

15. In an essay, explore the character of Abigail Williams at the end of Act III. Is her motivation the same as it was earlier in the play? Do you think she expected what was happening to go this far? Do you think she expects to fulfill her wish to be with John Proctor? As you write, consider the responses of the other characters to what she says and does.

Oral Response

16. Go back to question 2, 8, 13, 14, or 15 or one assigned by your teacher, and take five to ten minutes to expand your answer and prepare an oral response. Find additional details in the play that will support your points. If necessary, make notes to guide your response.

Rubric for Evaluating Extended Responses

0	1	2	3	4
Blank paper Foreign language Illegible, incoherent Not enough content to score	Incorrect purpose, mode, audience Brief, vague Unelaborated Rambling Lack of language control Poor organization	Correct purpose, mode, audience Some elaboration Some details Gaps in organization Limited language control	Correct purpose, mode, audience Moderately well elaborated Clear, effective language Organized (perhaps with brief digressions)	Correct purpose, mode, audience Effective elaboration Consistent organization Sense of completeness, fluency

Name _____ Date _____

The Crucible, **Act IV,** by Arthur Miller

Open-Book Test

Multiple Choice and Short Answer

Write your answers to all questions in this section on the lines provided.
For multiple-choice questions, circle the letter of the best answer.

1. The scene at the beginning of Act IV with Sarah Good and Tituba reinforces the influence
    of _____ on the people of Salem throughout the play. Choose the correct answer and
    explain your response.
    a. God   c. Judge Hathorne
    b. the Devil   d. Abigail Williams

    _____

    _____

2. Abigail and Mercy Lewis have been gone for three days. Where does Parris think they
    have gone? Explain the significance of Abigail's disappearance.

    _____

    _____

    _____

3. Describe the effect of a person saying something in a floundering way.

    _____

    _____

    _____

4. Select the sentence that best describes why Danforth allows Elizabeth to speak to
    John Proctor. Explain your answer.
    a. He hopes she will convince him to confess so that he will not hang.
    b. He wants them to have a chance to be reunited before they are hanged.
    c. He thinks Elizabeth should tell her husband that she is pregnant.
    d. Reverend Hale has told him he should allow them to speak before they hang.

    _____

    _____

5. Choose the best explanation of why John Proctor anguishes over having his signed
    confession made public. Explain your answer.
    a. It will not save his soul.
    b. It will not keep him from being hanged.
    c. He regrets that he has not confessed sooner.
    d. His name represents who he is as a man and who he is to his descendants.

    _____

    _____

    _____

6. Use the graphic organizer to review John Proctor's dialogue and action that is pivotal to the play's theme. Then explain how the character of John Proctor relates to the theme of the play.

John Proctor	
with Elizabeth Proctor:	**with Abigail Williams:**
with Judge Danforth:	**with Mary Warren:**
with Reverend Hale:	**actions:**

_____

_____

_____

7. Select the best description of how Elizabeth Proctor has changed during her imprisonment. Explain your answer, citing evidence from her actions and words.
   a. Her judgment of others has become harsher.
   b. Her judgment of others has been tempered.
   c. She has lost her faith in God.
   d. Her faith in God has strengthened.

_____

_____

_____

8. One definition of the word *crucible* is "a severe test." Explain how this meaning of the word applies to the message of Miller's play, *The Crucible.*

_____

_____

_____

9. Briefly state the theme of *The Crucible.*

_____

_____

_____

10. Review the biographical information about Arthur Miller. On the lines below, briefly apply the theme of *The Crucible* to the contemporary event that motivated Miller to write the play.

_____

_____

_____

Extended Response

11. Use a chart to review what has taken place in each act of *The Crucible.* Then write a summary of the play, briefly explaining the theme, or insight, that Miller conveys.

Act I	Act II	Act III	Act IV

12. Abigail Williams has been a pivotal character in the first three acts of the play. At the beginning of Act IV, it is discovered that she has run away with one of the other girls. Explain how Abigail's disappearance affects the resolution of the play. Think about what might have happened had she still been in Salem when John Proctor was asked to confess.

13. In an essay, explain the significance of Elizabeth's last statement—the last line of the play. Use examples of the play's earlier dialogue and action to support your explanation, and include your impression of what Miller was trying to convey with the final comment.

14. Write an essay in which you explore the probability of a current "witch hunt." Has society learned from experiences like the Salem witchcraft trials and McCarthyism? In your essay, use examples from the play that support your ideas about how easy it is for people to get caught up in mass hysteria, bringing on the tragedy of a "witch hunt."

15. Think about the title of *The Crucible.* The word *crucible* means "a container for melting or purifying metals" or "a severe test." In an essay discuss which meaning you think Miller had in mind when he titled the play. Also consider whether the central idea of his play implies both meanings?

Oral Response

16. Go back to question 2, 6, 10, 13, 15, or one assigned by your teacher, and take five to ten minutes to expand your answer and prepare an oral response. Find additional details in the play that will support your points. If necessary, make notes to guide your response.

Rubric for Evaluating Extended Responses

0	1	2	3	4
Blank paper	Incorrect purpose, mode, audience	Correct purpose, mode, audience	Correct purpose, mode, audience	Correct purpose, mode, audience
Foreign language	Brief, vague	Some elaboration	Moderately well elaborated	Effective elaboration
Illegible, incoherent	Unelaborated	Some details	Clear, effective language	Consistent organization
Not enough content to score	Rambling	Gaps in organization	Organized (perhaps with brief digressions)	Sense of completeness, fluency
	Lack of language control	Limited language control		
	Poor organization			

ANSWERS

UNIT 1: BEGINNINGS (TO 1750)

"The Earth on Turtle's Back"
by Onondaga

"When Grizzlies Walked Upright"
by Modoc

from *The Navajo Origin Legend*
by Navajo

and **from *The Iroquois Constitution***
by Iroquois

Open-Book Test (p. 1)

Multiple Choice and Short Answer

1. Sample answers: Skyland—Arrows should show Wife moving from Skyland down through Water. Water—to Earth; Muskrat moving from Water to Earth; and Turtle should be Earth—placed on Earth with no arrows. Summary: The Chief's wife came from Skyland and fell through the hole in the tree into the Water. The birds caught her and held her until the Muskrat brought up the Earth and placed it on the Turtle's back, where the Earth became large enough so that she could stand upon it.

2. Sample answer: Students should be able to discern that in the physical world, the word "sacred" used in conjunction with "directions" assigns a higher importance to the concepts of North, South, East, and West. In addition, the Chief's belief that his wife's dream must be obeyed shows the spiritual significance of dreams for the Onondaga.

3. Sample answers: Turtle = strength; "place it on my back," Muskrat = courage; "I will bring up earth or die trying," Birds = compassion; "We must do something to help her," Water birds = intelligence; " . . . have heard that there is Earth far below the Waters."

4.c Explanation: They assumed the bear was not their ancestor, because one of their ancestors wouldn't kill an Indian. There is no support in the text for answers a, b, or d.

5.b Explanation: The key word in this question is "development." Answer b is the only answer that traces development. Answer a mentions correct myth elements, but being burned does not relate to the development of the bear. Answers c and d have some incorrect items.

6. Sample answer: The grandchildren of the Sky Spirit were part bear and part Spirit, so they would not have killed their ancestors.

7. Sample answer: It was the morning of the twelfth day (which clearly meant something to the Navajos); sacred buckskins were carried; men and women dried themselves with cornmeal, an item of significance, in colors that had significance. All of these elements pointed to it being a special day.

8. Sample answer: Wind (d) is the only element in this myth that clearly gives life. The Mirage People (a) and the tips of the eagle feathers (c) contribute to movement but do not give life. The buckskin (b) was only a covering.

9.c Explanation: The text clearly states that the lord makes a promise to observe the constitution. In addition, he has to furnish the wampum, hold it in his hand to make the pledge, and then send it to the other side. Answer a: The new status of the lord is mostly symbolized by the deer's antlers. Answer b: The connection of the lords to one another is implied but not stated. Answer c: While there is an implied promise to uphold the values of the other lords, it is not clearly stated.

10.b Explanation: In this context, *deliberation* refers to the process of discussion and decision-making, as does *consideration*. *Effort*, a, and *patience*, c, are certainly needed for this process, but the synonym has to include the act of discussion as well. *Tenderness*, d, does not relate to the decision-making process.

Questions are classified in these categories:

Comprehension	1 (E), 3 (A)
Interpretation	4 (A), 6 (A)
Literary Analysis	5 (A), 8 (A), 9 (C)
Reading Strategy	2 (C)
Vocabulary	7 (C), 10 (E)

E=Easy, A=Average, C=Challenging

Extended Response

11. (Average) Examples of community might come from the instructions given to the lords by the Iroquois Constitution; an example of nature might come from the wind in "When Grizzlies Walked Upright" or *The Navajo Origin Legend*; an example of religion might come from the prayer of the lords before they meet as a council in the Iroquois Constitution or the concept of the "sacred" directions in "The Earth on Turtle's Back."

12. (Challenging) Sample answers:

Myth	"Earth"	"Grizzlies"	*Navajo*
Animals	turtle	bear	eagles
Nature	Great Tree	snow/ice	wind
People	Wife	Indians	tribe
Super-natural	Earth grew	Sticks became alive	Corn became people

Students should write an essay in which they can support the powerfulness of a particular influence on the myth's believability.

13. (Average) Examples: From *Navajo Origin Legend*: the yellow and white cornmeal later become the first man and woman, or the Mirage People can be seen as dreamlike and powerful; From "When Grizzlies Walked Upright": The bears changing from walking on 2 feet to 4 feet shows the control of man over animals, or the girl's hair being caught by the wind shows the dangerous power of nature; From "The Earth on Turtle's Back": the deep voice of the Turtle carries an impression of strength, or the tightly shut paw of the Muskrat connotes her determination.

14. (Average) Principles described in students' essays might include honesty (as promoted in basic belief systems such as the Ten Commandments), appreciation for nature (as expressed in traditional religious prayers of thanks), the eagle watching for danger (as it relates to the concept of a nation having a standing army), or the lords' council (which relates to the democratic system of government and having a Congress).

15. (Challenging) Support: A great leader is seen in The Great White Roots, which embody peace and strength; the instruction that the lords should not be led into trivial discussions; and the admonition to have thick skin against anger, offense, and criticism. Contrast: The Native Americans' connection to a Great Creator conflicts with our concept of the division of church and state; their expectation that lords will be held in high regard does not coincide with our mistrust of political leaders.

Oral Response

16. In their oral response, students should cite specific information from the myths or the Constitution that substantiates their presentations and expands on their earlier responses.

"A Journey Through Texas"

by Alvar Núñez Cabeza de Vaca

"Boulders Taller Than the Great Tower of Seville"

by García López de Cárdenas

Open-Book Test (p. 4)

Multiple Choice and Short Answer

1.c Explanation: They put hot stones from the fire into water–filled calabash gourds and replaced the stones as they lost heat.

2. Sample answer: "soon" and "all night"

3. Sample answer: "These can trade everywhere" implies that Native American women are seen as neutral and will not be harmed; they are also perhaps more expendable than the men who are afraid to venture forth.

4. Sample answer: The explorers adopted a "new custom" in the middle of their travels. They initially were traveling with one tribe. Then they switched to another tribe that had food and housing; they could not join the two tribes together as traveling companions, because the tribes were enemies.

5. Sample answer: De Vaca wanted to continue westward, which he expressed as "towards sunset." Students may mention that he ended up at the Gulf of Mexico, but it is not a correct answer, since we have no evidence that his goal was so specific.

6.d Explanation: The sentence relates to food consumption. Answer a: The explorers did not grow food. Answer b: The explorers had no food to offer. Answer c: There were no choices available.

7. Sample answer: They set out with much food, since they would not see other people for a while. Explanation: The lands were inhospitable, and they needed to be well-prepared.

8.c Explanation: Answer a does not reveal why he would put this information into a narrative; answer b ignores that the explorer wanted to examine the river, not the canyon; answer d is unsupported by the text.

9.a Explanation: Answer a is the only answer that is supported by the text.

10. Sample answer: The main impression is that the journey is difficult. Examples from text: "uninhabited land"; "settlements more than twenty days away"; opposite side of river seemed to be 3–4 leagues away; the canyon is cold; the large size of the boulders makes travel hard; "obstacles."

Questions are classified in these categories:

Comprehension	9 (A)
Interpretation	3 (A), 10 (E)
Literary Analysis	1 (E), 4 (C), 5 (A), 8 (A)
Reading Strategy	2 (A), 7 (C)
Vocabulary	6 (E)

E=Easy, A=Average, C=Challenging

Extended Response

11. (Easy) Students may offer examples of Native American tribes avoiding contact with each other. They should indicate that the tribes viewed each other as enemies.

12. (Easy) Students should pay attention to the Introduction, in which de Vaca's healing powers are mentioned. Since the Native Americans experienced illness while with his group, they would have expected that because of his reputation he could heal them.

13. (Average) De Vaca: terrain – flat with water; climate – warm; human interaction – extensive. De Cárdenas: terrain – a rocky canyon; climate – cold; human interaction – minimal

14. (Challenging) Chart: (sample answers)
Narrative: "Journey"; Factual Information: how tribes lived, descriptions of villages; Personal Information: fears of Native Americans, relations between tribes
Narrative: "Boulders"; Factual Information: descriptions of boulders, climbing, rivers, description of how water was carried; Personal Information: well-received by natives
Essay: In "Journey," there was more emphasis on people, food, and customs. In "Boulders," there was more emphasis on the terrain and the difficulty of exploration.

15. (Average) In "Journey," the fear of travel was so intense that the Native Americans became ill and died; if they established homes, they stayed in one place; and they did not want to lead the explorers upriver. In "Boulders," the Native Americans were at least comfortable enough with travel to prepare for it by storing water underground for their return trip.

Oral Response

16. In their oral response, students should cite specific information from the exploration narratives that substantiates their presentations and expands on their earlier responses.

from *The Interesting Narrative of the Life of Olaudah Equiano*

by Olaudah Equiano

Open-Book Test (p. 7)

Multiple Choice and Short Answer

1.b Explanation: He "envied" the "inhabitants of the deep." Answers a, c, and d are not supported by the text.

2.b Explanation: The ability to see the sailors' activity was far less important than the slaves' conditions.

3.c Explanation: He describes "hardships which are inseparable from this accursed trade." Answers a, b, and d are not supported by the text.

4.d Explanation: Equiano specifically refers to the slave traders' "improvident avarice."

5.d Explanation: Students need to read the directions carefully, so that they find the opposite word d. Answer a is a synonym; b and c describe the experience of the slaves generally.

6.b Explanation: They could use it to document their rationale for abolishing slavery.

7.a Explanation: The paragraph refers to property and animals. Although b, c, and d represent important details, they do not reflect the overall emphasis of the last paragraph.

8.a Explanation: Answer a correctly represents the harshness of the voyage. Although b is factually correct in referring to aspects of the voyage, it is more neutral than "loathsome." Answers c and d are irrelevant, because neither has a negative connotation.

9. Sample answer: Equiano was curious about the use of the quadrant; he observed the clouds—he could have been a scientist or a navigator.

10.c Explanation: The key to this question is the phrase "most useful" in the directions. Answers a, b, and d may be factually true, but the usefulness of this narrative is that it is a first-person account that documents the horrors of slavery.

Questions are classified in these categories:

Comprehension	2 (A)
Interpretation	4 (A), 9 (C)
Literary Analysis	3 (E), 6 (C), 10 (A)
Reading Strategy	1 (A), 7 (A)
Vocabulary	5 (E), 8 (A)

E=Easy, A=Average, C=Challenging

Extended Response

11. (Average) Students should note that the Barbados slaves told the ship slaves that they would be working and safe, and that they would soon see their countrymen. According to Equiano, "this report eased us much," reassuring the ship slaves.

12. (Average) EXAMPLES OF SLAVE TRADERS' LACK OF CARING FOR SLAVES
They crowded the slaves together.
They flogged the slaves for trying to eat the fish they caught.
EXAMPLES OF SLAVE TRADERS' CARING FOR SLAVES
They brought Equiano to the deck.
Students' essays should focus on the dominant idea of the slaves as property rather than people. The caring for them by slave traders was minimal.

13. (Easy) Students should mention that people jumped ship, choosing "death [over] slavery," because the conditions were so brutal. The heat, closeness of human bodies, and the stench were too much for some to bear.

14. (Average) Students should select at least some of the following textual references that make clear the commercial nature of slavery: "merchants," "parcels," "merchant's yard," "sold," "buyers," "pent up" like sheep—all of these terms substantiate that African Americans were seen as property rather than as people.

15. (Average) Students should focus on the most dramatic words and elements of Equiano's narrative. They should mention at least some of the following: no fresh air, crowded conditions, severe illness and death, and the startling concept that conditions were bad enough that people wanted to die.

Oral Response

16. In their oral response, students should cite specific information from Equiano's narrative that substantiates their presentations and expands on their earlier responses.

from *Journal of the First Voyage to America*

by Christopher Columbus

Open-Book Test (p. 10)

Multiple Choice and Short Answer

1.a Explanation: They were financing his journey. There is no evidence in the excerpt to support b, c, or d.

2. Sample answers: "groves of lofty and flourishing trees," "as green as April in Andalusia."

3.d Explanation: The answer is supported by several quotations that discuss the concept of value.

4. Sample answer: The lakes and surrounding foliage are described as "enchanting," which could mean "exquisite"; the fruit from the trees is described as "delicious," which could also mean "exquisite."

5. Sample answer: Further exploration is justified, because he found valuable items and he established a trade relationship with the natives.

6.a Explanation: He could have gained something from the knowledge. Answer b is not supported because he is looking for wealth, so he cannot be wealthy. Answer c is wrong, because there is no mention of embarrassment in the excerpt. Answer d is wrong, because he cannot be well–educated and "ignorant" at the same time.

7. Sample answer: His details provided the information that the natives were non–threatening and therefore would make the island easy to investigate or conquer. His details also gave a description of the island's bounty, indicating its potential monetary value.

8. Sample answer: His description noted that there was much water, many fruit trees and foliage, and he indicated there was much "fertility."

9.d Explanation: Supported by "as I find gold or spices." There is nothing in the excerpt to support any of the other answers.

10.c Explanation: Answer c is the item of primary importance to the king and queen, since they are financing the expedition. The other answers are important only to Columbus.

Questions are classified in these categories:

Comprehension	1 (A), 9 (E)
Interpretation	2 (E), 3 (A), 5 (C)
Literary Analysis	7 (A), 10 (C)
Reading Strategy	8 (C)
Vocabulary	4 (A), 6 (E)

E=Easy, A=Average, C=Challenging

Extended Response

11. (Average) Venn diagram: circle with Columbus only: increased understanding of global travel, survival information. Circle with King & Queen: contact with leaders of islands, possibilities of colonization. Intersecting space (both): gold or other valuable items, agricultural possibilities, friendly relationship with natives. Essay should focus on why there is a difference in the importance of these different factors to the participants—in other words, what is at stake for each of them.

12. (Average) Students should use quotations or paraphrases to support Columbus's order that nothing be touched or taken. They should also use details to show that he gave the natives gifts in exchange for water (that he did not take anything by force), and that the natives seemed to enjoy the transaction.

13. (Average) Students should use information from the text to support the reactions of the natives, including that they were "delighted," "showed great pleasure," and that they appeared with full calabashes and agreed to return the following day.

14. (Easy) Students should use details from the selection to indicate that natives fled from their homes at the explorers' approach and details that describe the abundance of the island.

15. (Challenging) Students should use details to explain that Columbus was discovering new territory and did not know, for example, whether snakeskins were of value, or about the properties of various fruit trees. By staying on San Salvador, he would be able to increase his knowledge and maybe apply it to the investigation of other islands.

Oral Response

16. In their oral response, students should cite specific information from the journal selection that substantiates their presentations and expands on their earlier responses.

from *The General History of Virginia*

by John Smith

from *Of Plymouth Plantation*

by William Bradford

Open-Book Test (p. 13)

Multiple Choice and Short Answer

1.d Explanation: The first president did not share food with the settlers; the food they did get was substandard.

2. Sample answer: Smith felt that President Ratcliffe had weak judgment and was lazy; however, Ratcliffe was clever enough to recognize Smith as a potential leader and single him out. Smith's opinion of himself was high, because he was hard-working and was able to motivate settlers to work with him to build lodgings.

3. Sample answers: 1. the notion of opposite poles; 2. the greatness of the land and sea; 3. the roundness of the earth and skies.

4.c Explanation: Answer a is incorrect, because Smith specifically says the Council should **not** be blamed. Answer b is incorrect, because Ratcliffe does not enter the picture until after the voyage, when he replaces Wingfield as President. Answer d: The Native Americans were not to blame; in fact, they fed the settlers.

5. Sample answer: What happened: The Native Americans fed the settlers; To whom does Smith give credit? God; Meaning of "desperate extremity": terrible circumstance.

6. Sample answer: 1.a God. 2. They were very religious. 3. Possible answers: The saving of John Howland's life; being brought safely over the ocean; the caretaking of the sick; the assistance of Squanto.

7. Sample answer: It puts both groups in the position of possibly having to fight against their own people while aiding one another.

8.b Explanation: Answer a is less important than how many died; answers c and d are details that support the main thought, but they do not represent the main thought.

9.b Explanation: Answers a and c are details that support the main idea; answer d is not in the text.

10.d Explanation: Answers a, b and c have no bearing on this context of the word "homely."

Questions are classified in these categories:

Comprehension	1 (A)
Interpretation	2 (E), 3 (E)
Literary Analysis	4 (C), 6 (C), 7 (A)
Reading Strategy	5 (A), 8 (A), 9 (A)
Vocabulary	10 (A)

E=Easy, A=Average, C=Challenging

Extended Response

11. (Easy) Why Smith was not killed: Pocahantas begged for his life to be spared. Possible value of Smith for Chief: He could get guns for the tribe; the compass indicated he might have other items to offer and teach them about.

12. (Average) Narrow escape: He avoids being put to death by Ratcliffe and others for the deaths of Robinson and Emry. Positive reasons to stay: Pocahantas has brought him food; he and his men admire her; he had seen an abundance of food.

13. (Average) Any of the six agreements is an adequate choice, provided the students can justify their answers with a rationale that relates to the account.

14. (Average) Possible answers—they gained experience with Native Americans; they could educate people as to the importance of adequate provisions; they could provide information about health issues; they could offer information about the climate; they could offer information about ocean navigation.

15. (Challenging) **The General History of Virginia**
Settlers' Experience with Native Americans: Went through ups and downs with Native Americans—at first they were going to kill Smith, but they later established a relationship.
Of Plymouth Plantation
Settlers' Experience with Native Americans: Meeting with Samoset
Positive outcome of having Squanto as a guide

Oral Response

16. In their oral response, students should cite specific information from the two narrative accounts that substantiates their presentations and expands on their earlier responses.

"To My Dear and Loving Husband"

by Anne Bradstreet

"Huswifery"

by Edward Taylor

Open-Book Test (p. 16)

Multiple Choice and Short Answer

1.b Explanation: Since "thee"=you, you are loved by your wife (the speaker)

2.d Explanation: Example: "My love is such that rivers cannot quench."

3.c Explanation: If he repays her with love, she will be happy, because all she desires is his love—nothing more.

4. Sample answer: "I prize thy love more than whole mines of gold" contains short words and a direct speaking style.

5. Sample answer: "Let us be so steadfast in our devotion to one another that the memory of our love will endure beyond our lifetime."

6.a Explanation: Any of the other answers is acceptable also, provided it can be justified. Answer a is the best choice, because a home has to be created and has many parts.

7. Sample answers: spinning wheel represents the poem's speaker; apparel represents the speaker's efforts at behavior that is worthy of God.

8. Sample answer: "Make everything I say and do holy, so I will be a good person who does honor to myself and to God."

9.b Explanation: The speaker wants his affections (emotions) to be part of his entire self as it becomes holy.

10.c Explanation: The elaborate language is justified by his use of it to glorify a relationship with God.

Questions are classified in these categories:

Comprehension	1 (C)
Interpretation	2 (E), 6 (E)
Literary Analysis	4 (A), 7 (A), 10 (C)
Reading Strategy	5 (A), 8 (A)
Vocabulary	3 (A), 9 (E)

E=Easy, A=Average, C=Challenging

Extended Response

11. (Average) Students should include that the speaker wants her husband to be rewarded because he is so loving and such a wonderful husband; she wants him to be rewarded for his goodness both during his lifetime on earth and after his death, in heaven.

12. (Challenging) The students' poems do not need to be overwritten and elaborate; they should, however, include a strong statement of the wife's love for her husband and her good wishes for him and their future together.

13. (Challenging) "To My Dear and Loving Husband" REFERENCES TO GOD/LIFE AND DEATH: "heavens," death ("live no more"), "Huswifery" REFERENCES TO GOD/LIFE AND DEATH: "O Lord," "Thy holy word," "Thy holy spirit," "holy robes," "Thee glorify" Essay: Students should emphasize that religion, the foundation of Puritan life, is exemplified in both poems.

14. (Average) If students are unable to find substitutes, their paragraphs can contain certain words that refer to parts of the spinning wheel. They should, however, try to be creative in changing at least some words. Primarily, they should try to retain the sense of a person seeking holiness.

15. (Easy) "To My Dear and Loving Husband" EXAMPLES OF REPETITION: If/if/if If ever man were lov'd by wife/If ever wife was happy in a man Riches/gold/reward Then while we live/When we live no more "Huswifery" EXAMPLES OF REPETITION: Spinning wheel and its various parts throughout poem Make me, Thy, Reel, Wheel, Dye/pinked/colors Students can select either poem. They should note that the use of repetition emphasizes certain images and ideas for the reader, so the reader carries away a very specific, strong impression.

Oral Response

16. In their oral response, students should cite specific information from the poems that substantiates their presentations and expands on their earlier responses.

from *Sinners in the Hands of an Angry God*

by Jonathan Edwards

Open-Book Test (p. 19)

Multiple Choice and Short Answer

1.a Explanation: They "have an opportunity to obtain salvation" and be born again.

2.b Explanation: "every one of you that are out of Christ." Answers a, c, and d are not in the text.

3.c Explanation: "There is nothing between you and Hell but air."

4. Sample answers: REPETITION IN *Sinners in the Hands of an Angry God*: the pleasure of God, the wrath of God, out of Christ, sinner USE OF EMOTIONAL APPEAL IN *Sinners in the Hands of an Angry God*: fear, guilt, envy, longing to be saved

5. Sample answer: abhors = hates; provoked = angered

6.c Explanation: The *case* is painful beyond the ability to speak. Answer a: There is no reference in the sentence to this. Answer b has no relation to the *torment* in the sentence. Answer d means *unending*, which does not make sense in the sentence.

7. Samples answer: out of Christ = not a believer. They "can now awake" by becoming believers.

8.a Explanation: The quotation denotes opportunity, ends the style of frightening the listeners, and begins to reassure them.

9.d Explanation: They can "awake and fly from the wrath to come"—they can avoid God's wrath and Hell, and enjoy salvation on earth now and later, in Heaven.

10. Sample answer: The sermon would seem to be the most effective way to present this speech, because, since Edwards was a preacher, his congregants had to respectfully listen to him while he was in his pulpit. Also, a sermon allows the speaker to create a tone or use gestures. Students may choose another answer, but they must support it.

Questions are classified in these categories:

Comprehension	1(A), 9 (E)
Interpretation	2 (E), 3 (A), 8 (A)
Literary Analysis	4 (A), 10 (C)
Reading Strategy	5 (C), 7 (A)
Vocabulary	6 (A)

E=Easy, A=Average, C=Challenging

Extended Response

11. (Average) Expressions: "Dreadful pit of the glowing flames" contains frightening imagery; "nothing between you and Hell but the air" makes listeners feel they are unprotected; "black clouds of God's wrath" is a strong image that makes listeners feel they have done something wrong. Essay: Students should explain both the images and their effectiveness.

12. (Average) Sample answers: Consequences: they may be "left behind"; they would be "pining"; they would "mourn for sorrow of heart"; they would "howl for vexation of spirit"; they would "be consumed." Essay: Students should point out that many congregants were probably scared into declaring themselves to be born again.

13. (Challenging) Sample answers: TOPIC: smoking. TONE: reasonable. PURPOSE: to get people to stop smoking. IMPORTANT POINTS: your health; others' health; bad habit; odor on clothing and breath. Speech: Students must include the above four elements in their speech; the speech must be written as thought it is going to be delivered orally.

14. (Easy) Sample answer: Students should include that Edwards tells listeners that they have an opportunity for deliverance: "one day's opportunity such as you now enjoy!" He changes his style, because he is now able to reach them, since they have become completely frightened and will be more open to hearing his message.

15. (Average) Students can answer this question in any way they wish, as long as they support their answer with a reasonable premise. Sample: I would not have introduced threats of damnation, and I would have spoken more positively. I would try to appeal to people's better judgment and higher values. Scaring people may create a temporary change of heart, but that is not very substantial. I would deliver the sermon with enthusiasm and kindness.

Oral Response

16. In their oral response, students should cite specific information from the sermon that substantiates their presentations and expands on their earlier responses.

UNIT 2: A NATION IS BORN (1750-1800)

from *The Autobiography* and from *Poor Richard's Almanack*

by Benjamin Franklin

Open-Book Test (p. 22)

Multiple Choice and Short Answer

1.b Explanation: Natural inclination = his own tendency; custom = habit or general practice.

2.c Explanation: Apparently, Franklin knew that he was embarking on a difficult task and would need to reinforce his efforts by seeing his progress. This self-knowledge shows he realized his limitations.

3.d Explanation: Answer d is correct, as evidenced within the selection. Answers a, b, and c are not in the text.

4. Sample answer: The context clue is "guard." Franklin feels that old habits and constant temptations are so powerful that one has to be very careful and aware, in order to achieve a life where moderate eating and drinking would prevail.

5. Sample answers: Haste—waste; rise—wise; healthy—wealthy; curse—worse; gains—pains; recover—get over. He chose these words because they are powerful, and pinpoint people's main concerns.

6. Sample answer: Students may agree or disagree, but they should support their view. Agree: His book became full of holes, as he scratched out notes and made others; he could not keep to his routine of filling out the book; he was unable to keep his things in their place. Disagree: He was able to make an orderly list of thirteen virtues; he organized a daybook to track his progress; he wrote his autobiography, which required organization.

7. Sample answer: Franklin's general opinion of people seems to be that they are imperfect and could use improvement. He also recognizes that they are admirable, despite their failings. An example of his opinion: "Love your neighbor; yet don't pull down your hedge," implies that people should be nice to one another but recognize each other's needs for privacy and boundaries.

8.d Explanation: He decided that a better way to keep his friends was to retain a few faults rather than to try to be perfect.

9. Sample answer:

ONE OF THE 13 VIRTUES	EXAMPLES OF THE VIRTUE
Temperance	good health; good constitution
Industry	early easiness of his circumstances; his fortune; his usefulness as a citizen; his reputation
Frugality	same as above
Sincerity	confidence of his country; his evenness of temper; cheerfulness
Justice	same as above

10. Explanation: They found him entertaining or amusing; they learned something new each day; they were eager to read to find out what new saying he would come up with.

Questions are classified in these categories:

Comprehension	1 (E)
Interpretation	2 (A), 3 (E)
Literary Analysis	9 (A), 10 (A)
Reading Strategy	6 (C), 7 (E), 8 (A)
Vocabulary	4 (E), 5 (C)

E=Easy, A=Average, C=Challenging

Extended Response

11. (Easy) Students may select whichever virtues they wish to discuss. Examples: He used order to achieve greatness as a scientist; he was a statesman known for his fairness, which relates to justice; he gave good advice with sincerity; and kept his tranquillity as a diplomat and statesman.

12. (Average) Sample answer: The man discovered that he had to work hard toward his goal, and that it was taking a long time. He then changed his feelings about pursuing his goal. Franklin uses the analogy to explain that perhaps he has been unreasonable in expecting himself to fulfill all thirteen virtues.

13. (Average) Students may choose any of the virtues to examine and reflect upon as to how reasonable it was for Franklin to try to achieve them. However, students must use two or more details to support their opinions.

14. (Average) Sample answers: weeding a garden is like cleansing oneself of bad habits; preparing the soil is like preparing oneself for change; discarding weeds is like discarding the worst parts of oneself; weeding a garden takes time and patience, as does self-improvement; weeding a garden produces ground hospitable for growth, as does ridding oneself of bad habits.

15. (Challenging) Students can have far-ranging answers to this question, but they should rely on some of Franklin's techniques. It is acceptable for them to model their work on his.

Oral Response

16. In their oral response, students should cite specific information from the autobiography that substantiates their presentations and expands on their earlier responses.

"The Declaration of Independence"
by Thomas Jefferson

from *The Crisis, Number 1*
by Thomas Paine
Open-Book Test (p. 25)

Multiple Choice and Short Answer

1. Sample answers:
MILITARY ACTION
Quartering troops in the colonies; taking away the laws and charters of the colonists; declaring colonists out of the King's protection; transporting mercenaries to America; kept standing armies without legislators' consent; officers harass colonists; the English trying to make military power independent of, and superior to, civil power.

IMPACT ON COLONISTS
Colonists have had to bear arms against one another; they have been incited to rebellion among themselves; they have been victimized by "Indian savages"; they have no trade with the rest of the world; their seas, towns, and lives have been destroyed; there is little real law in the colonies.

2. Sample answer: He is referring to the King of England. The label he uses is "tyrant." He also describes the King as "unfit."

3.b Explanation: " . . . we have petitioned for redress in the most humble terms." The reaction on the part of the British has been "repeated injury"— ignoring the pleas and increasing military activity.

4. Sample answer: Section 1: He states that the colonists must justify their position. Section 2: He explains basic assumptions about freedom. Section 3: He cites a long list of English abuses. Section 4: He cites the positive activities of the colonists. Section 5: He concludes with a common resolve to separate from England and pledge loyalty among colonists.

5.a Explanation: These rights are "unalienable" because they are given to each human being by the Creator (God) and are therefore beyond the reach of men's power. Answers b, c, and d are directly contradicted by the document.

6.d Explanation: The English feel they have the right to restrict the colonies in whatever way the King chooses. Answers a and b refer to colonist sympathizers, and answer c refers to the colonists.

7. Sample answer: "Infidel" refers to a person who does not believe in God. Paine is saying that he cannot believe that God has given up an interest in the governing of the world and will allow the colonists to be tyrannized by the English.

8. Sample answer: "the summer soldiers and the sunshine patriot"—people who will serve when it is convenient for them; he who serves "deserves the love and thanks of man and woman."

9. Sample answer: "Even the expression is **impious** for so unlimited a power can belong only to God." Translation: The power of restricting humans' activities is not in the hands of governments, but of God. Both the words "impious" and "infidel" are effective, because he is invoking the righteous wrath of religion against the way in which the English government is behaving.

10. b Explanation: is the only answer supported by the text: all of the colonists—"I call not upon a few, but upon all"; to support a war declaration—"could have induced me to support an offensive war."

Questions are classified in these categories:

Comprehension	1 (A), 8 (E)
Interpretation	3 (A), 10 (A)
Literary Analysis	4 (C), 6 (A)
Reading Strategy	2 (A), 9 (C)
Vocabulary	5 (E), 7 (A)

E=Easy, A=Average, C=Challenging

Extended Response

11. (Easy) Students can select from the many offenses listed, but they should focus on those that infringe on basic freedoms, eliminate the rule of law, and use military force.

12. (Average) Students should include some of the following in their essay: the King has refused to agree to necessary laws; he has not allowed his governors to act on important issues; the King has ignored the colonists' needs for action concerning laws; he has called the legislature together at inconvenient places and times; he has dismissed legislative gatherings at will; he has prevented elections; he has interfered with immigration laws.

13. (Average) Students may choose either analogy. They should relate the father-son story to Paine's plea for the colonists to be "generous" parents and endure the hardships of war in order to provide a better life for their children. They should compare the thief to the British, who have committed acts of murder and war, with no respect for the colonists' freedom.

14. (Average) Students may choose either document to support. They should include details from both selections. They should focus on particular aspects, such as the effectiveness of an emotional or reasoned appeal, or the effectiveness of a certain writing style.

15. (Challenging) Sample answers "The Declaration of Independence":

Emotional appeals: The King is acting against the will of God; every person is entitled to life, liberty and the pursuit of happiness; officers have harassed people; the King has deprived the colonists of trial by jury; the King has abolished the free system in Canada; he has caused the colonists to rise up against one another.

Appeals to reason: The King shows a disregard for law and the process of law; the colonists have petitioned the King; the colonists have warned the British; the colonists have reminded the English that theirs is a common heritage; the colonists have tried to appeal to the English people's sense of justice.

The Crisis:

Emotional appeals: The British have acted to "bind" the colonists; the colonists have earnestly sought to avoid war; the colonists must act to protect their children's future; the British are behaving like common thieves.

Appeals to reason: The difficulty of the conflict will make the glory of the victory sweeter for the colonists; the price of freedom is celestial in its worth; God is on the side of the colonists, since God would not be able to be a just God and stand by as the British usurp their freedoms.

Oral Response

16. In their oral response, students should cite specific information from the selections that substantiates their presentations and expands on their earlier responses.

"To His Excellency, General Washington" and "An Hymn to the Evening"

by Phillis Wheatley

Open-Book Test (p. 28)

Multiple Choice and Short Answer

1.c Explanation: She encourages him, exemplified by the line "thy ev'ry action let the goddess guide." Answers a, b, and d are not supported by the text.

2.d Explanation: is supported by "glorious toils," "they seek the work of war," and "Columbia's fury found."

3. Sample answer: "Pensive" means thinking seriously; England has finally realized the colonies' strength and seriousness of purpose.

4.b Explanation: Other nations are concerned with the outcome, because they value their own sense of independence.

5. Sample answers:
QUOTATION: 1. "*her* armies"; 2. "fury"; 3. "Columbia"; 4. "Britannia droops"
CHARACTERISTIC: being a female; able to be angry; a goddess; lowers its head
GIVEN TO: America; America; America; England; England
IMPRESSION: America is worthy of empathy.; America is capable of retaliation.; America has power; England realizes its mistake.

6.d Explanation: Answer d is supported by "Astonish'd ocean feels the wild uproar / The refluent surges beat the sounding shore."

7.a Explanation: Answer a is supported by "what beauteous dyes are spread!" at the beginning and "placid slumbers" toward the end of the poem.

8.a Explanation: "Him" = God; Actions: 1) God provides light for the day, and 2) God provides the evening's darkness.

9.a Explanation: The subject of the poem will "wake more heav'nly, more refined"—in other words, more in connection with God and nature—therefore, more holy.

10.d Explanation: The heaviness of the night (the scepter) causes the speaker's eyes to close and sleep to come.

Questions are classified in these categories:

Comprehension	1 (A)
Interpretation	2 (A), 6 (E)
Literary Analysis	5 (C), 8 (A), 10 (A)
Reading Strategy	4 (A), 7 (A), 9 (C)
Vocabulary	3 (A)

E=Easy, A=Average, C=Challenging

Extended Response

11. (Easy) Students can say that the Washington poem is more powerful because it could be used to inspire a whole country. They may say they find the hymn more powerful for them personally. Either position is correct, provided they support it with details.

12. (Average) Sample answers (adjectives followed by nouns): glorious toils, refulgent arms, unnumber'd charms, astonish'd ocean, refluent surges, golden reign, bright array, guardian aid, destined round, heaven-defended race, pensive head, cruel blindness.
Essay: Students should choose strong adjectives to demonstrate their points. There are some adjectives in this poem that are not as powerful as others (e.g., "golden hair"); these should not be used.

13. (Average) Sample answers: In the first poem, she contrasts America with Great Britain, the

fairness of gods and goddesses with the warlike deeds those on earth must perform, and aspects of nature with earthly deeds. In the second poem, she contrasts night with day and dark with light.

14. (Average) Sample answers: (Poem 1) heaven's light, the veil of night, tempest, night of storms; (Poem 2) the eastern main, pealing thunder, west glories in red, sable curtains of the night, Aurora. Students' essays should focus on Wheatley's ability to use nature images.

15. (Challenging) Sample answers: She is clearly intelligent, demonstrated by her choice of words (most quotations from either poem will substantiate this); she loves language and uses it well (most quotations from either poem will substantiate this); she is a patriot (her fervor in the first poem shows this); she has an artistic imagination (a quotation that visually describes an aspect of the sunset in the second poem will show this); she is knowledgeable about myths (shown in first poem with use of gods and goddesses); she has studied history (shown in first poem when she discusses the war with France).

Oral Response

16. In their oral response, students should cite specific information from the poems that substantiates their presentations and expands on their earlier responses.

"Speech in the Virginia Convention"
by Patrick Henry

"Speech in the Convention"
by Benjamin Franklin

Open-Book Test (p. 31)

Multiple Choice and Short Answer

1.b Explanation: " . . . in proportion to the magnitude of the subject ought to be the freedom of the debate. It is only in this way that we can hope to arrive at the truth, and fulfill the great responsibility . . . "

2.a Explanation: In the myth, Circe enchants men with her singing and distracts them.

3.c Explanation: The actions of the British imply anything but friendship or cooperation. Answers a and b are the opposite of what is implied by the context. Answer d is not implied at all by the context.

4. Sample answer: Words—lamp; judging; sir. Phrases—we must fight; we have. Sentence structure—He asks many questions; he also asks and answers.

5. Sample answer: There are several sentences that support the charge; the general answer is that Britain has accumulated armies and navies near America, for which she has no reasonable excuse.

6. Sample answer: Since he is held in such high regard and is admitting his flaws, he is hoping that his humility will have the effect of causing others to reexamine their views and become less rigid in their opposition to parts of the Constitution.

7.c Explanation: "to have the advantage of their joint wisdom . . . From such an assembly can a **perfect** production be expected?"

8. Sample answer: He recognizes that they need to present a united front for the public, both in America and abroad. Students may also select the quote that begins "Much of the strength . . . " that relates to "opinion."

9. Sample answer: Good attributes: goodness, wisdom, integrity. Outside expectations: that the delegates are confused and babbling; that the States plan to separate; that the delegates plan on "cutting one another's throats."

10.d Explanation: He emphasizes the need for unity. Answers a, b and c are not supported by the text.

Questions are classified in these categories:

Comprehension	1 (A)
Interpretation	6 (C), 8 (C)
Literary Analysis	4 (A), 7 (E), 9 (A)
Reading Strategy	2 (A), 5 (A), 10 (A)
Vocabulary	3 (A)

E=Easy, A=Average, C=Challenging

Extended Response

11. (Easy) "We must fight"; "an appeal to arms . . . is all that's left"; "three millions . . . armed in the holy cause of liberty." Students should note that these are powerful examples of how far he was willing to go to fight for freedom—he was literally willing to die for it.

12. (Average) Keeping back his opinions would be "an act of disloyalty toward the Majesty of Heaven"; "An appeal to arms and the God of hosts . . ."; "those means which the God of nature . . . "; "There is a just God . . . "— Students should show some comprehension of the concept that he was using the most powerful concept he could think of (God), which he knew would have a strong impact.

13. (Average) "But when will we be stronger?"; "Will it be the next week, or the next year?"; "Will it be when we are totally disarmed . . . ?"; "Shall we gather strength by . . . ?"; "Shall we acquire the means of effectual resistance . . . ?"

Essay: Students may include some of the following: that speeches that have repetitive sound can effectively convey an argument;

rhetorical questions make audiences curious and attentive, as they wonder whether the question will in fact be answered.

14. (Average) Students should mention at least part of the following: Franklin is concerned that people may go back and discuss their objections with others outside the Convention, and that this may result in being unable to garner widespread support for the Constitution. Of even greater concern is that both at home and abroad they may lose the beneficial effects of their previous hard work, and their government will become less productive. He has set the example of keeping his concerns to himself outside the Convention.

15. (Challenging) Patrick Henry—"It is natural to man to indulge in the illusions of hope." Modern application: In relation to finding a cure for AIDS or cancer, we need to be more active, rather than hope a solution will just magically appear. Benjamin Franklin—"Much of the strength . . . depends on . . . the general opinion of the goodness of . . . government . . ." Modern application: The public needs to have a better sense that politicians and government officials are worthy of our trust.

Oral Response

16. In their oral response, students should cite specific information from the speeches that substantiates their presentations and expands on their earlier responses.

"Letter to Her Daughter from the New White House"
by Abigail Adams

from *Letters from an American Farmer*
by Michel-Guillaume Jean de Crèvecoeur

Open-Book Test (p. 34)

Multiple Choice and Short Answer

1. Sample answers: There are several possible answers, depending upon the students' interpretation. Any example is correct, as long as it supports the premise. Students may cite the first sentence, in which Adams mentions getting lost on the Frederick Road, as it may seem unlikely that the President's wife would publicly acknowledge this kind of mishap. Students might also mention that the reference to a city being "only so in name" may seem too critical for public reading. Certainly the sentence "This is so great an inconvenience, that I know not what to do, or how to do" is one that would only be used privately.

2.d Explanation: Answers a, b, and c are not in the text.

3. Sample answer: Her statement about Georgetown's lack of beauty is purely subjective, so it is an opinion. She compares it to another town that is obviously not attractive—Milton—but she believes that Milton is still better than Georgetown.

4.c Explanation: The irony is that there are plenty of forests nearby, but no one is available to do the work.

5. Sample answer: The new house is the White House, since Abigail Adams is the wife of the second President. It is in Washington, D.C. One example of a clue about the house is on page 196, when she makes a reference to the fact that the chamber for the President (her husband) is comfortable.

6. Sample answer: She means that she is in a place where things are not as she has come to expect at home. There are labor problems, the area is less than attractive, and the city is not very developed. It is ironic that the President's wife would use these words, because she and her husband should feel very connected to their country in its seat of government, not as though she is in a foreign place.

7. Sample answer: It is a place of refuge. In their old countries, Europeans were "wretches" where there was "no bread," "no harvest," and they "met with nothing but the frowns of the rich" and "the severity of the laws."

8. Sample answers:
FACTS: Immigrants receive ample reward for their labors; they can buy land; they can become freemen. People who come to America often have a mixed heritage. Americans came from all over Europe.
OPINIONS: People have taken root and flourished in America; they leave behind their old prejudices; the labors of Americans will one day change the world.

9.b Explanation: Crèvecoeur believes that it is better to be working for oneself than having to pay off others—his examples are a prince, an abbot, and a lord—from the fruits of one's labors.

10.d Explanation: Additional clues: "a country that had no bread for him, whose fields procured him no harvest."

Questions are classified in these categories:
Comprehension   2 (E)
Interpretation   4 (A), 9 (A)
Literary Analysis   1 (E), 5 (A)
Reading Strategy   3 (A), 6 (C), 8 (A)
Vocabulary   7 (A), 10 (A)
E=Easy, A=Average, C=Challenging

Extended Response

11. (Easy) Students should use at least some of the following details in their essays: one who

"wanders about . . . works and starves . . . can that man call . . . any other kingdom his country?"; " a country that had no bread for him"; "no harvest"; "severity of the laws"; "not numbered in any civil lists."

12. (Average) Students should use supportive details, especially from the first and final pages of the letter, to show that Adams went from complaining about her new environment to making the most of it. At the end of the letter, she says , ". . . the more I view it, the more I am delighted with it." Clearly, she is beginning to see the potential of her new home.

13. (Average) Students may choose any sentence from the text, as long as they can rewrite it. Example: The beginning sentence could be rewritten in the following manner—The poor people of Europe have traveled and found their way to America; and they do not bother to ask the name of one another's country.

14. (Average) Students may choose any sentence, as long as they can write in the personal, humorous style of Adams and the effusive style of Crèvecoeur. In addition, they should provide some rationale for why the styles work well (or don't work well) for their topics.

15. (Challenging) Students may choose from many examples. Examples: Adams points to the possibilities for the new seat of government (which later evolves into a beautiful building), a metaphor for the possibilities in young America; she also alludes to the hospitality of several people, an attribute of friendliness that could apply to many Americans. Crèvecoeur views America as a place where people can take "root and flourish!" America has long been known as the "land of opportunity."

Oral Response

16. In their oral response, students should cite specific information from the selections that substantiates their presentations and expands on their earlier responses.

UNIT 3: A GROWING NATION (1800–1870)

"The Devil and Tom Walker"
by Washington Irving
Open-Book Test (p. 37)

Multiple Choice and Short Answer

1. Sample answer: They are miserly and miserable people who live in a broken-down, uncared-for environment.

2.b Explanation: In addition, Tom's wife waited for hens to lay eggs, so that she could hoard them.

3.c Explanation: Answers a and d are not supported by the text. Answer b is not correct, because Tom Walker is not yet mentioned in the story.

4. Sample answer: They were proud people who were not easily brought down; there were many people whom Irving would have considered as sinners.

5. Sample answer: His attitude towards his wife: He dislikes her to the point of physically fighting with her. Towards the swamp: In that desolate place, he is not afraid, because he was already such a sad soul. He stops there to rest, rather than hurry on, as someone more fearful would have done. Towards the devil: He is was not afraid of the Devil; in fact, he sneers at him.

6. Sample answer: The "common people's" attitudes are that the Indians were savages who made sacrifices. The Devil has the same opinion of Native Americans as he did of white men—that they are all savages.

7.d Explanation: She hides the hen's eggs; she has secret hoards; she urges her husband to make a bargain with the Devil; she goes to make her own bargain with the Devil.

8. Sample answer: "However Tom might have felt disposed to sell himself to the Devil, he was determined not to do so to oblige his wife . . ."

9. Sample answer: Two quotations: "Let us get hold of the property . . . and we will endeavor to do without the woman." And "Old Scratch must have had a tough time of it!"

10. Sample answer: People were wildly putting their money into unreliable ventures, supported by "the great speculating fever . . . had raged to an alarming degree."

Questions are classified in these categories:

Comprehension	2 (E)
Interpretation	3 (A), 9 (A)
Literary Analysis	1 (A), 5 (C), 8 (A)
Reading Strategy	4 (A), 6 (C), 10 (A)
Vocabulary	7 (A)

E=Easy, A=Average, C=Challenging

Extended Response

11. (Easy) Examples of religion: Tom loudly declares his devotion each Sunday; he censures his neighbors; he carries a Bible and keeps one in the office. Students may choose whether they believe Tom's efforts did or did not have an effect on his life, as long as they support their stance with details.

12. (Average) Both this passage and the one that describes Tom's placing the Bible near him while he engages in usurious practices—as well as the passage that describes his interest in reviving the persecution of Quakers and Anabaptists—shows that Tom has a misplaced zeal. His belief that the Bible would protect him, even though he still sinned, or that he could outwit the Devil by burying his horse, confirms the same kind of childlike belief that drove him to make a bargain with the Devil to begin with.

13. (Average) Students may cite other important incidents. Rising action: 1) Tom gets lost in the woods; 2) The Devil offers him a bargain; 3) Tom mentions the incident to his wife; 4) Tom's wife disappears, and he takes the bargain; 5) Tom becomes rich; 6) Tom tries to protect himself from the Devil. Climax: 7) The Devil kills Tom. Falling action: 8) The people clean up Tom's effects; 9) The people observe his spirit wandering in the woods. 10) The story has become a proverb. Conflict: the decision that Tom and his wife have to make about striking a deal with the Devil. Resolution: They strike the deal (and pay the price). The setting is in, and around, Boston. The major characters are Tom, his wife, and the Devil.

14. (Average) Students' answers will vary, but they should include key events such as the suspense of the meeting between the Devil and Tom Walker, or the underlying greed of Tom and his wife, or the ruthlessness of the Devil's bargain.

15. (Challenging) Students' answers will vary. The Devil and the supernatural aspects of the story are sources for students to examine, as is the bitter and unyielding behavior of both Tom Walker and his wife. The supernatural elements of the story can have a powerful impact on the reader, because they are scary. Perhaps readers will take this tale as a warning to be careful of their own avarice.

Oral Response

16. In their oral response, students should cite specific information from the story that substantiates their presentations and expands on their earlier responses.

"A Psalm of Life" and "The Tide Rises, The Tide Falls"

by Henry Wadsworth Longfellow

Open-Book Test (p. 40)

Multiple Choice and Short Answer

1.b Explanation: Possible quotation: "We can make our lives sublime / And, departing, leave behind us / Footprints on the sands of time."

2. Sample answer: Message: to live life to the fullest. Possible quotations: 1) "Be a hero in the strife!"; 2) "To act, that each tomorrow / Find us farther than today"; 3) "Act in the living present!"; 4) "Let us, then, be up and doing."

3. Sample answer: Many possible images: drums (the road to the grave); the battlefield (life); footprints (our mark in the world); main (life's possibilities).

4. Sample answer: Students may choose any stanza to rewrite, as long as they are able to convey its main concept. Sample: (Stanza 1) Do not tell me in this poem that life is empty. If we sleepwalk through life, we have missed a great opportunity. Even though sometimes things may seem grim, there are still many possibilities for fulfillment in life.

5. Sample answer: Longfellow draws an analogy with a battle to symbolize the difficulties we all face in life (including death). Other symbols are the field (the passage of time); a bivouac (the temporary nature of life); a hero (our opportunity to rise to the challenges of life); and strife (life's challenges). The mention of "dumb, driven cattle" shows us an image of how we do not wish to behave or be perceived.

6.d Explanation: Supporting quotation: ". . . nevermore / Returns the traveler to the shore . . ."

7.d Explanation: The waves of the ocean represent the image that *effaces*; the symbolism is that the ocean is death, wiping out our impression on the world.

8. Sample answer: The pattern uses the "alls" rhymes repeatedly; the last line, which matches the title, is also repeated in every stanza. This pattern reinforces the sense of the repetition of the ocean's waves, and, symbolically, the inevitability of death.

9. Sample answer: The images of beginnings and life are in these lines. They differ from the theme of the poem by pointing out that life goes on, even without those who die.

10. Sample answer: The calling of the sea is the call to death, and the waves are the natural, repetitive events that lead us into the end of our lives. The images are very effective, because they are somewhat unexpected. They signal a gentle, natural, almost calming passage from life into death.

Questions are classified in these categories:

Comprehension	1 (E), 2 (A)
Interpretation	5 (C)
Literary Analysis	4 (A), 8 (A), 10 (A)
Reading Strategy	3 (C), 6 (A), 9 (A)
Vocabulary	7 (A)

E=Easy, A=Average, C=Challenging

Extended Response

11. (Easy) The theme of "A Psalm of Life" is hope. Possible quotation: " . . . that each tomorrow finds us farther than today." The theme of "The Tide Rises, The Tide Falls" is the inevitability of death. Possible quotation: "The twilight darkens . . . " Students may select other quotations, including the two titles, to support their themes. The two themes are related in that they both focus on death, but they are different

in that they approach death from either an optimistic or pessimistic point of view.

12. (Average) He is trying to convey that we can leave behind "footprints" that inspire others, as do "the lives of great men." Our deeds can inspire others who are perhaps "shipwrecked" and need encouragement.

13. (Average) Possible images and meanings: 1) sand (time); 2) the tide (time); 3) the ocean (death); 4) shipwrecked (distraught).

14. (Average) Students' answers should focus on the positive meaning of footprints in "A Psalm of Life," which presents them as imprints on humanity that can inspire others: "footprints on the sands of time . . . [that] a forlorn and shipwrecked brother, seeing, shall take heart again." In "The Tide Rises, The Tide Falls," footprints are erased by death, and the view is much more negative: "The little waves . . . efface the footprints in the sands."

15. (Challenging) Students' ideas about the themes may vary, but they should explain the symbolism correctly, as it is explained in the textbook. The curlew calls as the twilight darkens, or as death approaches. The hostler calls as the morning breaks, and life goes on. Longfellow uses these contradicting ideas to deepen the complexity of the poem, so that it is not just about death, but about life continuing.

Oral Response

16. In their oral response, students should cite specific information from the poems that substantiates their presentations and expands on their earlier responses.

"Thanatopsis"
by William Cullen Bryant

"Old Ironsides"
by Oliver Wendell Holmes

"The First Snowfall"
by James Russell Lowell

from *Snowbound*
by John Greenleaf Whittier

Open-Book Test (p. 43)

Multiple Choice and Short Answer

1.c Explanation: supported by "Thou go . . . sustained and soothed by an unfaltering trust" and "All that breathe will share thy destiny."

2. Sample answer: the last bitter hour; shroud; pall; the narrow house; cold ground; pale form; tears; eternal resting place; sepulcher; tomb;

last sleep; rest; destiny; innumerable caravan; mysterious realm; chamber; silent halls; grave.

3.d Explanation: Answer d is supported by "all these . . . shall come / And make their bed with thee."

4.b Explanation: Answer b is supported by the text. Answers a, c, and d are not indicated in the text.

5. Sample answer: Holmes is almost being sarcastic. He certainly does not want the ship to be destroyed. However, he is concerned that greedy people will make the most of the ship's destruction, and he would rather see it literally sink than have it demeaned or disrespected.

6. Sample answer: Unstressed: I; and; by; the; -dow; The; -less; of; the; And; the; -den; -ries; of; -birds; like; -ing; by. Stressed: stood; watched; win-; noise-; work; sky; sud-; flur-; snow-; brown; leaves; whirl-.

7. Sample answer: The "mound in sweet Auburn," the "leaden sky," and snow that was a "mound heaped so high" all remind him of the death of his first daughter. "Flake by flake," at another, more painful time, the snow hid the scar of his loss. As he is kissing his daughter who is standing in front of him, he is thinking of the child he lost.

8.a Explanation: Other words: cheerless; gray; darkly circled; sadder light; thickening sky.

9. Sample answer: Stressed: prompt; -ci-; breath; fa-; wast-; Boys; path; pleased; when; farm-; boy; such; sum-; less; joy; bus-; feet; drew. Unstressed: A; de-; -sive; man; no; Our; -ther; -ed; a; Well; for; did; -er; Count; a; -mons; than; Our; -kins; on; our; we.

10. Sample answer: At the beginning of the poem, there is a feeling of the frightening aspects of the impending storm—"thickening sky," "ominous prophecy." By the poem's end, some snow has been shoveled to reach the animals, a fire has been lit in the hearth, and food is cooking, so there is a much more cheerful tone—"content to let the north wind roar."

Questions are classified in these categories:

Comprehension	2 (A), 4 (A)
Interpretation	3 (A), 5 (C)
Literary Analysis	6 (E), 9 (E)
Reading Strategy	1 (A), 7 (C), 10 (A)
Vocabulary	8 (A)

E=Easy, A=Average, C=Challenging

Extended Response

11. (Easy) Students' answers will vary, but they should use details that convey the natural aspects of death that Bryant is trying to convey, as opposed to the forced death of the ship that Holmes is trying to prevent.

12. (Average) Students will choose a variety of stanzas. They should paraphrase accurately. In addition, their essays should reflect an understanding of the poet's intent.

13. (Average) Examples: "The eagle of the sea" conveys the power and majesty of Old Ironsides; "Chanticleer's muffled crow" shows the intensity of the weather in "The First Snowfall"; "robins the babes in the wood" provides a gentle image of Lowell's daughter's gravesite; there are several animals in **Snowbound** that give color and life to the poem, as well as setting a homey scene for the reader.

14. (Average) Possible answers: thickening sky; chill no coat could keep out; a dull bitterness of cold; the wind's strong pulse; starry flake; all night long; all day the hoary meteor fell.

15. (Challenging) Students' answers will vary, but they should mention that the task was to shovel a path to the barn to reach the animals, which filled them with "joy." They created a path that resembled "dazzling crystal," making them imagine Aladdin's cave. They delighted in the various reactions of the animals.

Oral Response

16. In their oral response, students should cite specific information from the poems that substantiates their presentations and expands on their earlier responses.

"Crossing the Great Divide"

by Meriwether Lewis

"The Most Sublime Spectacle on Earth"

by John Wesley Powell

Open-Book Test (p. 46)

Multiple Choice and Short Answer

1.d Explanation: Although answers a and b are partly correct—they do run out of food, and they do establish camp quickly—they are not the account's focus. Answer c is unsupported by the text.

2. Sample answer: the fraternal hug of the chief; the meeting was affecting; one woman was a sister of another; two women had been prisoners together.

3. Sample answer: 1) The explorers make it clear their intentions are peaceful; 2) The explorers make it clear that the American government is the source of trade and peace; 3) The explorers want to travel westward to trade with the Native Americans; 4) The explorers need to be able to successfully complete their journey, so they can return with goods to trade.

4. Sample answer: After unloading baggage (conveying their intent to stay), he and his

company set up a comfortable, shaded spot where the Native Americans can sit while they parley. His concern for their comfort shows that he intends for the negotiations to be peaceful and friendly.

5.c Explanation: Lewis wants it to be very clear—obvious—to the Native Americans that his company and the American government have good feelings towards the Native Americans. He expresses this sentiment so the Native Americans will not harm anyone, and will allow them to explore farther into the West.

6.b Explanation: It is supported by the suggestion to pick up Mt. Washington or the Blue Ridge Mountain and throw either of them into the canyon, and still they would not fill it.

7. Sample answer: rains and rivers carve the canyon; more than 6,000 feet of rock has been eroded; clouds have formed the mountains.

8. Sample answer: size: the little clouds seem to be individualized; distance, location: the skies come down into the gorges and cling to the cliffs; faring here and there; relationships in space: no demarcation between sky and earth is seen when the clouds cover the mountaintops.

9.c Explanation: The final sentence suggests a level of appreciation of beauty usually available only in Paradise.

10. Sample answer: They "carve out valleys and canyons and fashion hills"; "The clouds are the artists sublime"; they "play"; they "creep"; they seem "to have wills and souls of their own and to be going on diverse errands."

Questions are classified in these categories:

Comprehension	1 (A), 3 (A)
Interpretation	4 (C)
Literary Analysis	2 (A), 7 (A), 10 (A)
Reading Strategy	6 (A), 8 (C)
Vocabulary	5 (E), 9 (A)

E=Easy, A=Average, C=Challenging

Extended Response

11. (Easy) Students may choose details that support the following premises: The two explorers' accounts are similar in that they are both impressed by their new discoveries. They are different in their focus. Lewis is focused on the relationship he is trying to establish with the Native Americans. Powell is focused on the natural beauty around him.

12. (Average) Lewis has to establish a good relationship with the Native Americans to be able to trade with them and to pave the way for further exploration (see introduction). He also notes that it is "mutually advantageous" to have a cordial relationship.

13. (Average) Describe it: Students may use geological or artistic descriptions. Compare it:

They may compare it to their own expeditions in nature, or to something they are familiar with. A variety of answers is fine, as long as students relate their comparisons to the Grand canyon. Associate it: Students may associate the size or grandeur of the canyon with something in their own lives. Analyze it: Students should describe how the canyon is created.

14. (Average) Students may answer that they feel Powell is most effective either when he is writing scientifically or artistically, as long as they support their answers. Sample response: He describes in some detail the "music" of the waters' sound, which he refers to as a "symphony."

15. (Challenging) Students may use several textual details to support this, or another, opinion: Powell changes from the accurate but somewhat distant scientist to a more romantic vision of the Grand Canyon, with which he is clearly infatuated.

Oral Response

16. In their oral response, students should cite specific information from the accounts that substantiates their presentations and expands on their earlier responses.

"The Fall of the House of Usher" and "The Raven"
by Edgar Allan Poe

Open-Book Test (p. 49)

Multiple Choice and Short Answer

1.c Explanation: His attempt does not work: he looks at it again "with a shudder even more thrilling than before."

2. Sample answer: He believed that the house had a peculiar atmosphere about it that had no freshness or beauty, but reeked of decay and produced a greyish vapor.

3. Sample answer: The special effect is one of impending doom. Possible answers for contributing details: "the first glimpse . . . a sense of insufferable gloom pervaded my spirit"; "rank sedges"; "bleak walls"; "vacant eyelike windows"; "decayed trees"; "black and lurid tarn."

4. Sample answer: I recognized the carvings on the ceilings, the wall tapestries, the blackness of the floors, and the fantastic trophies. At first, I did not want to acknowledge their familiarity to me. Nonetheless, they conjured up frightening, and new, images for me.

5. Sample answer: his action was alternately vivacious and sullen; his voice varied greatly; he had an over-sensitivity to light and sound; he

struggled greatly with fear; he was unable to leave the house.

6.a Explanation: The narrator constantly analyzes his reactions to the situation. He tries to find a reason for all his impressions, and to shake off the feelings of superstition.

7. Sample answer: continual knocking; repetition of "Nevermore"; repetition of certain words, such as "Lenore," "prophet if bird or devil,"; rhyming pattern of each first line—for example, "dreary" and "weary"; many words that end in "or" sound.

8.a Explanation: He had the "mien of lord or lady" and was "stately," so the Raven did not feel he needed to humble himself in any way.

9. Sample answer: I smiled, a change from my sad demeanor, to think of this Raven. I sat down before the bird and tried to figure out what was going on. I wondered why this strange and threatening-looking bird kept saying, "Nevermore." What could he mean by it?

10.c Explanation: The narrator can tell that the bird is not a coward, because his countenance is so stern, despite the fact that he has wandered far in the night.

Questions are classified in these categories:

Comprehension	2 (C)
Interpretation	1 (A)
Literary Analysis	3 (A), 5 (A), 6 (C), 7 (A)
Reading Strategy	4 (A), 9 (A)
Vocabulary	8 (E), 10 (A)

E=Easy, A=Average, C=Challenging

Extended Response

11. (Easy) Students should cover the following themes, which they can support with a variety of story details: The narrator feels a sense of responsibility, both because they were childhood friends and because he has received a desperate letter. He fulfills his responsibility by reading and painting with Roderick, and listening to him talk endlessly. He also helps Roderick to bury his sister.

12. (Average) Possible answers: the house, his sister, the influence of his family tradition. Students should support their views with examples of the house's declining condition, the sister's illness, and the Usher tradition of straight patrilineal descent.

13. (Average) Students should discuss his artwork and his music. One piece of art described in the story shows a tunnel buried deep beneath the earth. His musical piece describes the glory of old that cannot be recaptured and is now "entombed." Both artistic expressions reveal Usher's obsession with decay and death.

14. (Average) Students should focus on the growing fear of the narrator in both selections, choosing examples that show the narrator's internal thoughts and feelings.

15. (Challenging) Students' answers will vary. Possible elements they may choose might include books, women, visitors, inclement weather, or the supernatural. Any of these elements are acceptable, as long as they can be documented in both selections.

Oral Response

16. In their oral response, students should cite specific information from the selections that substantiates their presentations and expands on their earlier responses.

"The Minister's Black Veil"
by Nathaniel Hawthorne
Open-Book Test (p. 52)
Multiple Choice and Short Answer

1. Sample answer: They are immediately ready to believe the worst about the minister; this demonstrates their narrow-mindedness. Examples: "I can't really feel as if good Mr. Hooper's face was behind that crape"; "I don't like it"; "Our parson has gone mad!"

2.c Explanation: Answers a, b, and d are not supported by the text; these answers also imply that the townspeople are less serious than they actually are.

3. Sample answer: "Did he seek to hide it from the dread Being . . .? "—Mr. Hooper had sinned greatly; "the veil hung straight down from his forehead"—Mr. Hooper is ashamed to reveal himself to the dead; —"ready . . . for the dreadful hour that should snatch the veil from their faces"—Mr. Hooper was referring to the moment of death, when all would be revealed to God; "the black veil involved his own spirit in the horror"—Mr. Hooper did not wish to see his own face, to know himself and his flaws; "this dismal shade"—He is either hiding his face for sorrow or for shame.

4. Sample answer: Even the most innocent member of the congregation feels that all of their misdeeds have become revealed. They feel guilty and overwhelmed by their own sense of sin: "the hearers quaked." The community carries the burden of an overactive conscience and an overzealous imagination.

5.b Explanation: Answer b is suggested by the experience he has when he bids farewell to the dead girl. His face becomes revealed to her, and he quickly pulls his veil over it. This suggests that the veil allows the dead to see him, and that he is aware of this phenomenon.

6. Sample answer: She loves him, but finally, she is overcome by the horror that surrounds the veil, and she leaves him. However, at the story's end, Hawthorne suggests that if Mr. Hooper were unable to protect his face, Elizabeth stands ready at his death bed to honor his wish that his face be always covered. Students may use details or quotations to support these facts.

7. Sample answer: The beneficial effect is that sinners feel able to talk to the minister. Possible interpretation (students may suggest others): Hawthorne may be trying to convey that we are only willing to admit sins in secret, which implies a limited confession. Maybe he is saying that we do not really want to become free of sin. Example: "Dying sinners cried aloud for Mr. Hooper . . ."

8. Sample answer: They jump to conclusions; they are judgmental; they lack courage; they wanted absolution for their sins; they are narrow-minded.

9.d Explanation: The clue word is "quivering," and the whole sense of the scene is one of fear and gloom.

10.c Explanation: Additional detail: "He had never lacked advisers."

Questions are classified in these categories:

Comprehension	1 (E)
Interpretation	5 (C), 6 (A)
Literary Analysis	3 (A), 4 (A), 8 (C)
Reading Strategy	2 (A), 7 (A)
Vocabulary	9 (E), 10 (A)

E=Easy, A=Average, C=Challenging

Extended Response

11. (Easy) Students' opinions may vary; this is acceptable, as long as they support their responses. Sample: Hawthorne repeatedly refers to Mr. Hooper as "good Mr. Hooper." It is as though Mr. Hooper has willingly taken on all the evilness of the townspeople, and he is the mirror who reflects it back to them. However, he continually tries to fulfill his normal responsibilities as a parson, even in the midst of dealing with this difficult new role.

12. (Average) Possible answers: Reverend Clark thinks Hooper has prayed much; he thinks Hooper is a blameless person and a role model for others; he thinks Hooper is a father in the church who should not leave a blot on his memory; he thinks Hooper has had a "pure" life; he thinks Hooper will go to his "reward" (Heaven).

13. (Average) Because Mr. Hooper has been, in his opinion, a model citizen and preacher, Reverend Clark wants him to cast aside the veil. When Mr. Hooper refuses, Reverend Clark assumes he is a sinner.

14. (Average) The "veil of eternity" is the one that separates the time of living from the time of dying. Mr. Hooper is ready to die and enter eternity. This symbol is hinted at earlier when people have a fancy of him walking with a dead maiden, and in his ability to calm sinners who are approaching their death.

15. (Challenging) Students' answers may vary, but they should touch on the veil as a symbol of secrecy and darkness. Hawthorne's larger message is that no one in the town is willing to try to communicate beyond the veil to the human being underneath; they are not able to overcome their own foibles. Hawthorne is saying that although the minister's veil may be the only visible one, we all wear them to cover our sins and our sorrow.

Oral Response

16. In their oral response, students should cite specific information from the story that substantiates their presentations and expands on their earlier responses.

from *Moby-Dick*

by Herman Melville

Open-Book Test (p. 55)

Multiple Choice and Short Answer

1.b Explanation: Answer b is supported by "the footprints of his one unsleeping, ever-pacing thought."

2. Sample answer: He rubs the piece, "heightening its luster." He knows the men may not share his bloodlust for the whale but will respond to money. He needs their help, so he decides to make it more worth their while to help him.

3. Sample answer: Starbuck's objections are that he has signed on for a business purpose, not for vengeance. Ahab's "vengeance will not fetch thee much in our Nantucket market." Ahab convinces him by first recounting his own need with great animation, but more so by reminding him that all others on board support him.

4. Sample answer: "foreboding invocation"; "low laugh from the hold"; "presage vibrations of the winds"; "hollow flap of the sails"; "Starbuck's downcast eyes."

5.c Explanation: "He would fain have shocked into them the same fiery emotion . . ."

6. Sample answer: Ray 1—1) "had Ahab time to think"; 2) Ahab can only feel, not think; Ray 2—1) "To think's audacity"; 2) Ahab believes that mortals don't have the right to think; Ray 3—1) "Thinking . . . ought to be a coolness and a calmness"; 2) Ahab thinks that humans are not capable of this; Ray 4—1) "Our poor hearts throb, and our poor brains beat too much"; 2) Ahab is saying that we feel too much and think too much.

7. Sample answer: Students may express Ahab's positive or negative feelings, since he has both. Sample answers: He calls the wind "glorious and gracious," because it does not veer from its intent; he calls it "unchangeable and strong," because it blows ships onward.

8.c Explanation: He sees that "against the wind [nature] he [Ahab] now steers for the open jaw"; His fear is confirmed, because "my bones feel damp inside me."

9. Sample answer: The sharks represent a warning in the story that if Ahab persists, he will die, and his ship will be destroyed, since sharks symbolize danger. They also symbolize that nature prevails against the will of humans, even when they are enraged. Sample quotes: "maliciously snapped at the blades of the oars"; "sharks following them in the same prescient way as vultures," "the unpitying sharks accompanied him."

10. Sample answer: Curses. Other words in sentence that suggest meaning: "The long, barbed steel goblets were lifted"; "cries"; the drinks were "quaffed down with a hiss."

Questions are classified in these categories:

Comprehension	3 (A), 8 (C)
Interpretation	2 (A), 4 (A)
Literary Analysis	1 (A), 5 (A), 9 (A)
Reading Strategy	6 (C), 7 (A)
Vocabulary	10 (E)

E=Easy, A=Average, C=Challenging

Extended Response

11. (Easy) Students can use details to substantiate some of these qualities of Ahab: He is strong and able to get his men to agree to his task; he encourages them; he does not ask them to do anything he will not do himself; he bends them to his will; he makes them victims of his obsession; he inspires them by getting them to agree to a common purpose; he is friendly and drinks with them; he relies on their support. In their answers, students may say he is effective, because he gets his men to obey him; or that he is ineffective, because he victimizes his men.

12. (Average) Students should explain that they both speak to nature (or God), reminding nature of their positive attributes, but in different ways. Starbuck reminds God of his loyalty to his task; Stubbs speaks of his self-reliance.

13. (Average) Students should use textual details to answer that it is Tashtego, trying to maintain the ship's flag even in its darkest hour. His action represents the persistence of human will, and the will to survive, even in the throes of death.

14. (Average) Students should make some mention that, like Ahab and the men of the ship who go along with him, the bird represents greediness that will be punished with death. The larger theme is that all living themes are subject to the whims of nature.

15. (Challenging) Melville's message is that nature continues, as it did before Ahab's obsession, and as it will beyond human measurements of time. Students may mention either the event of the men helplessly watching the whale destroy their ship, or how Ahab is ironically killed by his own hand. Both of these events serve to emphasize the inability of humans to combat or contain natural forces.

Oral Response

16. In their oral response, students should cite specific information from the book excerpt that substantiates their presentations and expands on their earlier responses.

from *Nature*, from *Self-Reliance*, "The Snowstorm," and "Concord Hymn"

by Ralph Waldo Emerson

Open-Book Test (p. 58)

Multiple Choice and Short Answer

1. Sample answer: There are several possible responses. Examples: the snake casting off his skin (like a man in nature casts off his years); his head is "bathed" by the air and becomes more relaxed; nature is not always dressed "in holiday attire," so it can have a melancholy effect on the spirit.

2. Sample answer: Students may agree by saying that Emerson says nature can be beautiful and melancholy, to suit either mood. They may disagree by saying that nature does not always match one's feelings. They should cite details.

3. Sample answer: "The name of the nearest friend . . . disturbance"; "I find something more dear and connate than in the streets or villages."

4.c Explanation: Answer c is supported by "the absolutely trustworthy was stirring at their heart."

5. Sample answer: Students may agree with Emerson, saying that society does indeed value "names and customs" rather than "realities and creators." However, they may also state the viewpoint that today's society is more accepting of individual accomplishment.

6. Sample answer: Each person's success is determined by the effort he or she puts into the task given to them by God: "A man is relieved and gay when he has put his heart into his work." But if he or she does not live up to his or her potential, "his genius deserts him."

7.b Explanation: Answer b is supported by the second stanza, and the line in the third stanza that refers to "the mad wind's nightwork."

8. Sample answer: He is impressed by the majesty of nature. Examples: "the house mates sit around the radiant fireplace"; "the frolic architecture"; "Art" is "astonished" by one night's work; "fanciful"; "myriad-handed."

9.d Explanation: The event was a battle in the Revolution.

10. Sample answer: He is mentioning their occupation to stress that they were not battle-hardened soldiers, but everyday people, who had to take up arms to protect themselves and their families, firing "the shot heard round the world." He draws a contrast between their everyday lives and the historical importance their battles came to have in America's history.

Questions are classified in these categories:

Comprehension	3 (A), 7 (A)
Interpretation	6 (C), 8 (A), 10 (A)
Literary Analysis	1 (A), 4 (A)
Reading Strategy	2 (A), 5 (A)
Vocabulary	9 (E)

E=Easy, A=Average, C=Challenging

Extended Response

11. (Easy) He enjoys and appreciates the work of nature. From **Nature:** Examples—"I have enjoyed a perfect exhilaration"; "I am glad to the brink of fear"; "We return to reason and faith"; "A man casts off his years." From "The Snowstorm": Examples—"the trumpets of the sky"; "the radiant fireplace"; "so fanciful"; "frolic."

12. (Average) The wind is portrayed as an artist. Examples: "artificer"; "curves his white bastions"; "nought cares he for number or proportion"; "fanciful"; "he hangs Parian wreaths"; "a swan-like form"; "frolic architecture."

13. (Average) Students may use any examples that provide the answer: The purpose of the poem is to commemorate a monument to the fighters of the American Revolution, sixty years later. It fulfills its purpose, since it makes a connection between the fighters and the generations who came later and were able to be free, because of their efforts.

14. (Average) Students will have a variety of examples from which to choose, but they should mention that the importance of each individual is paramount to Emerson. In **Self-Reliance**, he pits the individual against society, saying that "society is a joint-stock company." In **Nature**, the individual is best served by becoming a tool of nature.

15. (Challenging) Students should focus on the spiritual references in the selections. Examples: "I am part or parcel of God"; "the currents of the Universal Being circulate through me"; "Accept the place that divine providence has found for you"; "Obeying the Almighty effort."

Oral Response

16. In their oral response, students should cite specific information from the selections that substantiates their presentations and expands on their earlier responses.

from *Walden* and **from *Civil Disobedience***

by Henry David Thoreau

Open-Book Test (p. 61)

Multiple Choice and Short Answer

1.b Explanation: Students may support the statement with many details. Examples: "then I let it lie, fallow perchance"; "I have frequently seen a poet withdraw, having enjoyed the most valuable part of a farm."

2. Sample answer: The traditional, or farmer's view, is that a farm is worth what it produces. Thoreau is making a case that the artist was able to derive most of the art from the farm, so that to his mind, the farmer is not left with much of value.

3. Sample answer: Thoreau means that a farm is like a jail, because it burdens a farmer with responsibilities, as though he is a prisoner. Students may agree or disagree with Thoreau's concept of commitment, saying that they do not wish to become overcommitted to the acquisition of material goods, or that they do wish to be committed to people and their communities.

4. Sample answer: what people should do: count only your fingers and toes, and lump the rest; let your affairs be as two or three; count half a dozen; keep your accounts on a thumbnail; eat one meal a day; use only five dishes. What people should not do: not have your affairs be a hundred or a thousand; don't count a million; do not eat three meals a day; do not use a hundred dishes; reduce other things in proportion.

5.c Explanation: Its significance is in this sentence: "Who does not feel his faith in a resurrection and immortality strengthened by hearing of this?"

6.d Explanation: Students may agree or disagree with Thoreau's stance. Example of detail: "**It** does not keep the country free" could be used to argue for or against government; that is, that a government organizes people to fight for their freedom (for), or that, as Thoreau says, the credit should be given to the character of the people (against).

7. Sample answer: He means that it is a non-vital force. In addition, although people may use it against one another and themselves, it does not have the energy of a living organism, so it does more damage than good.

8.a Explanation: The context clue is "tradition."

9. Sample answer: He asks for "**at once** a better government." He also expects that "every man make known what kind of government will command his respect."

10.c Explanation: Thoreau means that "enterprise" has taken place in direct proportion to how quickly the government has removed its interference.

Questions are classified in these categories:

Comprehension	1 (A), 9 (E)
Interpretation	5 (A), 7 (A)
Literary Analysis	2 (A), 4 (A)
Reading Strategy	3 (C), 6 (C)
Vocabulary	8 (E), 10 (A)

E=Easy, A=Average, C=Challenging

Extended Response

11. (Easy) Students might say that Thoreau would be a writer or a poet, or that he could still somehow pursue his dream of self-reliant living amidst nature. They might also say he could end up as a homeless person, since he would be reluctant to purchase private property. Many answers are acceptable, as long as students relate their answers to his philosophy in a realistic way.

12. (Average) Students may use a variety of details from the text; they should demonstrate an understanding that Thoreau is speaking wistfully of his lost innocence, and his feeling that as we grow older, we lose touch with the simpler, and most important, aspects of life.

13. (Average) Students may choose from several examples. Possible answer: **Walden**: One might conclude from Thoreau's rejection of man's purpose as "to glorify God" that he is not religious, but in fact, he demonstrates his spirituality by saying that "God will see that you do not want society" and his analogy between humans and a bug's resurrection.

14. (Average) Possible answers: "The character inherent in the American people has done all that has been accomplished" (Meaning: It is not the government, but the governed, who empower the nation.); "If you have built your castles in the air . . . now put the foundations under them" (Meaning: Whatever your purpose is, fulfill it by giving yourself entirely to it.); "Cultivate poverty like a garden herb"; (Try to focus on poverty, not wealth; on simplicity, not complexity); "If a man does not keep pace with his companions, perhaps it is because he hears a different drummer"; (Meaning: We are all individuals and deserve respect for our differences.)

15. (Challenging) Students may use a variety of examples, as long as they mention the basic premises of Thoreau's philosophy of individual reliance, simplicity, and the search for a life of quality. As long as students can support their opinions, answers that state that Thoreau is inconsistent in these essays are also acceptable.

Oral Response

16. In their oral response, students should cite specific information from the essays that substantiates their presentations and expands on their earlier responses.

Emily Dickinson's Poetry
Open-Book Test (p. 64)
Multiple Choice and Short Answer

1.d Explanation: There is nothing in the poem to indicate an attitude of either (a) annoyance or (c) amazement. Answer b is not indicated in the poem.

2. Sample answer: me / immortality; away / Civility; chill / tulle; day / Eternity; Immortality / Civility / Eternity.

3.d Explanation: It is supported by "as these that twice befell," the two events that brought her pain.

4. Sample answer: Examples of slant rhymes: society / Majority; Gate / Mat; nation / attention; one / stone; choose / close. Example of exact rhyme: Door / more; unmoved / unmoved; known / stone.

5. Sample answer: It is the particular slant of light in winter afternoons that is Dickinson's visual image. The larger idea which she is discussing is death.

6.b Explanation: The context clue is "the Heft of Cathedral Tunes," or the heaviness of church music. Students may say that the word "oppresses" is effective, because light is usually not oppressive—so Dickinson is using contrast to get her point across. They may also say the use of "oppresses" is effective, because it conveys the heaviness of thoughts about death.

7. Sample answer: She suggests that the privacy and solitude of the soul, and therefore its

depths, are much greater than those we associate with space, sea, and death. She implies that the soul is boundless by comparing it to the most boundless concepts we know, and therefore it should be valued highly.

8.c Explanation: *Finite* is contrasted with *infinity*. Answers a, b, and d are not supported by the text.

9. Sample answer: The brain will contain the sky with ease, because it has the capacity to think of all things. Ordinarily, our visual image of the sky is so vast, that our visual image of a physical brain might be smaller. But, in reality, the brain is larger. Dickinson also adds, for emphasis, that the brain can encompass not only the sky, but "You—beside—."

10. Sample answer: Examples: Water (concrete) / Thirst (abstract); Peace (abstract) / Battles (concrete); Love (abstract) / Memorial Mold (concrete).

Questions are classified in these categories:

Comprehension	9 (A)
Interpretation	3 (A), 7 (A)
Literary Analysis	2 (A), 4 (E)
Reading Strategy	1 (A), 5 (A), 10 (E)
Vocabulary	6 (C), 8 (A)

E=Easy, A=Average, C=Challenging

Extended Response

11. (Easy) Students should mention that Dickinson deals primarily with death, using any of several examples provided in these poems. They may also say that she deals with the soul or the individual. These answers are acceptable, as long as they are supported by examples.

12. (Average) Students may say that either the soul or the brain is more valued by Dickinson. Either answer is acceptable, if it is supported. They may also say that the soul and brain are both of value to Dickinson, without saying that she values one over the other. This answer is also acceptable, as long as it is supported. In any case, students should refer to the other "solitudes" that are compared with the soul. They should mention the sky, the sea, and God, in reference to the brain.

13. (Average) Students should mention that Dickinson has an internal focus on the life of the soul and the mind, as opposed to the external focus on the world that another writer might have. Students may justify their premises with any examples that suffice.

14. (Average) Examples: Slant rhymes: listens/Distance ("There's a certain Slant); privacy/ Infinity ("Solitude of space"); Room/Storm ("I heard a Fly buzz"); firm/Room ("I heard a Fly buzz"); space/ these ("Solitude of space"). Exact rhymes: Blue/do ("The Brain"); Pound/Sound ("The Brain"); told/Mold ("Water");

throe/snow ("Water"); Door/more ("The Soul"). Students may say her use of slant rhymes is effective, since its unexpectedness gets the reader's attention.

15. (Challenging) Students may mention the weather, the sunlight, the sea, space, the sky, water, or the land and the landscape. They should be able to offer some imagery that is conjured by the use of these words, and how that imagery affects the poem's strength.

Oral Response

16. In their oral response, students should cite specific information from the poems that substantiates their presentations and expands on their earlier responses.

from *Preface to the 1855 Edition of Leaves of Grass*; from *Song of Myself*; "I Hear America Singing"; "A Noiseless Patient Spider"; "By the Bivouac's Fitful Flame"; "When I Heard the Learn'd Astronomer"

by Walt Whitman

Open-Book Test (p. 67)

Multiple Choice and Short Answer

1.d Explanation: Answer d is supported by "new life of the new forms"; "action has descended to the stalwart and well-shaped heir who approaches, and that he shall be fittest for his days."

2. Sample answer: Examples: "hospitality which forever indicates heroes"; "ruggedness and nonchalance that the soul loves"; "tremendous audacity of its crowds"; "prolific and splendid extravagance."

3. Sample answer: Whitman's emphasis on the individual is confirmed by his saying that he celebrates and values himself, as should others. Since he uses varying line lengths, he emphasizes his need to write in a style that feels right to him. His first two stanzas are much shorter than the third and fourth, where he permits himself to get into more detail. His style has very much the feeling of prose.

4.b Explanation: Answer b is supported by "retiring back a while." Answers a, c, and d are not indicated by the text.

5.d Explanation: Answer d is supported by "These are really the thoughts of all men . . ."; "This is the common air that bathes the globe."

6. Sample answer: Students may interpret this image in many ways: as the moon "up there"; the sky "up there"; the vast universe of nature or God ("what have you to confide in me?" "Will you speak before I am gone?").

7. Sample answer: mechanics singing blithe and strong; carpenter singing as he measures plank and beam; mason as he makes ready for or leaves work; boatman singing what belongs to him; deckhand singing on steamboat; shoemaker singing on his bench; hatter singing as he stands; mother or young wife singing at work; girl singing, sewing or washing.

8. Sample answer: delicious, robust, friendly, open, strong, melodious.

9.c Explanation: In the first poem, the searching of the soul is likened to the creation of the spider's web; in the second poem, the image is of a person sitting by an army campfire, whose mind wanders through memory, trying to recapture lost moments.

10. Sample answer: Although Whitman labels his experience as "unaccountable," it is attributable to the proofs, figures, columns, and other scientific measures of the sky. He immediately feels better by going outside to have the sense of a real experience with nature.

Questions are classified in these categories:

Comprehension	7 (E), 9 (A)
Interpretation	6 (A), 10 (A)
Literary Analysis	1 (A), 3 (C)
Reading Strategy	2 (A), 5 (A), 8 (E)
Vocabulary	4 (A)

E=Easy, A=Average, C=Challenging

Extended Response

11. (Easy) Possible answers: the wild gander; the moose; the cat; the chickadee; the prairie dog; the sow; the hen. As expressed in "I am enamor'd of growing outdoors" and "Of men that live among cattle," he is clearly a lover of outdoor life.

12. (Average) Students should note that it is apparent from his mention of the grass (an ongoing phenomena), and his belief that "the smallest sprout shows there is really no death," Whitman seems to believe that our souls are still alive after we die.

13. (Average) Students may choose from any of the several examples. Their answers should focus on the poetic aspects of America.

14. (Average) Students may answer that the comparison is not effective, because they find it unattractive. In this case, they need to carefully support their answer. However, most students will probably agree that the soul is "noiseless" and "patient," and shares other qualities with a spider, such as a need to be connected to someone or something in "measureless oceans of space."

15. (Challenging) Alternate answers are acceptable here, as long as they are supported. Students may focus on his attachment to America and the individual spirit that propels it as the

underpinnings of Whitman's writing. In **Leaves of Grass** and "I Hear America Singing," he effectively uses the whole of the United States to express a concept of vigor and youth. Additionally, students may focus on Whitman's exploration of the soul, as expressed in the shorter poems and in sections of "Song of Myself."

Oral Response

16. In their oral response, students should cite specific information from the writings that substantiates their presentations and expands on their earlier responses.

UNIT 4: DIVISION, RECONCILIATION, AND EXPANSION (1850–1914)

"An Episode of War"

by Stephen Crane

"Willie Has Gone to the War,"

words by George Cooper, music by Stephen Foster

Open-Book Test (p. 70)

Multiple Choice and Short Answer

1.b Explanation: Right after he sets out the coffee, the lieutenant is shot. None of the other answers are supported by the text.

2.d Explanation: The context clues are "his eyes toward the battle" and "distance."

3. Sample answer: The danger that the officer was in both frightened and awed his men: it gave him a "majesty," and it also made them fear that any additional touch of theirs might damage him further.

4. Sample answer: general on a black horse; the blue infantry; the green woods; the aide galloping and then suddenly stopping his horse; the bugler; maniacal horses; the shells booming in the air; the glistening guns.

5.c Explanation: Answer (c) is correct, supported by the final line of the story.

6. Sample answer: He had to amputate it and could see the officer's distress. The doctor was trying to distract the officer from an unfortunate reality.

7. Sample answer: "The whispering waters repeat the name that I love"; "And pine like a bird for its mate"; "soft is the sigh of the gale."

8. Sample answer: They were trying to avoid the painful reality of war, since there were many people who had to stay strong at home while they waited for soldiers to return. They were

also trying to encourage people to maintain strong values, such as faithfully waiting for a loved one.

9.d Explanation: Context clues are: "our home in the glade"; dale; brookside; "where the lily bells grow"; daisies; "leaves of the forest"; roses.

10. Sample answer: Repetition of the last line of each verse, and repetition of the refrain, makes the song sound romantic and mournful. It also emphasizes that the singer will wait.

Questions are classified in these categories:

Comprehension	3 (A), 4 (A)
Interpretation	1 (A)
Literary Analysis	5 (E), 7 (A), 10 (E)
Reading Strategy	6 (C), 8 (A)
Vocabulary	2 (A), 9 (A)

E=Easy, A=Average, C=Challenging

Extended Response

11. (Easy) 1) "Why, man, that's no way to do. You want to fix that thing." 2) "Good-morning"; "Well, let's have a look at it." 3) Possible answers: "What mutton-head tied it up that way?"; "Come along. Don't be a baby." 4) Possible answers: "Oh, a man."; "I don't suppose it matters so much as all that."

12. (Average) Students should mention that the meaning of others' comments was to make the lieutenant feel that he didn't know how to handle himself: "that he did not know how to be correctly wounded." He felt scorned by the doctor and overly pitied by his family.

13. (Average) Students may have several opinions: the lieutenant is thrown off by the man's calmness; he is seized with panic at his own predicament; he feels helpless and wants to do something active instead of being passive. Any of these answers (or another) is acceptable, as long as students support their answer.

14. (Average) Students' answers will vary. They may mention that the most realistic parts of the song are those that describe loss ("and weep for my lov'd one"); that demonstrate that nature goes on, even during wartime ("the blue bird is singing his lay"); that evoke memories ("dearly I love the old place!") that describe the passage of time ("the leaves . . . will fade"; "the roses . . . will die"); or that state the current reality ("Willie has gone to the war": "Willie my lov'd one is gone!").

15. (Challenging) Students' answers may vary. They may offer several examples: the officer serving coffee to his men implies that he understands the importance of giving them support in battle; the silent mutual reaction to his wound implies a unified company; the men "crowded forward sympathetically," so they clearly had some feeling for their leader; they viewed him as someone both brave and doomed.

Oral Response

16. In their oral response, students should cite specific information from the selections that substantiates their presentations and expands on their earlier responses.

"Swing Low, Sweet Chariot" and "Go Down, Moses"

Spirituals

Open-Book Test (p. 73)

Multiple Choice and Short Answer

1.b Explanation: The "Jordan" is a religious metaphor, as well as a metaphor for slavery and freedom.

2. Sample answer: The angels imply heaven and harmony. They would most likely be welcoming and friendly to the singer.

3. Sample answer: *Home* might mean any of the following to the slaves—their ancestral home in Africa; their home on the plantation, after a hard day's work; their home of heaven; their home of sought-after freedom in the North; or a more general meaning of home as a sanctuary.

4.d Explanation: The only answer that makes sense in the song's context is d.

5. Sample answer: Students' answers may vary. They may say that "Swing low, sweet chariot" is more important, because it sets a tone and implies a heavenly or pleasant journey. They may also say that "coming for to carry me home" is more important, because it implies the journey's final destination.

6.d Explanation: Answer d is the most powerful, because it describes the action needed.

7. Sample answer: The creators of this song may have wanted to repeat this line to reinforce their wish. They were addressing the slave owners, and they may have hoped that if the owners heard the song enough, the owners would respond someday.

8.a Explanation: The two different oppressors in this song are the pharaoh of Egypt and the slave owners. The enslaved people are the Israelites and the slaves.

9.c Explanation: Answer c) is supported by "dead."

10. Sample answer: "Way down in Egypt land" implies a strong connection to biblical history. By using "way down," the song implies how far away in distance Egypt is, even as it is close in experience.

Questions are classified in these categories:
Comprehension   1 (E)
Interpretation   2 (A), 4 (A)
Literary Analysis   5 (C), 6 (A)
Reading Strategy   3 (A), 7 (A), 10 (A)
Vocabulary   8 (A), 9 (E)
E=Easy, A=Average, C=Challenging

Extended Response

11. (Easy) Students may offer many answers. "Swing Low, Sweet Chariot": Sweet chariot; coming for to carry me home; swing low; coming; home; carry. "Go Down, Moses": Go Down, Moses; Let my people go; Egypt land; Way down; Tell old Pharaoh. The phrases in both songs express a longing for a better life.

12. (Average) Students should mention several of the religious references in each song. "Swing Low": the angels, home, Jordan. "Go Down, Moses": Moses, Israel, Egypt, the smiting of the first-born. Students might also mention that the speaker is addressing God or some agent of God in each song. Students may choose "Swing Low" as more effective, because it promises the beauty of heavenly release. They may choose "Go Down, Moses" as more effective, because it uses biblical references.

13. (Average) Most students will probably write that the slave owners would prefer to hear slaves singing "Swing Low," which sounds peaceful and inoffensive. "Go Down, Moses" might inspire slaves to either fight their owners or to try to escape, since "Moses" was thought to refer to Harriet Tubman.

14. (Average) In "Swing Low," the speaker is addressing the chariot of freedom or heaven during the refrain. In the verses, the speaker addresses other slaves or people looking to enter heaven. In the refrain of "Go Down, Moses," the speaker addresses God, Moses, and maybe Harriet Tubman—anyone who may be a source of help. In the verses, the speaker addresses other listeners, who could be slaves.

15. (Challenging) Students will probably choose "Go Down, Moses," and its story of Harriet Tubman, as a more accurate depiction of the history of the slaves. However, some may argue that "Swing Low, Sweet Chariot" has a timeless, resigned quality that captures the mood of the slaves. Some students may even promote the idea that the two songs capture two different moods and are both valid. All of these answers are acceptable, providing they are well-supported.

Oral Response

16. In their oral response, students should cite specific information from the spirituals that substantiates their presentations and expands on their earlier responses.

from *My Bondage and My Freedom*

by Frederick Douglass

Open-Book Test (p. 76)

Multiple Choice and Short Answer

1. Sample answer: "I lived in the family of Master Hugh."

2.d Explanation: He writes that it "was necessary for her to have some training, some hardening. . . . "

3. Sample answer: Students may answer that he is correct, because he is a person, and no one deserves to be treated as a slave. He also may think he is better than other slaves, because he has such a fierce desire to learn. Students may also answer that he is incorrect, because in reality, he is a slave, whether or not he deserves to be. Either answer is acceptable.

4. Sample answer: Her husband was the impetus for her change. "He . . . was injured in his domestic peace," because "her home [was stripped] of its early happiness."

5. Sample answer: she was a "model of affection and tenderness"; "her fervent piety"; her "watchful uprightness"; "no sorrow nor suffering for which she had not a tear"; she smiled at "innocent joy"; "she had bread for the hungry"; she clothed those in need; she comforted mourners.

6. Sample answer: Her happiness and her family's is destroyed, because her basically good nature is being overridden. Having made the decision to change her ways, she then has to compound her fault by acting as though it was the right thing to do.

7.c Explanation: Answer (c) is supported by "had begun to teach me," which indicates kindness.

8. Sample answer: He had been taught the alphabet, and after that, he was insatiable; he was often found reading a book; he carried a dictionary in his pocket; he gave his friends bread so they would teach him.

9.b Explanation: There are several context clues: "fury"; "wrath"; "traitor"; "spy."

10. Sample answer: He minds the condition of slavery rather than any specific elements of it. He feels that it is an evil of which he and Mrs. Auld were both victims, although he more than she.

Questions are classified in these categories:
Comprehension   2 (C), 5 (E)
Interpretation   6 (A)
Literary Analysis   1 (E), 3 (A), 8 (A)
Reading Strategy   4 (A), 10 (C)
Vocabulary   7 (A), 9 (A)
E=Easy, A=Average, C=Challenging

Extended Response

11. (Easy) He never met a boy who defended the slave system; they all had hopes that he would someday be free; they helped to teach him; they did not believe that God intended him to be a slave.

12. (Average) Mrs. Auld watched over him in order to try to keep him in a state of ignorance and slavery. It didn't work, because Douglass had already discovered learning. He got around her by having his friends help him.

13. (Average) Possible answers (early behavior): She had begun to teach him; she was kind and tenderhearted; she had humanity in her heart; she had a simplicity of mind; she first treated him as a human being; she felt me to be more than that [chattel]. Possible answers (later behavior): She "set her face as a flint" against Douglass's learning to read; she lost all of her Christian qualities; she would rush at him to snatch reading matter from him; she would suspect him of reading, if he was separated from the family; she was offended by his downcast look.

14. (Average) Students may choose either position, as long as they can support it. It seems as though Douglass makes a case for her being a kind person, who has been influenced by the times she lives in. He suggests this especially when he writes "just as she herself would have acted," attributing to her the strength of character that he possesses.

15. (Challenging) Students' answers will vary. They should mention that his realization that he was a slave "for life" was very painful to him. The concept of liberty was thrown in his face by all aspects of nature. He still resolved to continue his acquisition of knowledge, because he was driven to it.

Oral Response

16. In their oral response, students should cite specific information from the autobiography that substantiates their presentations and expands on their earlier responses.

"An Occurrence at Owl Creek Bridge"

by Ambrose Bierce

Open-Book Test (p. 79)

Multiple Choice and Short Answer

1. Sample answer: Given that the subject matter concerns a man about to be hanged, the tone is remarkably distant.

2. Sample answer: It is objective, because it contains observations, rather than thoughts or feelings. "A man stood upon a railroad bridge . . ."

3.b Explanation: They show it by being silent and motionless.

4.c Explanation: it reveals a change to the third-person limited point of view. The other answers show the objective point of view, which is how the story begins.

5. Sample answer: The sound of his watch becomes increasingly loud and annoying to him; he has frantic thoughts of escape.

6. Sample answer: Section II flashes backwards; section III shifts to the present; at the end, he dies (shifts to the present). The effect is one of making the story more dramatic and dreamlike, in contrast to the orderliness of the preparations for his hanging.

7.c Explanation: supported by "arcs" and "pendulum."

8. Sample answer: The horseman is a Federal scout. He tricked Farquhar. Although Farquhar took the bait and tried to burn the bridge, for which he is responsible, he may not have thought to do it on his own.

9.d Explanation: supported by "a smile" and "joy."

10. Sample answer: The sequence is Farquhar has a conversation with a Federal scout; Farquhar is strung up in preparation for being hanged; The soldiers stand at parade rest; The sergeant releases the plank on which Farquhar is standing; Farquhar sees his wife waiting for him at home; Farquhar dies.

Questions are classified in these categories:

Comprehension	3 (A), 8 (E)
Interpretation	1 (C), 5 (A)
Literary Analysis	2 (A), 4 (A)
Reading Strategy	6 (A), 10 (A)
Vocabulary	7 (A), 9 (A)

E=Easy, A=Average, C=Challenging

Extended Response

11. (Easy) Students should include the fact that Farquhar is duped as evidence of this maxim. They should also mention that he is the character who was prepared to live out this maxim, but, instead, he is the one who is tricked unfairly.

12. (Average) Possible answers: Sound—his watch, the humming of bugs, whispers; Sight—veins of leaves, streaks of color, diamonds and rubies; Smell—fragrance of blooms.

13. (Average) Students should acknowledge that sensory descriptions are useful in writing from a third-person limited point of view. They contrast starkly with the objective point of view in the earlier descriptions from the first scene.

14. (Average) Students should note that the critical object is the railroad. The Union army needs it to transport goods and soldiers.

15. (Challenging) Students may include any of the elements of Farquhar's imaginary escape.

Oral Response

16. In their oral response, students should cite specific information from the story that substantiates their presentations and expands on their earlier responses.

"The Gettysburg Address" and "Second Inaugural Address"

by Abraham Lincoln

"Letter to His Son"

by Robert E. Lee

Open-Book Test (p. 82)

Multiple Choice and Short Answer

1. Sample answer: Lincoln is reminding people of the history of the nation, and the ideals of freedom for which their ancestors fought.

2.b Explanation: supported by the words "dedicate" and "hallow."

3.c Explanation: He is implying that the soldiers are the most worthy people of all (more so than Lincoln or his audience).

4. Sample answer: The audience was probably comprised of Union sympathizers. His purpose was to strengthen the resolve of the Union, so their soldiers could continue to fight with strength.

5. Sample answer: He is trying to present the strongest argument he can against the South's insistence upon the continuation of slavery.

6.d Explanation: supported by "none . . . charity for all . . . bind up the nation's wounds."

7. Sample answer: "All dreaded the coming war"; "neither side expected the magnitude" of the war; asking listeners to act "with charity for all," to help "bind up the wounds," and "to care for him [someone]" in need.

8. Sample answer: Use of "I" and several statements of his personal opinion; "As far as I can judge"; "I fear that mankind"; "The South . . . has been aggrieved . . . as you say."

9.d Explanation: He believes that the founding fathers wanted a nation that would stand together to uphold the Constitution.

10. Sample answer: He does not wish to fight either to preserve or split the Union. He will only fight in self-defense, as a last resort.

Questions are classified in these categories:

Comprehension	9 (E)
Interpretation	3 (A), 10 (A)
Literary Analysis	4 (A), 5 (A), 8 (A)
Reading Strategy	1 (A), 7 (C)
Vocabulary	2 (A), 6 (E)

E=Easy, A=Average, C=Challenging

Extended Response

11. (Average) Students' answers will vary, but they should mention that one area of agreement was that neither man wanted war or secession. A point of disagreement might be that Lee felt that the South had been "aggrieved" by the North, a fact with which Lincoln would probably take issue.

12. (Easy) Possible answers: "All men are created equal" (one of the foundations of democracy and the eradication of slavery); "These dead shall not have died in vain" (the concept of wars serving a greater purpose); "government of the people, by the people, for the people" (foundation of democracy); "with malice toward none" (the importance of a united country); "with firmness in the right, as God gives us to see the right" (the recognition that we try to be moral people).

13. (Average) Possible answers for references: the nation's great task is the new birth of freedom; the nation's ability to withstand war has been tested; the war has absorbed the nation's energy; he accuses one side of starting war, and the other of accepting it; he argues against perpetuating slavery in new territories. In general, students should focus on Lincoln's attempts to both heal the nation and redirect it away from slavery.

14. (Average) Possible answers: Lincoln uses God to substantiate his argument that slavery is wrong, thereby making his argument more powerful. Lee refers to Christianity as an instrument of civilization that is not sufficiently developed in humans to prevent them from engaging in war.

15. (Challenging) Possible answers: Lincoln—"The world will little note . . . what we say here" (importance: Ironically, the world has noted it. Therefore, people should be aware that their acts may carry consequences they did not expect.); "Both read the same Bible . . . and each invokes His aid against the other" (importance: We should be aware that we carry diverse opinions about how things should be). Lee—"I fear that mankind . . . " (importance: We have to be aware of our own lack of civilized behavior and guard against it); "The framers of our Constitution . . . " (importance: We should be mindful of all of the dedication that went into creating our nation).

Oral Response

16. In their oral response, students should cite specific information from the selections that substantiates their presentations and expands on their earlier responses.

from Civil War Diaries, Journals, and Letters

Open-Book Test (p. 85)

Multiple Choice and Short Answer

1.d Explanation: since Chesnut cites no evidence for this opinion. Answer a represents Chesnut reporting what she heard; answer b is a factual observation of dinner conversation; answer c is Chesnut's factual observation about dinner companions. (All of the factual answers can be proven.)

2. Sample answer: Her husband was instantly made into an aide-de-camp (it's possible that many men were immediately called into service); their family dinner table has become the center of conversation among military and political officials; men volunteer for service as privates; Chesnut cannot sleep; she prays; people are standing on their rooftops; Chesnut's dress catches fire; no one eats; Chesnut and her companion take tea in her room.

3.c Explanation: supported by "quietly enough" and "unruffled."

4. Sample answer: "When anything unusual was to be done . . . I shaved"; "my heart thumping like muffled drumbeats"; "promotion was a little uncertain and slow"; the coat made him "feel like a little nubbin of corn"; reference to "Virginia mud"; he discovered that "suggestions were not so well appreciated" in the army; "no wisdom was equal to a drillmaster's" orders; recruits have to learn "not to think or suggest, but obey"; he learned in "humility and mud"; he cut his uniform to see out of it.

5.a. Explanation: he was "twenty years of age" and excited about travel and promotion opportunities.

6. Sample answer: Facts: General Ewell's order to assume the offensive; The breastworks ran at right angles to the ones the soldiers were on; there was a double line of entrenchments; they were exposed to "enfilading fire"; a battery of artillery opened upon the soldiers. Opinions: "the gallant little brigade"; "six fearful hours"; "I do not recall the banners of any other regiment"; "daring to attempt what could not be done by flesh and blood"; "it is to be presumed that General Daniel acted in obedience to orders."

7. Sample answer: Students may offer a variety of possible answers: Based on the modest tone of the letter—he reports details but minimizes the difficulties—he does not want to appear conceited. Jackson may also be superstitious about glorying too energetically in the early days of the war. It is also possible that he is writing this letter only to reassure his wife about his safety and does not want to publicize his troops' activity.

8. Sample answer: "Men squealed, women fainted, dogs barked, white and colored people shook hands . . . "

9.b Explanation: supported by the repeated reports to the rail company president and the use of the court system.

10. Sample answer: Students answers may vary. They should imply that Truth is a patient, persevering person, as shown by her willingness to repeatedly attempt to get on the train, and her unwillingness to get off.

Questions are classified in these categories:

Comprehension	5 (A)
Interpretation	7 (C), 9 (A), 10 (A)
Literary Analysis	2 (A), 4 (A), 8 (E)
Reading Strategy	1 (A), 6 (A)
Vocabulary	3 (E)

E=Easy, A=Average, C=Challenging

Extended Response

11. (Easy) Possible answers: In the first account, African Americans are overjoyed at the first news of the end of slavery, and the reality has not yet settled in. Sojourner Truth, on the other hand, is dealing with the reality of trying to put policy into practice, a far more difficult and painful effort.

12. (Average) Example (students may choose other accounts): Comparison between Goss's and McKim's accounts—Similarities: Both of them contain many details; both are told from the perspective of soldiers of a low rank; both contain some opinion and some fact. Differences: McKim seems to have more experience; he is describing a much more difficult event; Goss is able to use humor, since his subject is less frightening; Goss's account is far more romantic, even in the real details he offers.

13. (Average) Students' answers will vary, depending upon how they have answered the previous question. If they write about Goss and McKim, it is very important to highlight the differences between the two accounts, because they are so pronounced.

14. (Average) Students' answers will vary. They should include some mention of the belief that slavery was or was not wrong ("But die it must"). They should also mention that some, like Goss, saw the war as an opportunity for adventure.

15. (Challenging) Students' answers will vary. They will probably say that these accounts are of value. Reasons might include that we need to know our history; that we can learn from our ancestors' mistakes; that we have to protect civil rights and can do so only by being aware of the severe racial divisions during that time. Students may argue that the accounts are not of value, but they need to effectively defend their viewpoints.

Oral Response

16. In their oral response, students should cite specific information from the accounts that substantiates their presentations and expands on their earlier responses.

"The Boys' Ambition" from *Life on the Mississippi* and "The Notorious Jumping Frog of Calaveras County"

by Mark Twain

Open-Book Test (p. 88)

Multiple Choice and Short Answer

1.c Explanation: Answers a, b and d are partially correct, but c is the most accurate response. Students may cite the first paragraph to support their answer choice.

2. Sample answer: His impression is that it is a sleepy Southern town that comes to life only when the steamboat arrives. Quotations to support this answer: "nobody to listen to the peaceful lapping of the wavelets"; "after ten more minutes the town is dead again"; "the town drunkard [is] asleep by the skids once more."

3. Sample answer: Students may choose the section on Twain's ambitions, where he makes fun of himself, saying he wants certain steamboat jobs because they are more "conspicuous" and glamorous. Students may also relate the description of the boy who went away as a steamboat apprentice and was the envy of all: "He would speak . . . in an easy, natural way that would make one wish he was dead."

4.d Explanation: supported by "lifts up the cry" and "S-t-e-a-m-boat a-comin'!"

5. Sample answer: Many boys were able to get work on board the ship. However, some, like Twain, were not allowed to participate, because their parents forbade it.

6. Sample answer: "I called on good-natured, garrulous old . . ."; he expected that Wheeler would "bore me to death" with a "tedious" remembrance that would be "useless" to Twain; the effort to trick Wheeler by using a name that will remind him of something else; Wheeler

"backed me into a corner" and "blockaded" Twain; he "reeled off the monotonous" version that follows.

7. Sample answer: feller (man); warn't (wasn't); curiousest (most curious); uncommon lucky (unusually lucky); ary (any); foller (follow); resk (risk or bet).

8.b Explanation: supported by "bull-pup" and "lay for a chance to steal something."

9. Sample answer: 1) "thish-yer" = this here; 2) "till you couldn't rest" = more animals than one could imagine; and 3) "you couldn't fetch nothing for him to bet on but he'd match you" = he could always come up with an animal for competition and betting purposes.

10. Sample answer: Twain does not expect to get any solid information and suspects he is being tricked by his friend in the East. He says in the beginning: "I have a lurking suspicion . . . "; at the end, he says: "'I did not think that a continuation of the history of . . ." would give him any information that he sought.

Questions are classified in these categories:
Comprehension	5 (A)
Interpretation	7 (C), 9 (A), 10 (A)
Literary Analysis	2 (A), 4 (A), 8 (E)
Reading Strategy	1 (A), 6 (A)
Vocabulary	3 (E)

E=Easy, A=Average, C=Challenging

Extended Response

11. (Easy) Students can use details from the story to describe the steamboat itself, which Twain does in painstaking detail. They can also use details from these pages to show the awakening impact that the ship has on the town. Whichever details they choose, students should be sure to convey Twain's love of steamboats.

12. (Average) Possible answers: the various ambitions of the town boys (paragraphs 1 and 2 of story); his mention of not wanting to be a judge like his father; wanting to be a "cabin boy" or a "deckhand"; the boy who went aboard a ship rose to "eminence," while Twain was "left in obscurity and misery"; he wished the boy was dead because of the casual way in which he talked about ships; the boy referred to places and events, and Twain accuses him of lying; town girls adored the boy.

13. (Average) Students should use the details they found for question #12. They should come to an opinion about which of Twain's feelings were appropriate, and which were not. (For example, Twain expresses a wish that the apprenticed boy would die, a clearly inappropriate and immature wish that Twain uses mostly to demonstrate his strong feelings at the time, and to reflect upon that time with some humor.)

14. (Average) Students should use details, such as the quotations that the boy uses to brag about his knowledge. Twain also mentions that he and other town boys "had a vague general knowledge" about St. Louis, but they were silenced by the boy's superior information. Twain is clearly not very worldly at this time in his life.

15. (Challenging) Students may choose any passage to rewrite, as long as the new version approximately replicates the old version. Their explanation of Twain's use of dialect should mention that by using dialect, he makes the trickery in the story come more alive (because Smiley is a sort of trusting, country fellow); that he uses dialect to help him exaggerate; or that the story seems friendlier to the reader, and therefore is more enjoyable.

Oral Response

16. In their oral response, students should cite specific information from the stories that substantiates their presentations and expands on their earlier responses.

"The Outcasts of Poker Flat"
by Bret Harte
Open-Book Test (p. 91)

Multiple Choice and Short Answer

1.d. Explanation: supported by "Mr. Oakhurst was right. . ."

2. Sample answer: The citizens rush impetuously to form a secret committee; they hang or banish people whom they judge to be wrong.

3.c Explanation: supported by "volley of expletives" and "alarming oaths."

4. Sample answer: Harte seems to view Mr. Oakhurst with some sympathy. Possible examples: He refers to him as "Mr."; he describes him as "calm" and "handsome," and as someone who wears "neat boots"; he refers to those who have won money from him, which implies that he plays cards somewhat fairly; Harte describes Mr. Oakhurst's giving away his horse; and Harte contrasts him with the extremely unsavory behavior of his riding companions—he is philosophic; he listens calmly.

5. Sample answer: Students may mention some of the following: Sandy Bar is less concerned with immoral behavior than Poker Flat (implying it is less settled); the mountain range and a "severe day's travel" are evidence of the difficulty of the terrain; they go into the colder regions of the Sierra Nevadas, where the "trail was narrow and difficult"; they are only halfway to where they need to go when they stop (the distances are vast); the spot where they stop is wooded and

surrounded by granite (a description of the terrain); the party is not well provisioned, as they need to be in this kind of territory.

6. Sample answer: Mr. Oakhurst kicks Billy when he is about to say something inappropriate and when he is about to laugh. Mr. Oakhurst seems to be trying to control the group, so that they will behave in a somewhat civilized manner, because Tom Simson is so innocent.

7. Sample answer: They plan to endure the snow together; they create a roof for the shelter and redecorate it; there is a "sound of happy laughter" that is not caused by drinking; they play instruments and sing together around the fire.

8. Sample answer: They view her as a child because she "didn't swear and wasn't improper." They "amuse" her and teach her how to decorate the cabin.

9.d Explanation: supported by "malediction" and "Just you go out there and cuss." The adjective's meaning is also supported by what the reader already knows of Mother Shipton's character.

10. Sample answer: His story-telling provides a welcome distraction from the lack of food and the weather; it also provides entertainment, since he tells it in a local accent; the story also contains messages about the heroic deeds of the gods, which provides Mr. Oakhurst with some thoughts about the group's (and his own) future.

Questions are classified in these categories:

Comprehension	1 (E), 10 (E)
Interpretation	6 (A), 8 (A)
Literary Analysis	2 (A), 5 (C)
Reading Strategy	4 (A), 7 (A)
Vocabulary	3 (C), 9 (A)

E=Easy, A=Average, C=Challenging

Extended Response

11. (Easy) Possible answers: Mr. Oakhurst is able to go without sleep, and he takes on the task of leading the group (strong); Mr. Oakhurst is unable to admit to Simson that Uncle Billy has stolen the mules, because he fears that he will upset and scare him, and Mr. Oakhurst kills himself rather than face death with the others (weak).

12. (Average) Students may use any details that apply to discuss the relationship they choose. Possible examples would be Mr. Oakhurst and Tom Simson or the older outcast women and Piney. In the early part of the story, we learn that Mr. Oakhurst returned Simson's money to him. Later he tries to save both him and Piney. The older women care for Piney, and the Duchess lies down with her to die. This behavior is ironic, because these older people have been banished specifically for immoral behavior, when they obviously have some remnants of humanity left in them.

13. (Average) Possible answers: "He was too much of a gambler not to accept Fate" (he realized that he couldn't control all of his life); He "did not drink," because his profession required coolness (he believed in keeping himself in control at all times); "He handed [Simson] his money back" (he didn't believe in taking advantage of people); "when a man gets a streak of luck, he don't get tired" (good circumstances cause people to be hopeful); "It's finding out when [luck's] going to change that makes you" (we are formed by circumstances that we can't control);"If you can hold your cards right along, you're all right" (he was trying to maintain an optimistic attitude and encouraged Tom not to give up hope); "handed in his checks" (although he tried to remain hopeful, he realized his fate was sealed, again stressing his feeling of being out of control).

14. (Average) Students may choose Uncle Billy, who is clearly a villain for leaving the rest of the group in distress. They may also choose the citizens of Poker Flat, who, without much thought, are willing to commit murder by hanging people they deem immoral, or subject them to banishment in hostile regions that will probably kill them. Students may also identify Piney's father as at least wrong in his lack of acceptance of the relationship between Piney and Tom Simson.

15. (Challenging) Possible answers: Poker Flat (a town trying to eliminate immoral behavior); Mr. Oakhurst (Mr.— conveys gentility; Oakhurst— conveys strength); the Duchess (implies someone who is rich—ironic, because she is in severely reduced circumstances); Uncle Billy (ironic, because he behaves in a manner completely unlike that of an uncle); The Innocent (descriptive label for Tom Simson); Piney (descriptive of the innocence and natural behavior of the young girl, as though she "pines," or is natural, like a tree).

Oral Response

16. In their oral response, students should cite specific information from the story that substantiates their presentations and expands on their earlier responses.

"Heading West"
by Miriam Davis Colt

"I Will Fight No More Forever"
by Chief Joseph

Open-Book Test (p. 94)

Multiple Choice and Short Answer

1. Sample answer: She believes that traveling alone would bring more of a hardship on her family, that they will benefit financially from being part of a larger group, and that her children will have a better future. She does not specifically mention the issue of safety, but as a wife and mother, it is certainly an additional concern— one that is enhanced by being in a group.

2. Sample answer: On January 15th, Colt is very matter-of-fact in tone, perhaps with a small hint of excitement. She is organizing her home in preparation for her family's journey. On April 22nd, she initially has a positive attitude in her description of the nighttime railway trip. However, some of the reality of the trip has disillusioned her, as she endures poor accommodations.

3. Sample answer: Students might choose either of two sections: her description of a "shadow" or her mention of "home-sickness." Colt gives the impression that, like other pioneers, she has fears and misgivings about the unknown, but she is willing to take hold of her anxieties to forge onward to a life she hopes will be fruitful.

4.a Explanation: suggested by "hopping in every direction."

5. Sample answer: Her concern is that the Southerners will discover she and her family are against slavery in the new territories, and that they may go so far as to kill the Free State settlers. Her dramatic use of the word "Bandits" paints a dramatic and effective picture for the reader. Her opinion seems to be somewhat accurate, but she may be incorrect in assuming that the Southerners will commit murder.

6.c Explanation: suggested by "Bandits," "commit," and "no doubt commit many a bloody murder."

7. Sample answer: Colt is dismayed by the lack of housing, the mismanagement of the members' funds, and the obvious hopelessness of some of the other women. Students may say that they are or are not affected by Colt's response. Students will probably be most affected either by the fact that there is no housing (since Colt has noted, during the entire journey, her anticipation of living in a house) or that the residents' mood is depressing.

8.d Explanation: Possible answer: Looking Glass, Toohoolhoolzote, the chiefs, old men, are all among the dead.

9. Sample answer: Students may choose several quotations, any of which are acceptable, as long as they support the idea of a evoking a strong response from the reader. Examples: any of the quotations about death; the cold; children; hunger; his heartsick feelings; his final surrender.

10.b Explanation: supported by "I am tired; my heart is sick and sad."

Questions are classified in these categories:

Comprehension	1 (A)
Interpretation	8 (E), 10 (A)
Literary Analysis	2 (A), 5 (A)
Reading Strategy	3 (A), 7 (A), 9 (C)
Vocabulary	4 (E), 6 (A)

E=Easy, A=Average, C=Challenging

Extended Response

11. (Easy) Possible answer: May 2nd represents a positive entry. Details: the weather is beautiful; the countryside is spacious; the women and children have a nice interlude under a tree; even though there is a wagon tongue that needs mending, she dismisses it, going on to relate the scene of an outside supper, or "pic-nic," which the travelers "expect" and enjoy. She mentions the beauty of several items in nature.

12. (Average) Students should use examples that support some of Colt's fears: having to be outside in the rain; having inadequate lodging; having inadequate food; having untainted water; living in crowded circumstances; "home-sickness'; the acts of the Southerners; the possible breakdown of their wagons; fear of the unknown ("shadows").

13. (Average) Students may find the money problems, the lack of building progress, or the lack of housing to be depressing. Colt's journal starts out with the expectation that everything in Kansas has been planned and organized very well, so the lack of a real "city" to live in is a major disappointment.

14. (Average) Students should mention that although Colt paints a difficult picture of the journey westward, she is conscious that she and her family have chosen this passage. Chief Joseph and his people are forced to change a way of life that they have become accustomed to and that has great meaning to them. In addition, Colt and Chief Joseph do not share the same view about who should possess the western lands.

15. (Challenging) Possible responses: His statement represents, in a larger sense, the historic defeat of the Native American at the hands of white soldiers and settlers over a period of many years. In addition, "from where the sun now stands" is a uniquely Native American way of measuring time (which will be lost if European settlers take over); "I will fight no more forever" may mean that Chief Joseph realizes he will die soon, or that the loss of his will to fight means that his will to live is diminishing.

Oral Response

16. In their oral response, students should cite specific information from the selections that substantiates their presentations and expands on their earlier responses.

"To Build a Fire"
by Jack London
Open-Book Test (p. 97)

Multiple Choice and Short Answer

1. Sample answer: The day was "cold and gray"; he turned off the main trail; "an intangible pall"; "a subtle gloom."

2. Sample answer: London indicates that he does not respect the man. He calls him a "newcomer"; the clues of the climate make "no impression"; he has no imagination; his strength in life is in "the things, not in the significances."

3. d Explanation: supported by "a vague and menacing apprehension." There is no basis in the text for answers a or b. Answer c is partly correct, but it does not answer the question about what London's purpose is in using the dog.

4. Sample answer: The man is aware of the snow-hidden ice skins and their danger, which is why he sends the dog to go forward first. He quickly moves when he finds he might be near one, and he listens for running water.

5. d Explanation: After this point, when he realizes how numb he is, he becomes "a bit frightened," which is a more appropriate reaction.

6. Sample answer: This sentence implies that the man will only have a limited impact on the cold ("the moment"), but that it will be a constant struggle. In addition, London is intentionally using the word "outwitted," because he is ascribing human attributes to nature, which cannot be outwitted or controlled by humans.

7. Sample answer: The tree is covered with fresh snow, which melts from the heat of the fire, falling on the fire and the man. The man could have prevented the problem by building the fire in the open.

8. c Explanation: A person who is conjectural might be a philosopher, or at least someone who concerns himself or herself with the universe and higher thoughts. A person who is not, like this man, thinks only about what is happening to him at the moment.

9. b Explanation: supported by "the sound of whiplashes in his voice."

10. Sample answer: his hands and feet become numb ("the wires were down"); he has to beat his hands against himself; he tries to keep moving; his tobacco spittle freezes on his beard; he shivers; he becomes apathetic.

Questions are classified in these categories:

Comprehension	4 (A)
Interpretation	2 (A), 3 (A)
Literary Analysis	6 (C), 7 (A), 10 (E)
Reading Strategy	1 (A), 5 (A)
Vocabulary	8 (E), 9 (A)

E=Easy, A=Average, C=Challenging

Extended Response

11. (Easy) Students should construct an essay that includes some of the following answers (and uses story details to support it): It's too cold to be traveling here; I hope this man has the sense to turn back; I hope he'll build a fire; I wonder where my next meal is coming from; I wish he wouldn't talk to me so meanly; I have no reason to be loyal to him.

12. (Average) Possible answers—rising action: 1) The man realizes that it is colder than he has experienced before, 2) The man avoids the hidden ice skins in the creek, 3) The man eats his lunch and forgets to build a fire, and then builds one, 4) He breaks through the ice and falls into water, 5) He builds a second fire under a tree. Climax 6) The tree dumps snow upon him and the fire. Possible falling action: 7)He tries to rebuild his fire, 8) His hands are too numb to use matches well, and he burns himself, 9) He tries to keep traveling, but falls several times, 10) He dies. Conflict: between man and nature; Setting: the Yukon; Major Characters the man and the dog; Resolution: the man dies, and the dog leaves him.

13. (Average) In general, since the danger increases in small increments, students will probably say the story is suspenseful as it is. However, they may have criticisms of the pacing. Various answers are acceptable, as long as they are rooted in the story.

14. (Average) Possible answers: The man treats the dog as a servant, not a companion. He speaks meanly to the dog, and does not respect that the dog may have superior knowledge of the hostile environment. In addition, the dog is also seeking warmth and comfort, a fact that goes ignored by the man. A conflict between them, which the man wins, is that the dog would prefer not to travel this path. By treating the dog badly and ignoring the reality of his situation, the man misses the opportunity not only to have a loyal companion, but one who might help him to survive.

15. (Challenging) Students' answers should reflect upon London's musings about the fact that the man is not much of a thinker. London is certainly critical of the man for his limited vision, which, in the end, dooms him to death. Students will probably agree that the man was short-sighted, but they may see his lack of a philosophical bent to be less of a problem than his lack of planning in a practical manner.

Oral Response

16. In their oral response, students should cite specific information from the story that substantiates their presentations and expands on their earlier responses.

"The Story of an Hour"
by Kate Chopin
Open-Book Test (p. 100)
Multiple Choice and Short Answer

1. Sample answer: Meaning: Her sister told Mrs. Mallard of her husband's death in a subtle way that allowed her to know the truth, but not in a blunt way that might upset her. Verbal irony: "revealed in half concealing"; also the use of "veiled" along with these other visual words.

2. Sample answer: Most women become paralyzed by such news; Mrs. Mallard wept wildly.

3.d Explanation: Context clues include "something coming to her"; "What was it? She did not know"; and "subtle."

4.c Explanation: The signs of new life contrast with the message of death she has just received.

5. Sample answer: "She said it over and over under her breath: 'free, free, free!'"

6. Sample answer: "Louise, open the door! I beg; open the door—you will make yourself ill. What are you doing, Louise? For heaven's sake open the door."

7.b Explanation: the context clues are "Josephine was . . . imploring for admission," "Louise, open the door!," and "For heaven's sake open the door."

8. Sample answer: Louise is shocked by the news of her husband's death; she feels the need to be alone in her room; she feels the beginning of a sense of newfound freedom; she exults in the discovery that she will be responsible for herself alone; she acknowledges some loving and some non-loving feelings towards her late husband; she is dismayed by his sudden reappearance.

9.a Explanation: Louise is actually shocked and disappointed to find her husband alive, since she had already accustomed herself to the exciting notion of living independently.

10. Sample answer: They may say the title is appropriate, because within an hour, dramatic events change people's lives. They may say it is not a good title, because it understates the situation greatly.

Questions are classified in these categories:

Comprehension	8 (A), 10 (A)
Interpretation	9 (A)
Literary Analysis	1 (A), 5 (E), 6 (A)
Reading Strategy	2 (A), 4 (A)
Vocabulary	3 (A), 7 (C)

E=Easy, A=Average, C=Challenging

Extended Response

11. (Average) Students should include the basic explanation that Louise does not stop to question her feelings. She is so relieved that she trusts her newfound instincts to guide her through her new life alone.

12. (Average) Students should cite quotations such as these: "a long procession of years to come that would belong to her absolutely" (she would no longer have to share her time); "she would live for herself" (there would be no one else to please or answer to); "no powerful will bending hers in that blind persistence" (she would not have to respond to the duty of a relationship that called for compromise); "no less a crime" (the loss of individual freedom brought about by marriage).

13. (Easy) Possible answers: verbal—"veiled hints that revealed in half concealing"; "a monstrous joy"; "the joy that kills"; dramatic—the reader knows, unlike Josephine and Richard, that Louise feels relief at her husband's death; the reader knows, unlike the doctors, that her husband's reappearance is not a pleasant surprise; situational—Louise feels free instead of in deep despair; Louise dies instead of her husband.

14. (Average) One male is Richards, who tries (ironically) to protect Louise twice, first from harshly delivered news of her husband's death, and second, from the shock of seeing that her husband is alive. The other male is her husband, Brently Mallard, who is not a significant character (he is not developed); but his absence in the beginning of the story, and his later appearance, is a plot device that adds to the surprise and suspense of the story.

15. (Challenging) Students may include some of the following information: In the first part of the story, the term implies that Louise is delicate— this is ironic, as we find she is very strong, at least emotionally. At the end of the story, Richards and Josephine once again try to protect this delicate creature, who ironically, collapses at joyful, rather than disastrous, news. Louise's "heart disease" seems to be that she has placed her heart with her husband rather than with her own best interests for many years.

Oral Response

16. In their oral response, students should cite specific information from the story that substantiates their presentations and expands on their earlier responses.

"April Showers"

by Edith Wharton

Open-Book Test (p. 103)

Multiple Choice and Short Answer

1. Sample answer: Students should note that the exposition "introduces the story's characters, setting, and situation."

2. Sample answer: Students should realize that Theodora was imitating the pen name of her favorite writer, Kathleen Kyd.

3. Sample answer: Students should note that at the story's climax, Theodora finds that the story printed in the *Home Circle* is not hers. We know this is the climax because it is the high point of suspense.

4. Sample answer: after Theodora sends her manuscript to *Home Circle*

5.b Explanation: She realizes that her story was rejected, and she is comforted by her father.

6. Sample answer: Students should realize that Kathleen Kyd is the pen name of Frances G. Wollop, a writer of romance fiction.

7. Sample answer: She is gratified by the reactions of others. "Her mother cried"; "her father whistled"; her friends were excited for her; Miss Brill called on her.

8. Sample answer: Students should note that she immediately went to Boston to get an explanation. They should support this with evidence from the story, such as, "She never knew how she got back to the station. She struggled through the crowd on the platform, and a gold-banded arm pushed her into the train . . ."

9. Sample answer: the reader "commiserates" with Theodora based on his/her disappointments

10. Sample answer: Students should define **commiseration** as "sympathy; condolence." They should use it in a sentence of their own.

Questions are classified in these categories:

Comprehension	6 (A), 8 (E)
Interpretation	2 (C), 7 (E)
Literary Analysis	1 (A), 3 (A), 5 (C), 9 (C)
Reading Strategy	4 (A)
Vocabulary	10 (A)

E=Easy, A=Average, C=Challenging

Extended Response

11. (Easy) Students should apply the saying to the story, citing evidence for their explanation. For example, they may say that the pain of the rejection that so dampens her spirits helps Theodora to grow out of her youthful pride and selfishness. Students might also say that her pain leads to a new understanding of her father and closeness with him.

12. (Average) Students should realize that Theodora felt miserable during her return trip from Boston. She thinks her father will be angry because of all the time she spent on the novel when she should have been taking care of chores at home. She also feels somewhat humiliated, knowing that everyone in town was expecting to see her name in the magazine. Most students will agree that Theodora is justified in feeling this way, especially since the confusion about the story was not her fault but, rather, the fault of the editor who put the acceptance letter in the wrong envelope.

13. (Average) Students should define the elements correctly and select the story events that correspond to each one. They will probably say that the exposition consists of Theodora's finishing and submitting her novel. The conflict is whether the novel will be accepted. The rising action consists of Theodora's problems with her family as she waits, the novel's acceptance (perhaps a false climax), and her continuing anticipation of its publication. The climax is the discovery that her novel has not been published. The resolution comes with the magazine's explanation of its error. The denouement is the meeting of Theodora and her father at the station and the comforting walk home.

14. (Average) Students will probably point out that the fact that Theodora has felt the need to hide her literary efforts from her family indicate that she is not a published writer yet. They might cite this passage as proof that "April Showers" is Theodora's first novel: "Kathleen Kyd's first story had been accepted to the Home Circle, and they had asked for more! Why should Gladys Glyn be less fortunate?"

15. (Challenging) Students should use examples from the story to support the idea that Theodora's pride is harmful. For example, they might say that it has blinded her to any faults in her own writing, which makes any improvement of it impossible. They might also cite her haughty attitude toward her potential audience. They might also mention that letting everyone in town know about her novel makes the final rejection even more bitter. Theodora's pride has also led her to neglect family duties, such as sewing buttons on her brother's coat.

Oral Response

16. In their oral responses, students should cite specific passages from the story that substantiate their presentations and expand on their earlier responses.

"Douglass" and "We Wear the Mask"
by Paul Laurence Dunbar
Open-Book Test (p. 106)
Multiple Choice and Short Answer

1. Sample answer: Dunbar is trying to let people know that in the early 1900s, the lack of economic opportunity for African-Americans in both the South and the North was making it even more difficult for them to survive than the period before the Civil War when they had been slaves.

2. Sample answer: Dunbar hopes his words will inspire others in the way that the life of Frederick Douglass inspired people.

3.d Explanation: Additional line: "The awful tide, that battled to and fro."

4. Sample answer: The vehicle is a boat. Other words and phrases: "we ride amid a tempest"; "the waves"; "pilot"; "bark."

5.b Explanation: He means that African-Americans are enduring angry criticism as though it is a weather-related (and uncontrollable) storm.

6. Sample answer: Know, ago, flow, fro; storm, form; stark, bark, dark; lies, eyes; guile, smile; cries, arise; vile, mile.

7.c Explanation: "We" represents African Americans.

8. Sample answer: the mask that grins; we smile; we sing.

9.d Explanation: Dunbar means that African-Americans are, through their masks, adding to the general level of deception in the world. They do this for their own reasons.

10. Sample answer: "Not ended then the passionate ebb and flow, / The awful tide that battled to and fro; / We ride amid a tempest of dispraise."

Questions are classified in these categories:
Comprehension	7 (A)
Interpretation	1 (C), 2 (A)
Literary Analysis	5 (A), 8 (A), 10 (E)
Reading Strategy	3 (A), 4 (E)
Vocabulary	6 (A), 9 (A)

E=Easy, A=Average, C=Challenging

Extended Response

11. (Easy) Possible answers: "ebb and flow"; "awful tide"; "to and fro"; "waves of swift dissension"; "the strong pilot"; "storm"; "to guide the . . . bark." Students' paragraphs may contain imagery of a boat in a storm.

12. (Average) Possible answers: Students should write essays that contain at least some of the following references: "evil days" (racial prejudice); "tempest of dispraise" (the lack of consideration and trust for African-Americans); "the storm" (the times they live in); "the lonely dark" (the sense that African-Americans have no support).

13. (Average) Possible answers: In "Douglass," Dunbar is asking both for Douglass in order to recall a sense of "Honor, the strong pilot," and to have the "comfort through the lonely dark" so that African-Americans know they are not alone in their fight. In "We Wear the Mask," Dunbar is asking Christ to hear the cries, so that someone will know of the anguish of African-Americans. In both cases, Dunbar reaches out to inaccessible people as a way to stress the distance between the difficulties of African-Americans' needs and their ability to get powerful assistance—it is a way of dramatizing their plight.

14. (Average) Students' essays should include some of the following information: Dunbar believes Douglass was a visionary ("Saw, salient, at the cross of devious ways"); a great speaker ("and all the country heard thee with amaze" and "thy voice high-sounding over the storm"); a great leader ("thy strong arm to guide the shivering bark"); a powerful presence ("the blast-defying power of thy form"); and a comfort to African-Americans ("to give us comfort through the lonely dark").

15. (Challenging) Possible answers: It is important to Dunbar that African-Americans maintain an outward appearance that seems happy. Students may answer that this is a suggested tactic so they can be more likely to advance or get better economic opportunities, or they may think Dunbar is suggesting hiding feelings as a matter of racial and historical pride.

Oral Response

16. In their oral response, students should cite specific information from the poems that substantiates their presentations and expands on their earlier responses.

"Luke Havergal" and "Richard Cory"

by Edwin Arlington Robinson

"Lucinda Matlock" and "Richard Bone"

by Edgar Lee Masters

Open-Book Test (p. 109)

Multiple Choice and Short Answer

1.c Explanation: supported by "I come to quench the kiss that flames upon your forehead."

2. Sample answer: The most likely identity of the speaker is a ghost. Students may extend this idea by suggesting it is the ghost of his lover, who refers to her old identity as "her" and "she." This line implies the speaker's identity: "Out of a grave I come to tell you this."

3. Sample answer: Students may say that the message is either that rich people are not always happy, or that one can't judge by appearances. Either answer is acceptable if it is well-supported.

4.d Explanation: suggested by "gentleman" and "crown."

5. Sample answer: "He was a gentleman from sole to crown. . . " "And he was always human when he talked."

6. Sample answer: Students should approximate these ideas: Her attitude is of one who has had a full, and mostly fulfilling, life. Her message is that she is frustrated by young people who do not understand or appreciate life and have little patience for its teachings.

7.a Explanation: In this context, "repose" means "death."

8. Sample answer: "It takes life to love Life," which suggests that one must embrace life fully, because it demands energy and effort. Other answers are acceptable, if students can support them.

9.c. Explanation: People in mourning come to him to create epitaphs for their loved ones.

10. Sample answer: Bone was new to the town and didn't know about its inhabitants. He later became more familiar with the townspeople.

Questions are classified in these categories:

Comprehension	1(A), 10 (A)
Interpretation	3 (A)
Literary Analysis	2 (A), 8 (A), 9 (E)
Reading Strategy	5 (A), 6 (A)
Vocabulary	4 (E), 7 (A)

E=Easy, A=Average, C=Challenging

Extended Response

11. (Easy) Possible answers: The speaker suggests that he approach his own death with some peace (whether now or in the future), supported by "if you trust her she will call." Other answers are acceptable, as long as they are supported well.

12. (Average) Possible answers: The speaker and others want a rich life ("wish that we were in his place"); a life that does not require such hard patience ("waited for the light"); and a life that does not contain daily hunger and poverty ("went without the meat, and cursed the bread").

13. (Average) Students may choose Lucinda Matlock or Richard Bone. They should include both joyous and sad details of Lucinda's full life, as well as her instructions to the next generation; or they should include the lessons that Richard Bone learns, and the role he plays in people's lives.

14. (Average) Students' answers will vary. Some will probably say that historians try to write the truth as well as they can. Others may say that

historians are influenced by the times and environments in which they live. Either point of view is acceptable, as long as it is well thought out.

15. (Challenging) Students may select Luke Havergal, his departed lover, the ghost, Richard Cory, the speaker in "Richard Cory," Lucinda Matlock, or Richard Bone. They must substantiate their choice with details that make the character worthwhile to know.

Oral Response

16. In their oral response, students should cite specific information from the poems that substantiates their presentations and expands on their earlier responses.

"A Wagner Matinée"
by Willa Cather
Open-Book Test (p. 112)
Multiple Choice and Short Answer

1.d Explanation: supported by "pathetic and grotesque"; "suddenly . . . ill at ease and out of place."

2. Sample answer: Students may offer various opinions, as long as they support them. Possible answer: She follows her husband to Nebraska and stays there with him for thirty years, raising her family with dedication; she must have loved him deeply to sacrifice her early success for this rough life.

3.c Explanation: supported by "I owed this woman most of the good that ever came my way."

4. Sample answer: If we only had the present-day point of view, we would think of Aunt Georgiana as an unsophisticated, poorly dressed woman from the country, who does not belong at a concert. Students may supply any details from the text that mention her poor, black clothing, or her somewhat lost demeanor.

5. Sample answer: He clearly has a great love of music, which she fostered in his early years by exposing him to great music, singing to him, and teaching him to play instruments.

6. Sample answer: Painful memories: he suffered from chilblains and shyness; his hands became raw from corn husking; he fell asleep while studying; he had to plow "forever and forever." Pleasant memories: he read Shakespeare with his aunt; he learned mythology from her; she taught him to play the organ; she talked to him about music.

7.a Explanation: supported by "as though they had been so many daubs of tube paint on a palette."

8. Sample answer: "The silence of the plains" refers not only to the vast quiet of the physical environment in which she has lived for thirty years, but a silence of her soul, that has not been exposed to the full range of culture which she loves.

9.b Explanation: supported by "waking her" and "passive."

10. Sample answer: Because it has been so long since she has experienced classical music, he does not know whether she still can appreciate or understand it. Examples: "I was unable to gauge how much of it had been dissolved in soapsuds . . ." and his reference to her having heard nothing but church music for years.

Questions are classified in these categories:
Comprehension	6 (A)
Interpretation	2 (A), 8 (C)
Literary Analysis	1 (A), 5 (A), 7 (A)
Reading Strategy	4 (A), 10 (A)
Vocabulary	3 (A), 9 (E)

E=Easy, A=Average, C=Challenging

Extended Response

11. (Easy) Examples: building a home; drawing water from a lagoon; cooking; putting children to bed; ironing; darning; milking. Examples of emotional support: awakening him to study; putting her hands over his eyes; teaching him to play music.

12. (Average) Students' answers should reflect the fact that Clark thought farm life was barren and lacked not only physical, but also emotional, fullness. They should use examples that describe the mundane details of each day or the visual picture of a flat, unchanging landscape.

13. (Average) Students' answers may vary; many approaches are acceptable, as long as they are supported. Possible answer: Although he is trying to be helpful, it appears that Clark has ironically opened a Pandora's box. He has exposed his aunt to something that was dead in her; at the end of the story, she is in pain, not wishing to return to her desolate life.

14. (Average) Students' answers will vary. They should, however, acknowledge that the intense religious devotion displayed by Aunt Georgiana ("She was a pious woman") represents one of the ways pioneers coped with their difficult way of life.

15. (Challenging) Students' answers may vary, but they should explore the theme that without her music, Aunt Georgiana is missing richness in her life. Clark expresses this loss with references to the soul, as when they are listening to the concert, and he hopefully asks himself: "It never really dies then, the soul?"

Oral Response

16. In their oral response, students should cite specific information from the story that substantiates their presentations and expands on their earlier responses.

UNIT 5: DISILLUSION, DEFIANCE, AND DISCONTENT (1914–1946)

"The Love Song of J. Alfred Prufrock"

by T. S. Eliot

Open-Book Test (p. 115)

Multiple Choice and Short Answer

1. Sample answer: Students should note that the speaker in a dramatic monologue addresses a silent listener at a critical point in the speaker's life. They might cite the first line of the poem, with its first-person and second-person pronouns, as a clue that the speaker is addressing a silent listener.

2. Sample answer: Students should describe the setting as a fall evening in a city. We know it is a city because of the references to hotels, restaurants, "narrow streets" (line 70), "lonely men in shirt-sleeves, leaning out of windows" (line 72), and we know it is the fall because of the reference to October (line 21).

3. Explanation: see lines 4–9. The streets seem empty and deserted. They are described as a "patient etherized upon a table." The streets are "half-deserted" where people are "restless" and engaged in "muttering retreats."

4. Students should note that the speaker addresses a silent listener, who can be a friend, an alter ego, or an audience.

5. Students should recognize the use of rhythm and repitition in the given lines. The rhythm of the first line flows gently as time passes. This line is repeated as the speaker tries to convince himself of the abundance of time.

6. Answers will vary. Students should begin by citing lines that contain musical devices, and should clearly explain the use of repitition, rhyme, alliteration, and rhythm in their chosen lines. They should strongly support their opinions regarding the effectiveness of the devices the poet uses.

7. Sample answer: He seems afraid that the best time of his life has passed, and that it is too late to take new chances.

8.b Explanation: In lines 35–45 he is very aware of how he thinks others see him—especially his signs of growing older—thinning hair, etc. In lines 80–86, again signs of aging are on his mind—he feels his time has passed. In lines 90–98, he seems frustrated that the time has passed to make a new impression on people and say what he really feels and means.

9. Words beginning in s; sea, sea-girls, and seaweed, are used in these lines. Students may suggest that the alliteration of s's gives the reader the impression of a soft whisper from the sea.

10. Sample answer: The mermaids symbolize beauty and happiness. He feels that both things are missing from his life.

Questions are classified in these categories:

Comprehension	2 (A)
Interpretation	3 (A), 8 (A)
Literary Analysis	1 (E), 4 (E), 7 (E)
Reading Strategy	5 (A), 6 (C), 9 (C)
Vocabulary	10 (A)

E=Easy, A=Average, C=Challenging

Extended Response

Guidelines for student response:

11. (Easy) Students should show that Prufrock is troubled by his inability to say what he feels. He also suggests that if he were younger—and less self-conscious—he might feel less inhibited about trying to act and behave differently.

12. (Average) Students should interpret the meaning of the poem using examples from the poem to support their ideas. While a poem can be like a song, this is not a song at all. Eliot may be using the title as an ironic statement to undermine the traditional conventions of a love poem.

13. (Average) As a dramatic monologue, we only get the thoughts and feelings of the speaker. There are no other voices in the poem, so we don't really know what anyone else thinks or feels about Prufrock, or his state of mind. The monologue reinforces the image we get of Prufrock as a lonely, isolated, introspective man. In a play or dialogue—other voices and opinions would appear and possibly challenge Prufrock. A short story, for example, would rely less on images to convey a portrait of the main character.

14. (Average) At the opening of the poem he clearly says, "let us go then, you and I." He is on his way to a tea party to tell a woman of his love to her. We see that he decides not to tell her. Later in the poem he describes feeling like an insect being examined by others. When he says in line 55 and 56 "And I have known the eyes already . . . the eyes that fix you in a formulated phrase" he may be speaking to someone else that may also be feeling helpless and exposed as he does here.

15. (Challenging) Prufrock is an image of the individual living in a time of rapid social and technological change. Students may say that his feelings are common when the world and social customs are changing quickly. They may also argue that his feelings are not common and more due to the unique personality and choices of the character.

Oral Response

16. In their oral responses, students should cite specific passages from the poem that substantiate their presentations and expand on their earlier responses.

Imagist Poets

Open-Book Test (p. 118)

Multiple Choice and Short Answer

1. Sample answer: Three main points: 1) avoid excessive language, and useless abstractions. 2) avoid ineffective description—show, don't tell. 3) don't break lines into awkward rhythm, and use rhyme carefully—in a surprising way.

2. Sample answer: He shows that as a child the woman has hair "still cut straight across my forehead / I played about the front gate, pulling flowers."

3. Sample answer: both petals on a branch and faces in a crowd seem temporary and easily moved—not likely to stay in one place if jostled.

4. Sample answer: Bright contrasting color creates a visual impression in objects that may seem ordinary and uninteresting when viewed in a picture.

5. Sample answer: He says the fire truck is "moving / tense / unheeded / to gong clangs / siren howls." The feeling of movement and sound suggest that it is on the way to a fire.

6. Sample answer: Even though the speaker knows the plums are saved for breakfast, he says they were "so sweet and cold," adding to the feeling that they had to be eaten.

7.b Explanation: "Silver dust lifted from the earth" is symbolic of more than earthly beauty. "Silver" suggests that the tree is shimmering and precious like the rare metal and "lifted from the earth" suggests that it is no longer of the earth.

8. Sample answer: Fruit will be able to fall again after the wind has "plowed" through the heat.

9.b Explanation: The goal of the "Imagist" style is to evoke complex ideas and emotions by focusing on ordinary things and objects in new ways.

10. Sample answer: Pound says that rhyme should be used carefully and in surprising ways. Students should cite examples from poems to support their answers.

Questions are classified in these categories:

Comprehension	1 (A)
Interpretation	6 (C), 8 (A), 9 (E)
Literary Analysis	3 (A), 4 (C), 5 (C)
Reading Strategy	2 (A), 7 (E)
Vocabulary	10 (E)

E=Easy, A=Average, C=Challenging

Extended Response

11. (Easy) Students should be able to identify words that describe color, taste, sound, and texture or touch in the selection and cite passages to support their answers.

12. (Average) Pound says that an Image in verse is "an intellectual and emotional complex in an instant of time." It can evoke the feeling of an object or scene in ways that paintings cannot—often with merely describing it. Students should cite evidence from Pound's essay in their answers and some examples of pictures and verses that perhaps deal with the same subject in different ways.

13. (Average) In the beginning we have physical descriptions of the woman and her husband as children. We read that she is bashful when they meet, but later she longs to go far to meet him. We can see the scene around her. At first she is playful—picking fresh flowers by the gate, later when they are apart, she says that the gate is overgrown with different mosses and the flowers are gone. Students may cite these images and others in their answers.

14. (Average) Students may focus on key words that demonstrate her feelings through actions, changes in the season that represent passing time and loneliness, or changes in her expressions and reactions to her husband over time.

15. (Challenging) Students should review the statements by Pound on the goals and strengths of Imagist poetry. What does he say it should do—and should leave to others? Students may say that this style is good for capturing an object or event at one moment in time, but not as good at showing changes across time—or more complex feelings as in "The River-Merchant's Wife" or in "The Love Song of J. Alfred Prufrock."

Oral Response

16. In their oral responses, students should cite specific passages from the poems that substantiate their presentations and expand on their earlier responses.

"Winter Dreams"

by F. Scott Fitzgerald

Open-Book Test (p. 121)

Multiple Choice and Short Answer

1. Sample answer: He dreams about being a golf champion, but in reality he is honored for being only the best caddy in the club.

2.d Explanation: d is the only appropriate answer. He has no other plans yet, and his encounter with Judy shocks him into rethinking his present situation and goals.

3. Sample answer: Dexter's reactions—"it made him clench his hands"; "[it made him] tremble"; "[he would] repeat idiotic sentences to himself"; "[he would] make brisk abrupt gestures of command"; "October filled him with hope"; "there was something gorgeous about the fall." He feels that his dreams are possible.

4. Sample answer: "She was entertained only by the gratification of her desires . . ."

5. Sample answer: He says very little about his wealth and career when having dinner with Judy for the first time. He is not embarrassed to admit that he is "making more money than any man" his age, but he doesn't brag about it either. Since he started his career in a very useful, small business he would attribute his success to good decision making and practical planning.

6. Sample answer: Since their first encounter, Dexter was enamored of Judy. When she becomes a young woman he is mesmerized by her beauty and makes it his goal to be with her. Her alternating indifference and attention toward him makes her even more desirable to him. Ultimately, his obsession with her makes it difficult to pursue joy and passion in other parts of his life.

7.c Explanation: She never seems shy, nervous, or lonely—she is always sought after and she uses her beauty and desirability to get what she wants.

8. Sample answer: He is confused and knows part of him still cares for her. He is afraid to lose her interest again.

9. Sample answer: Even though he wants some stability in his life, he is still attracted to Judy and what she represents. He sees her attention as a source of pride for himself, and wants to see if she is still interested in him. "There was nothing sufficiently pictorial about Irene's grief to stamp itself on his mind."

10. Sample answer: A *pugilistic* youth would provoke a fight. The angry young man was so *pugilistic* he would start fights with strangers.

Questions are classified in these categories:

Comprehension	7 (E)
Interpretation	3 (A), 4 (E)
Literary Analysis	1 (C), 5 (C), 6 (A), 9 (C)
Reading Strategy	2 (A), 8 (A)
Vocabulary	10 (A)

E=Easy, A=Average, C=Challenging

Extended Response

11. (Easy) We are repeatedly told about Judy's beauty and physical appearance to emphasize the way others saw her, especially Dexter. Dexter's appearance remains unknown, in part, to emphasize that the focus of the story is on Dexter's personality and emotional state. Fitzgerald may be showing us what he feels are the qualities most admired in men and women at the time: women were admired for their appearance, while men were admired for their intellect.

12. (Challenging) Students should note that Dexter does most of his dreaming during the winter months and they are about making plans for the summer. When he is a boy, his first dream is to be a golf champion. But when he later realizes that won't happen, he decides to make changes. His pursuit of Judy is the largest lasting dream—one that does not come free—but he still manages to carry on with other goals and make other decisions. Students may say that not all dreams lead to negative results when realistic expectations are weighed against unrealistic ones. In their answers, students should cite several instances from the story in which Dexter has to make choices.

13. (Average) Students comments should reflect that Dexter's regarded her beauty as something that would always exist. When he learns that she has changed—and that others no longer see her in the same way he did—he may feel that his passion for her in the past was unjustified. Her beauty represents something ideal and almost unattainable. It was also one of his dreams that he had to give up—knowing that she had changed finally ended another dream.

14. (Average) Students should identify some of the key attributes and actions of the characters. They may see Dexter as someone fascinated by wealthy society and what it contains, but also ambivalent about his eventual membership in it. He chooses to attend a prestigious college and join an exclusive golf club, but he also seems to regard its members with disdain. But, later he becomes infatuated with Judy Jones who seems to embody the beauty and the coldness of wealthy society.

15. (Average) Students should note that Dexter makes this statement after hearing that Judy may no longer be as beautiful as she once was. But, when he cries, he says it is "for himself now." He suggests that he has lost a part of himself rather than the affection of another person. He seems most upset knowing that finally all of his youthful dreams have ended. This suggests that the theme of the piece is that even though youthful dreams are sometimes a way to plan for the future, those whose lives are based on the pursuit of illusions are bound to face disappointment.

Oral Response

16. In their oral responses, students should cite specific passages from the story that substantiate their presentations and expand on their earlier responses.

"The Turtle" from *The Grapes of Wrath*
by John Steinbeck
Open-Book Test (p. 124)

Multiple Choice and Short Answer

1. Sample answer: Students should note that the turtle carried some oat seeds across the road, as revealed in this passage: "And one head of wild oats was clamped into the shell by a front leg."

2. Sample answer: both represent the struggle to survive

3. Sample answer: "sleeping life waiting to be spread"

4. Sample answer: The turtle persists in his mission, just as the people of the Depression persisted.

5. Sample answer: Students should see that the sedan driver swerves to avoid hitting the turtle. The text tells the reader that "She saw the turtle and swung to the right, off the highway." The fact that she left the highway shows that she was trying to avoid the turtle, who was on the highway.

6. Sample answer: reproduction

7. Sample answer: people took to the road, to California to escape the dust bowl, much like the turtle labored across the road.

8. Sample answer: a tiddly-wink is a small disc that flips. The turtle is shaped like a tiddly-wink.

9. Sample answer: Students should note that a fetlock has something to do with a horse, since Steinbeck mentions foxtails that might "tangle in a horse's fetlocks."

10. Sample answer: Students should define **protruded** as "pushed or thrust outward." They should use the word in a sentence of their own. Their cluster diagrams might include the following synonyms: ***projected, jutted out, stuck out, bulged, swelled,*** and ***distended.***

Questions are classified in these categories:

Comprehension	1 (A), 5 (E)
Interpretation	6 (A), 7 (A)
Literary Analysis	2 (A), 3 (A), 4 (C)
Reading Strategy	8 (E), 9 (E)
Vocabulary	10 (A)

E=Easy, A=Average, C=Challenging

Extended Response

11. (Easy) Students' diagrams and essays should use examples from the story to show how Steinbeck humanizes the turtle. For example, Steinbeck refers to the turtle as "he" or "him" throughout, calls his front feet "hands," and speaks of his "fierce, humorous eyes." Students might also mention that focusing closely on the turtle's journey across the road makes it seem larger than life and heroic, as when the turtle hoists himself over the parapet. Students will probably agree that humanizing the turtle makes the reader care about him and identify with his struggles.

12. (Average) Students should describe the setting as not only dry but also as rather remote and far from any city. Even though it is dry, it is not barren, and there is much evidence of "sleeping life waiting to be spread and dispersed." There is also much life in the grass, in the form of ants, ant lions, grasshoppers, sow bugs, and at least one land turtle. There is a somewhat steep (from the turtle's viewpoint) embankment leading to the highway, and a four-inch-high concrete shoulder to the road.

13. (Average) Students may take either position as long as they support it with details from the story. They could cite such examples as scaling the embankment, having the red ant run into his shell, and being hit by the truck. Students who disagree might argue that because the turtle is an animal, the term "hardships" doesn't really apply. The turtle is just following instincts to survive in trying to make his way across the road.

14. (Average) Students should recognize that the head of wild oats represents life, growth, renewal, and reproduction—the strong life force of nature. The fact that the seeds are planted against all odds and under such hardship hints that life will find a way to survive, no matter what.

15. (Challenging) Students can either agree or disagree with the statement but should support their position with details from the story. Those who agree might conclude that the seeds are more important to the theme of reproduction than the turtle, who is just one of many vehicles for seeds. They might cite the first paragraph, in which the focus is on seeds and the turtle has not yet appeared, and the last few sentences, in which the "planting" of the seeds is described. Those who disagree could mention the detailed emphasis on the turtle throughout the body of the story, which leads the reader to forget the earlier focus. They may argue that without the turtle, the seeds it carries would not survive.

Oral Response

16. In their oral responses, students should cite specific passages from the story that substantiate their presentations and expand on their earlier responses.

"anyone lived in a pretty how town" and "old age sticks"

by E. E. Cummings

"The Unknown Citizen"

by W. H. Auden

Open-Book Test (p. 127)

Multiple Choice and Short Answer

1.d Explanation: The "floating" of the bells suggests music.

2. Sample answer: Students should note that the theme of the poem is that true humanity is squelched by conventional society. They might cite any number of lines as support, including this one: "they / said their nevers they slept their dream," which implies that the characters are guided by negatives (nevers) and let their dreams get away from them.

3. Sample answer: Students should realize that in line 7, Cummings is satirizing the people who live safe, conforming lives. "Sowed their isn't" suggests that they did not sow any "wild oats," and "they reaped their same" suggests that their lives were not unusual in any way.

4.b Explanation: Students should realize that the "gr" in line 19 is an echo of the scolding tone of the old people in the previous lines, and it is meant to suggest growling and the general complaining attitude of the old people.

5. Sample answer: Students should see that the theme of "old age sticks" is that age diminishes the free spirit of youth. They might cite any number of lines as support, including the entire first stanza.

6. Sample answer: Students should see that the group (youth) is growing old in that stanza. It says so right in the text: "&youth goes / right on / gr / owing old."

7.b Explanation: "he held the proper opinions"

8. Sample answer: Students should note that Auden is saying the modern society is discouraging people from acting boldly. They might use any number of lines as support, including these: "He was found by the Bureau of Statistics to be / One against whom there was no official complaint."

9.c Explanation: Students should recognize that the reference to holding the "proper opinions for the time of year" is satirical because it suggests that an opinion is like a clothing style and is determined by seasons and fashion.

10. Sample answer: Students should define *statistics* as "the science of collecting and arranging facts about a particular subject in the form of numbers." They should use the word in a sentence of their own.

Questions are classified in these categories:

Comprehension	6 (E)
Interpretation	2 (A), 5 (A), 8 (C)
Literary Analysis	3 (C), 7 (A), 9 (C)
Reading Strategy	1 (A), 4 (C)
Vocabulary	10 (A)

E=Easy, A=Average, C=Challenging

Extended Response

11. (Easy) In their responses, students should interpret how the citizen might feel about being treated as a statistic. They should also suggest how he might want to be treated instead. For example, they might say he would be upset to be considered a statistic. He might wish that the government had been more actively concerned with his happiness and freedom, rather than with his conformity. Their charts should list specific examples from the poem of how the citizen was treated during his life.

12. (Average) Students should acknowledge that Auden's attitude toward the modern version of sense of the word "saint" is that he despises it because it implies someone who never takes risks. It is clear that Auden would not want to call such a person a friend, and if he met such a person, he might ask why the person was so conforming. He might ask such questions as "Are you free?" and "Are you happy?" He would expect that the answer would be no, since the Unknown Citizen never did anything that expressed his own difference from the crowd.

13. (Average) Students should support their speculations with evidence from "The Unknown Citizen." For example, Auden dislikes a society that puts a high premium on conforming. He appears suspicious of the materialistic focus of modern life, by which people are encouraged to react to advertisements by buying things they can't really afford (the Installment Plan).

14. (Average) Students should recognize that Cummings sees "anyone" as part of a common humanity, not important enough or different enough to merit the capital letters that are used for proper nouns, the names that distinguish an individual from the masses. When he describes the women and men in the town as being "(both little and small)," he is emphasizing the small-mindedness of these people.

15. (Challenging) Students should choose appropriate elements to support the statement. For example, the poem mixes subject matter about human rituals such as marriage and burials with repeated lines about natural cycles—"spring summer autumn winter" and "sun moon stars rain." Students might also argue that Cummings writes about faceless people (someones and everyones) instead of individual characters to convey a sense of the universal.

Oral Response

16. In their oral responses, students should cite specific passages from the poems that substantiate their presentations and expand on their earlier responses.

"The Far and the Near"

by Thomas Wolfe

Open-Book Test (p. 130)

Multiple Choice and Short Answer

1.b Explanation: Their waving was "beautiful and enduring . . . beyond all change and ruin . . ."

2. Sample answer: Students should see that the engineer wants to meet the women. The quote that supports this is as follows: ". . . he resolved that one day, when his years of service should be ended, he would go and find these people and speak at last with them whose lives had been so wrought into his own."

3.c Explanation: He expects to find an extraordinary woman. She turns out to be a disappointment.

4. Sample answer: "extraordinary happiness"

5. Sample answer: Up close, things are not as perfect as they seem from afar.

6. Sample answer: The town is completely "unfamiliar" to him.

7. Sample answer: Students should realize that Wolfe is striving for an effect of insight into the feelings and emotions of the engineer. Their diagrams and essays should mention such words and phrases as **old man, sick with doubt and horror, strange and unsuspected, gone forever,** and **never be got back again.**

8.c Explanation: Students should recognize that the engineer finally realizes that the earth, even though it was "within a stone's throw of him," had always been out of his reach, for he "had never seen or known" it. It has become clear to him that even though the women are dear to him in his mind, they have no such reciprocal thoughts about him.

9. Sample answer: Students should realize that the engineer's expectations were unrealistic from the beginning. He feels paternal toward these women he has never met, as shown in these words: "He felt for them . . . such tenderness as a man might feel for his own children. . . ." It is foolish for him to expect that they will feel the same tenderness for him.

10. Sample answer: Students should note that an animal with a timorous manner would act frightened, since **timorous** means "full of fear."

Questions are classified in these categories:

Comprehension	2 (A)
Interpretation	1 (C), 8 (A)
Literary Analysis	3 (A), 7 (A), 9 (C)
Reading Strategy	4 (E), 5 (C), 6 (E)
Vocabulary	10 (A)

E=Easy, A=Average, C=Challenging

Extended Response

11. (Easy) Students should use details from the story to support their interpretation of the engineer's feelings. For example, students might say that the women always make time during their day for this one gesture. This otherwise insignificant gesture makes the engineer feel hopeful and believe that there is always some good in the world.

12. (Average) Students should recognize that the little house gives the engineer such "extraordinary happiness" because he feels that he has a connection with it and its occupants. Every day for twenty years, the woman had come out to wave when the engineer blew the whistle on the train. Whatever else happened in his life, this was the one constant, and he feels a personal affection for the woman and her daughter. He feels that the house is "something that would always be the same, no matter what mishap, grief or error might break the iron schedule of his days."

13. (Average) Students' story maps should show the engineer as the major character, the setting as somewhere along the tracks on the outskirts of a little town, the rising action as the events leading up to his decision to visit the women, the anticlimax as his disappointing meeting with the women, and the falling action as the moments he walks away from the women's cottage. The conflict is within the engineer and the resolution is his insight that his perception was wrong. In their essays, students should clearly demonstrate why the story's ending is anticlimactic. They should use details from the story to support their assertions. For example, when the engineer visits the women, he discovers that there is no particular reason why they wave—their wave is not really the brave, free gesture that he imagined it to be.

14. (Average) Students should recognize that the theme of the story is that up close, things are rarely as perfect as they seem from afar. Support for this view includes the engineer's disappointing realization that he should not have visited the women.

15. (Challenging) Students should interpret the engineer's state of mind at the end of the story by explaining why he feels confusion, doubt, and hopelessness and what has changed. For example, students might say that the engineer

feels the way he does because his perspective has completely changed. As a person with an important job, he had confidence that led him to shape what he saw from the majestic distance of his train into idealized, magical visions. Up close, from a more realistic perspective, the people and things he embellished in his visions are ordinary and even unpleasant.

Oral Response

16. In their oral responses, students should cite specific passages from the story that substantiate their presentations and expand on their earlier responses.

"Of Modern Poetry" and "Anecdote of the Jar"
by Wallace Stevens

"Ars Poetica"
by Archibald MacLeish

"Poetry"
by Marianne Moore

Open-Book Test (p. 133)

Multiple Choice and Short Answer

1. Sample answer: Students should recognize that the central theme of "Of Modern Poetry" is that a modern poem must reflect the people of the time. This is supported by the following lines: "It has to be living, to learn the speech of the place. / It has to face the men of the time and to meet / The women of the time."

2.d Explanation: Humans can use their imagination to affect nature.

3.b Explanation: A simile makes a comparison between two subjects using **like** or **as**.

4. Sample answer: Students should recognize that the theme of "Ars Poetica" suggests that a poem should appeal more to the senses. Evidence from the poem can include any of the sensory images, such as "the flight of birds."

5. Sample answer: "motionless in time / As the moon climbs."

6. Sample answer: "A poem should be palpable and mute / As a global fruit."

7. Sample answer: Students should note that Moore suggests that poems fuse the real and the imagined, just as the idea of a real toad in an imaginary garden does.

8. Sample answer: Students should note that Moore is saying that when one reads poetry disdainfully, one can find truth in it.

9. Sample answer: Students should recognize that Moore is saying that it is not right to criticize factual writing.

10. Sample answer: Students should define *slovenly* as "untidy," and they should use the word in a sentence of their own.

Questions are classified in these categories:

Comprehension	1 (A)
Interpretation	2 (C), 4 (C)
Literary Analysis	3 (A), 5 (E), 6 (E), 7 (C)
Reading Strategy	8 (A), 9 (A)
Vocabulary	10 (A)

E=Easy, A=Average, C=Challenging

Extended Response

11. (Easy) Students may choose any of the other three poems in the selection and identify lines or images that are memorable to them. For example, they might choose MacLeish's "A poem should not mean / But be" because it is such a strong and simple definition of a poem. Or students might consider the opening lines of Moore's "Poetry" significant because the poet admits to sharing readers' negative feelings about poetry. Students will probably feel that the "imaginary gardens" image is effective because it gives a vivid impression of fantasy mixed with reality, which captures what poetry is all about.

12. (Average) Students might cite the following lines in support of the statement: "The wilderness rose up to it, / And sprawled around, no longer wild" and "It took dominion everywhere." They should point out that the jar, as something created by humans, represents civilization. The fact that it has taken "dominion" suggests that humans have power over nature and can either enhance it or destroy it.

13. (Average) Students may take either position as long as it is supported by details from the two poems. Those who feel that examples are most effective might suggest that if a poem cannot be explained, it can only be likened to something else, like a "globed fruit" or "the flight of birds." They may point out that Stevens also uses examples in likening a poem to "an insatiable actor." Students who prefer Stevens's approach may argue, for example, that his description of what a poem does or must do, such as "learn the speech of the place," makes it easier to grasp his idea of poetry.

14. (Average) Students may agree or disagree with the statement as long as they back up their view with evidence from the poem. Those who agree might say that Moore's concrete images indicate that poetry should be as clear as those images. She wants poetry to be something for "hands that can grasp." Students may note, however, that Moore is too critical of difficult poetry, and that the effort to understand it is worthwhile.

15. (Challenging) Students may take either position as long as it is supported by examples from "Anecdote of the Jar." Some students may think the poem is realistic because it is filled with realistic, concrete images. Other students may think the poem is unrealistic because the concrete image of the jar symbolizes the much broader abstraction of human civilization and because the concrete image of the Tennessee wilderness stands for the natural world in general.

Oral Response

16. In their oral responses, students should cite specific passages from the poems that substantiate their presentations and expand on their earlier responses.

"In Another Country"

by Ernest Hemingway

"The Corn Planting"

by Sherwood Anderson

"A Worn Path"

by Eudora Welty

Open-Book Test (p. 136)

Multiple Choice and Short Answer

1. Sample answer: Students should note that the narrator feels separated from the three Italian soldiers who had won medals because the other soldiers have done brave deeds in battle, but the narrator has not. The supporting detail is as follows: "I was a friend, but I was never really one of them after they had read the citations, because it had been different with them and they had done very different things to get their medals."

2. Sample answer: Students should realize that the major never misses a day with the machines only because self-discipline is important to him. It has nothing to do with a belief that the machines will help him, because the major obviously does not believe that they will.

3. Sample answer: Students should recognize that the major is indifferent toward the doctor. They might mention that when the doctor asks the major if he has confidence, the major says "No," which indicates that the major has no faith in the doctor's methods.

4. Sample answer: Students should note that the narrator refers to himself as "I" and uses other first-person pronouns throughout the story.

5. Sample answer: Students should note that a story is told from the third-person limited point of view when an outside narrator who does not participate in the action tells the story and conveys the thoughts of one of the characters.

6. Phoenix talks about him and buys him a gift.

7. Phoenix describes him as "all wrapped up."

8. She tricks him into chasing a dog so she can retrieve the nickel.

9.a Explanation: Students should recognize that because of the limited third-person narration, the reader does not get into the mind of Phoenix, so it is impossible to know the truth about her grandson.

10. Sample answer: Students should define **limber** as "flexible." Synonyms might include **yielding, bendable, pliant, elastic, pliable, springy, supple, lithe,** and **plastic.** Antonyms might include **inflexible, stiff, firm, rigid, solid, unbending,** and **unyielding.** Students should use the word **limber** in two sentences of their own.

Questions are classified in these categories:

Comprehension	1 (C), 3 (E)
Interpretation	6 (A), 7 (A)
Literary Analysis	4 (C), 5 (A), 8 (A), 9 (E)
Reading Strategy	2 (E)
Vocabulary	10 (A)

E=Easy, A=Average, C=Challenging

Extended Response

11. (Easy) Students should describe Hal's character, using details from the story that relate to his involvement with the Hutchensons. They might mention that he appears to be a good person in befriending Will in Chicago. He appears to be very kind and caring, since he visits the Hutchensons regularly and is reluctant to give the Hutchensons the news of their son's death. Except that he was educated in Chicago and is a high school principal, we know nothing else about him.

12. (Average) Students should recognize that Phoenix's reactions to the many obstacles she encounters tells us that she is resilient and takes difficulties in stride. For support, they should use details from the story, such as this: when she gets to the creek and has to cross on the log, she says "Now comes the trial," but crosses quickly despite her fear.

13. (Average) Students should use examples from the stories to compare Phoenix Jackson and the major. For example, both characters respond to their troubles by maintaining a hard discipline with little complaint: Phoenix regularly makes the difficult journey, and the major comes to the hospital daily and keeps his grief mostly to himself. If students believe that Phoenix's grandson is dead, then she and the major are alike in their difficulty in accepting the death of

a loved one. For differences, students should refer to their nationalities, gender, education, and circumstances.

14. (Average) Students' essays should describe the loneliness and loss faced by the characters, such as the various physical injuries of the men, the loneliness of the narrator when he notices the separation between himself and the other men, and the emotional loss suffered by the major when his wife died.

15. (Challenging) Students should use examples from the stories in discussing the role of the narrators and their involvement with the events. They may mention, for example, that the narrator of "In Another Country" plays a more direct role in the story's events, although he also tells about other characters. The first-person point of view brings the reader closer to the tragedies of war. In "The Corn Planting," much of what the narrator reports is hearsay from Hal, such as the letters from Will and his parents' reaction to them. At the end, the narrator becomes a direct observer and provides a unique perspective on the strangeness of the old couple's act.

Oral Response

16. In their oral responses, students should cite specific passages from the stories that substantiate their presentations and expand on their earlier responses.

"Chicago" and "Grass"

by Carl Sandburg

Open-Book Test (p. 139)

Multiple Choice and Short Answer

1. Sample answer: Students should note that in the first five lines of "Chicago," the narrator is addressing Chicago by its various nicknames.

2. d Explanation: apostrophe—Sandburg is addressing Chicago as if the city were a person.

3. Sample answer: Students should note that the narrator means that the young man laughs even though he is bound to lose some battles.

4. b Explanation: Students should recognize that the phrase "Flinging magnetic curses" appeals to the sense of hearing.

5. Sample answer: Their diagrams should list other images associated with the sense of hearing, such as "lifted head singing," "laughing with white teeth," "laughing as a young man laughs," "Laughing even as an ignorant fighter laughs," and "Laughing the stormy, husky, brawling laughter of Youth."

6. Explanation: Students should explain that the beating of the pulse and the heart can be apprehended with the sense of touch.

7. Sample answer: Students should note that Sandburg is trying to create an image of a future tour group passing over the battlefield in a train.

8. Sample answer: Students should note that the speaker is the grass itself, as indicated by the line "I am the grass."

9. Sample answer: Sandburg is portraying grass (nature) as more powerful than human events.

10. Sample answer: Students should define **cunning** as "skillful in deception; crafty; sly." They should use the word in a sentence of their own.

Questions are classified in these categories:

Comprehension	7 (E)
Interpretation	3 (A), 9 (A)
Literary Analysis	1 (C), 2 (E), 8 (E)
Reading Strategy	4 (A), 5 (A), 6 (A)
Vocabulary	10 (A)

E=Easy, A=Average, C=Challenging

Extended Response

11. (Easy) Student essays should discuss the charges against the city and the verdict of the speaker, using examples from the poem. For example, they might point out that the speaker actually agrees with the critics that Chicago is a city of poverty and crime, yet he finds its youthful vitality, its will to work hard, and its ability to laugh at adversity admirable.

12. (Average) Students should support the given interpretation of "Chicago" by using examples from the poem. For example, they might mention the following lines: "They tell me you are wicked and I believe them . . . And having answered so I turn once more to those who sneer at this my city, and I give them back the sneer and say to them: Come and show me another city with lifted head singing so proud to be alive . . . laughing as a young man laughs."

13. (Average) Students should pick an image that captures other aspects of the city giving strong reasons for their choices. For example, they might choose an image of building: structures rising from the prairie created by the people—architects, businesspeople, and workers interacting as a team to make a better life for all.

14. (Average) Students should state a possible theme for "Grass" and support their answer with details from the poem. For example, they might say that the theme is that nature heals the damage that war wreaks on society. As support, they could cite the following lines: "Pile the bodies high. . . . Shovel them under and let me work."

15. (Challenging) Students may choose either interpretation as long as they support it with details from the poem. For example, students who understand the poem as a reflection on the statement "Time heals all wounds" may say that it stresses the fact that the physical scars of war are quickly erased by nature. Those who read the poem as an illustration of the pointlessness of war might suggest that as the physical scars of war disappear, so the reasons for fighting the war may be forgotten.

Oral Response

16. In their oral responses, students should cite specific passages from the poems that substantiate their presentations and expand on their earlier responses.

"The Jilting of Granny Weatherall"
by Katherine Anne Porter
Open-Book Test (p. 142)
Multiple Choice and Short Answer

1. Sample answer: Students should note the Granny Weatherall is disturbed because she refuses to acknowledge that she is not well. As proof, they might mention that she says, "There's nothing wrong with me."

2. Sample answer: a young woman. John Weatherall died when he was young.

3. Sample answer: Students should recognize that Granny's thoughts reveal that her predominant character traits were strength and industriousness, as shown in the fact that she "had fenced in a hundred acres once, digging the post holes herself and clamping the wires with just a negro boy to help."

4. Sample answer: Students should state that in stream-of-consciousness writing, the author presents the character's thoughts as if they were coming directly from a character's mind. The technique mimics the unorganized flow of insights, memories, and reflections that occur in people's minds.

5. Sample answer: John Weatherall died when his wife was still a young woman. John was a good husband: "Better than I hoped for even."

6. Sample answer: Students should recognize that Father Connolly is in the room so he can give Granny the last rites. Proof of this is the following line: ". . . Father Connolly murmured Latin in a very solemn voice and tickled her feet." He is putting oil on her feet as part of the last rites, but Granny interprets it as tickling.

7. Sample answer: Students should see that Granny seems to value the character trait of being orderly. This is supported by the following line, among others, from the story: "It was good

to have everything clean and folded away, with the hair brushes and tonic bottles sitting straight on the white embroidered linen . . ."

8.a Explanation: Students' diagrams and answers should reflect that the only choice that takes place in the present is that Granny wants to give Cornelia the amethyst set. All the other answer choices are revealed in flashbacks as things that happened in the past. Their diagrams should list other events from the past, such as the time Granny Weatherall fenced in a hundred acres. They should list other events from the present, too, such as Granny thinking about sending gifts to the nuns.

9. Sample answer: Students should recognize that Granny Weatherall associates Father Connolly's presence with her jilting because she had faced the priest alone when George didn't show up for their wedding. They might cite the following line as support: "What if he did run away and leave me to face the priest by myself?"

10. Sample answer: Students should define **dyspepsia** as "indigestion." Then they should use the word in a sentence of their own.

Questions are classified in these categories:
Comprehension   1 (E)
Interpretation   5 (A), 7 (A), 8 (C), 9 (A)
Literary Analysis   2 (E), 4 (E), 6 (C)
Reading Strategy   3 (A)
Vocabulary   10 (A)
E=Easy, A=Average, C=Challenging

Extended Response

11. (Easy) Students may choose different interpretations as long as they support their opinions with events from the story. For example, they might feel that the title signifies the importance of the jilting to Granny and its continuing effect on her. Others might suggest that Granny's approaching death evokes many of the same feelings in her that her jilting did.

12. (Average) Students may choose either position, as long as it is supported with details from the story. For example, students who agree might suggest that Granny committed a blunder in her youth by agreeing to marry George. She admits her adulthood was a struggle, especially after John died. Most students will probably state that Granny Weatherall would disagree with the last part of the statement, as she does not seem to regret much in her old age, except a chance to tell George he did no lasting damage. Those who disagree might say that Granny seems too spunky to agree with such a depressing blanket indictment of life.

13. (Average) Students should recognize that the flashbacks reveal that Granny Weatherall was a source of comfort to her children when they were young. This is supported by the following

passage: "Lighting the lamps had been beautiful. The children huddled up to her and breathed like little calves waiting at the bars in the twilight. . . . The lamp was lit, they didn't have to be scared and hang on to mother any more." They should complete the chart by listing other flashbacks in the story and explaining what each one reveals. For example, they might mention her memory of digging post holes for the fence by herself, which demonstrates her strength and capacity for hard work.

14. (Average) Students might see the theme as something like this: Even the moment of death often provides no relief from one's memories of life's troubles. They should support their opinion with details from the story, such as Granny's recollection of the terrible moment in her life when she was jilted by George.

15. (Challenging) Students should define stream of consciousness and state how well it indicates how close Granny is to death, supporting their answers with specific details. For example, they might say that stream of consciousness reflects the thoughts coming directly from a character's mind and that it creates a realistic and vivid personal view of death approaching a character. They could contrast Granny's coherence at the beginning, where she carries on a conversation with the doctor, and her growing difficulty in communicating as the story progresses. They might also say that, at first, she can distinguish between present events and memories of her past but loses this ability toward the end of the story.

Oral Response

16. In their oral responses, students should cite specific passages from the story that substantiate their presentations and expand on their earlier responses.

"Race at Morning" and "Nobel Prize Acceptance Speech"

by William Faulkner

Open-Book Test (p. 145)

Multiple Choice and Short Answer

1. Sample answer: Students should note that Mister Ernest doesn't shoot the buck because he wants the buck to live so they can hunt it again next November. The passage that supports this is as follows: " 'Which would you rather have? His bloody head and hide on the kitchen floor yonder and half his meat in a pickup truck on the way to Yoknapatawpha County, or him with his head and hide and meat still together over yonder in that brake, waiting for next November for us to run him again?' "

2. Sample answer: "And then we seen him again" is an example of slang dialect, as it uses "seen" instead of "saw."

3. Sample answer: Students should recognize that the action takes place at the narrator's cabin on the river. Support for this is in this passage: ". . . Mister Ernest rid Dan up to the door of the cabin on the river he let us live in . . ."

4. Sample answer: His parents abandoned him, so Mister Ernest took him in.

5. Sample answer: Mister Ernest says that *maybe* is the "best word in our language" and one that "mankind keeps going on."

6. Sample answer: Students should write the sentence as follows: Because Mister Ernest and I were going to get him.

7. Sample answer: Their charts should show five other examples of dialectical speech and also show the standard English version of each.

8. Sample answer: Students should recognize that Faulkner's explanation of why young writers today have forgotten the "problems of the human heart in conflict with itself" is that they are worried about being blown up by the bombs of an international war.

9. Sample answer: Faulkner faults writers for writing "not of the heart but of the glands."

10. Sample answer: Students should define *bayou* as a "sluggish, marshy inlet," and they should use it in a sentence of their own.

Questions are classified in these categories:

Comprehension	1 (A), 8 (A)
Interpretation	7 (C), 9 (C)
Literary Analysis	2 (E), 5 (E), 6 (A)
Reading Strategy	3 (E), 4 (A)
Vocabulary	10 (A)

E=Easy, A=Average, C=Challenging

Extended Response

11. (Easy) Students' answers should describe the character traits of Dan, Eagle, and the buck. For example, they might describe Dan as an intelligent and powerful horse; Eagle as a smart, experienced, and determined lead dog; and the buck as an intelligent, brave, and wily deer, knowing just how to elude the hunters following its trail and the many who are arrayed along its path. Students may conclude that all these characters are reasonably well developed as minor characters. They will probably say that the buck is the most important of these characters because without it, the hunt could not occur.

12. (Average) Students should recognize that the narrator means that hunting and farming are necessary and equal parts of a full life. They should use passages from the story that support this view, such as: ". . . all of a sudden I

thought about how maybe planting and working and then harvesting oats and cotton and beans and hay wasn't jest something me and Mister Ernest done three hundred and fifty-one days . . . but it was something we had to do . . . to have the right to come back into the big woods and hunt for the other fourteen."

13. (Average) Students' essays should assess the intelligence of the narrator and provide examples to support their conclusions. Students might point out that although the narrator's use of language indicates a lack of formal education, he demonstrates high intelligence in evaluating events and analyzing issues, as in his realization that the 351 days spent working and the 14 days spent hunting each year are not different or of unequal value but opposite sides of the same thing.

14. (Average) Students should recognize that Faulkner's main point is in his "Nobel Prize Acceptance Speech" is that the writer's most important duty is to help human beings endure and prevail. They should quote passages from the essay as support.

15. (Challenging) Students should identify events or situations in which Mister Ernest and the narrator are struggling with internal conflicts. Mister Ernest, for example, demonstrates an internal conflict over the values of hunting when he pursues the buck all day only to pass up the opportunity to shoot the deer when he has the chance. In his explanation that hunting and farming are not two different things but "jest the other side of each other," the narrator reveals that he is working to resolve an internal conflict over the values of work relative to the need for recreation.

Oral Response

16. In their oral responses, students should cite specific passages from the story or from the speech that substantiate their presentations and expand on their earlier responses.

Robert Frost's Poetry
Open-Book Test (p. 148)
Multiple Choice and Short Answer

1. Sample answer: Students should recognize that, to the speaker, the wall symbolizes suspicion, mistrust, and bias. It is clear that the speaker does not want the wall, for he tries to talk the neighbor out of having it. He tells the neighbor that "My apple trees will never get across / And eat the cones under his pines," and thinks about asking, "'**Why** do they make good neighbors?'"

2. Sample answer: Students should see that the neighbor means that he doesn't want to get to know the speaker any better. To him, the fence is good because it keeps people on their own property.

3. Sample answer: The family returns to work because they know that life must continue and that death is a part of life.

4. Sample answer: Students should see that the night represents loneliness and doubt to the speaker. He says "I have looked down the saddest city lane," suggesting that he does not see the night as a happy time.

5. Sample answer: Students should note that an iamb is an unaccented syllable followed by an accented one. They might cite any group of four iambs as examples, including any complete line from "Stopping by Woods on a Snowy Evening."

6. Sample answer: Students should note that blank verse is unrhymed iambic pentameter, or unrhymed lines that consist of five iambs each, such as "When I see birches bend to left and right."

7.b Explanation: blank verse, which re-creates natural speech.

8. Sample answer: 1) He has many tasks before he rests; 2) he has much to do before he dies.

9. Sample answer: "The only other sound's" the wind and snowfall.

10. Sample answer: Students' Analysis Maps should define **rueful** as "sorrowful." Synonyms might include **sad, contrite, remorseful, regretful, sorry, grieving,** and **mournful.** Antonyms might include **glad, blissful, blithe, cheerful, happy, contented, delighted, gladdened,** and **joyful.** Students should use the word in two sentences of their own.

Questions are classified in these categories:

Comprehension	1 (E), 4 (A)
Interpretation	2 (C), 3 (C)
Literary Analysis	5 (A), 6 (E), 8 (A)
Reading Strategy	7 (C)
Vocabulary	10 (A)

E=Easy, A=Average, C=Challenging

Extended Response

11. (Easy) Students' essays should reflect a number of different examples of Frost's thematic use of regret. For example, students may cite the example of the boy who is killed by the saw in " 'Out, Out—.' " ("Then the boy saw all— / since he was old enough to know, big boy / Doing a man's work, though a child at heart— / He saw all spoiled.") They may point out the mournful refrain at the end of "Stopping by Woods on a Snowy Evening" or the speaker's wish to return to childhood and simple joy in "Birches." Students may mention that such longings are a part of human nature that is instantly recognizable and

familiar. They may note that even at their relatively young age, they have a sense of lost childhood or regret about times gone by.

12. (Average) Students should see that the theme of "Stopping by Woods on a Snowy Evening" is the conflict between the attractions of duty and rest. The speaker has stopped to admire the beauty of the snow-covered woods, but he cannot stay long, even though he would like to. He feels pulled away from this moment of rest by the thought that he has "promises to keep."

13. (Average) Students' essays should reflect that while the story told in the poem seems a simple one, it actually reflects complicated ideas about the human condition and the American sensibility. The reasons for not wanting walls might include unspoiled natural beauty, easier access to the countryside, a stronger bonding with neighbors, and so on. Reasons for building and keeping walls might include such ideas as maintaining privacy and land rights, avoiding legal battles, and a desire to keep family affairs within the family. The poem points up the American ideas of open spaces and pioneering on the one hand, and rugged individualism and ownership on the other.

14. (Average) Students should recognize that, for the speaker in "Birches," swinging on birch trees most clearly symbolizes a temporary return to a youthful, carefree state. They should cite lines from the poem as support, such as, "I like to think some boy's been swinging them," "I should prefer to have some boy bend them / As he went out and in to fetch the cows— / Some boy too far from town to learn baseball / Whose only play was what he found himself," and "So was I once myself a swinger of birches. / And so I dream of going back to be."

15. (Challenging) Students should explore "Stopping by Woods on a Snowy Evening" in terms of the three parts Frost considered essential: the point or idea, the details that develop it, and the technique. For example, they might state the main idea as the conflict between desire for rest and duty; the details in the attractiveness of the woods and the little horse's eagerness to keep going; and the rhythm and rhyme scheme that sound like a moving sleigh.

Oral Response

16. In their oral responses, students should cite specific passages from the poems that substantiate their presentations and expand on their earlier responses.

"The Night the Ghost Got In"
by James Thurber

from *Here Is New York*
by E. B. White

Open-Book Test (p. 151)

Multiple Choice and Short Answer

1. Sample answer: Students should note that this detail contributes to the essay's humor because it emphasizes the family's tendency toward mishaps. It also prepares the reader for the idea that more mishaps will be reported in the essay.

2. Sample answer: Students' charts and answers should reflect that the example of hyperbole is the underlined part of this sentence: "Bodwell was at the window in a minute, shouting, frothing a little, shaking his fist."

3. Sample answer: Students should realize that the cop means to say "hysterical," based on the excitement level in the household.

4. Sample answer: Students should realize that the theme of the essay is that jumping too quickly to conclusions usually leads to trouble. This is supported by the entire chain of events that leads from the conclusion that a ghost had gotten into the house.

5.d Explanation: All of the other items are directly involved in the plot.

6. Sample answer: ". . . pedestrians instinctively quicken step" when passing the Empire State Building.

7. Sample answer: Students should recognize that the sentence exemplifies the following characteristic of the informal essay: the expression of the author's opinion.

8. Sample answer: He says that New York City is the "loftiest" of cities.

9. Sample answer: The city offers "the sense of belonging to something unique, cosmopolitan, mighty, and unparalleled."

10. Sample answer: Students should note that if a person who suffered from *claustrophobia* were to get into an elevator, he or she would not be comfortable because of the fear of being in a confined space.

Questions are classified in these categories:

Comprehension	3 (E)
Interpretation	4 (A), 8 (E)
Literary Analysis	1 (C), 5 (A), 7 (C), 9 (E)
Reading Strategy	2 (A), 6 (A)
Vocabulary	10 (A)

E=Easy, A=Average, C=Challenging

Extended Response

11. (Easy) Students' responses should give a clear idea of the eccentricities of these characters through specific examples of their personalities and actions. For example, students might cite the mother's urge to throw another shoe and her belief that the wounded policeman really was a deserter as eccentric features, which come close to crossing the line of credibility. They might find the grandfather's reception of the police eccentric, but somewhat believable, given the implication that the old man is not in his right mind.

12. (Average) Students should recognize that the grandfather bounding out of bed in his nightshirt and leather jacket is one of the aspects of the essay that would not be funny without Thurber's embellishment. In fact, the vision of the grandfather sleeping in his leather jacket is a bit sad, considering the fact that the grandfather is not really in the best of mental health. They might find other examples as well, and they should support their choices by explaining why each would not be funny in and of itself.

13. (Average) Students should show White's wide-ranging interests and feeling for humanity through specific examples. For example, they might cite his sympathetic admiration for New Yorkers living under pressure, as an example that nothing human is alien to him. They could see evidence of his keen eye in such vivid examples as the young man writing to his girl or the overwhelmed newlywed visitors eating a dispirited meal. As evidence of White's intelligence, they might mention his clear analysis of New York's neighborhood pattern.

14. (Average) Students should note that White probably means that New York has small neighborhoods, each of which is almost self-sufficient. They should cite passages in the essay that suggest this, such as "Each neighborhood is virtually self-sufficient. usually it is no more than two or three blocks long and a couple of blocks wide."

15. (Challenging) Students should give some general criteria for where they draw the line between humor and unkindness and illustrate it with specific examples. For example, they might state that when Thurber calls attention to things people can't help, such as the grandfather's mental problems or the police's speech patterns, and exaggerates them, he crosses the line. In contrast, they might decide that White's depiction of tourists doesn't cross the line because he is more descriptive than critical.

Oral Response

16. In their oral responses, students should cite specific passages from the selections that substantiate their presentations and expand on their earlier responses.

from *Dust Tracks on a Road*
by Zora Neale Hurston
Open-Book Test (p. 154)
Multiple Choice and Short Answer

1. Sample answer: She was curious about the whites because they represented something outside her experience, living as she did in a small segregated town in the South. Details might include: the fact that she accosted the whites and asked if she could travel "a piece of the way with them;" the fact that she continued to do this even after her parents found out and punished her for it; the sentence, "The village seemed dull to me most of the time."

2. Sample answer: Huston's grandmother worried so much about Hurston's "forward ways" because "she had known slavery." She knew the ways of an earlier time when black people were lynched for minor offenses.

3. Sample answer: Any reasonable answer is acceptable if supported by detail from the text. A possible answer: The dust tracks represent the path to a new life. Supporting detail: The tracks led out to the world beyond her village. Also, the narrator says she resolved to be like Hercules, who "put his hand in that of Duty and followed her steep way to the blue hills of fame and glory."

4. Sample answer: White people visiting from the North were curious about black schools in the South: "A Negro school was something strange to them . . . "

5. Sample answer: What Zora Did or Said: 1) She observed the visitors closely; 2) She was already familiar with the passage she had to read and she read it well; 3) She lied about loving school. Was This Unusual Behavior?: 1) Yes, because she was the only student confident enough about her reading to take the time to observe the visitors; 2) Yes, because most of the students stumbled over their reading; 3) No, probably not.

6. Sample answer: Hurston did most of her reading on her own. Despite the fact that she did **not** love school, she did acquire a keen love of literature.

7. Sample answer: 1) to portray the culture of her community; 2) to share the experiences of her life; 3) to show how she struggled against racism and prejudice; 4) to inspire others to educate themselves.

8. Sample answer: Hurston's mother locked Hurston in her room once as punishment for repeating gossip. Hurston passed the time reading the Bible, the only book in the room. The parts she liked best were tales of action and adventure from the Old Testament, such as the stories of David and the enemies he slew.

9.d Explanation: Hurston tells us she was not interested particularly in the morals of a story. She tells us she preferred the Old Testament. She tells us she preferred the Old Testament. She tells us she loved many stories about gods and goddesses. Answer d is the only choice that can be inferred.

10. Sample answer: *Brazenness* means boldness or impudence. Zora's brazen behavior could be: accosting white people and going off with them; flicking her skirt behind her at school; lying to the teacher about loving school.

Questions are classified in these categories:

Comprehension	5 (A)
Interpretation	1 (A), 2 (C), 3 (C), 4 (A)
Literary Analysis	7 (A), 9 (A)
Reading Strategy	6 (C), 8 (C)
Vocabulary	10 (A)

E=Easy, A=Average, C=Challenging

Extended Response

11. (Easy) Aspects of Hurston's character: brazen (talking openly to white people; inviting herself to go with them; flicking her skirt at her schoolmates to show her scorn at them; openly observing the white women); eagerness to learn (her avid reading on her own); love of action (her preference for action stories). In their essays, students can show in a variety of ways how these characteristics took her far from home, into new fields; how, for an African-American woman of her time, these characteristics helped her overcome prejudice. They may also indicate how these characteristics perhaps led her into poverty and obscurity.

12. (Average) Students should recognize that the schoolchildren felt threatened when the visitors came to observe them because of the pressure put on them by their own teachers, who were concerned with making a good impression on the visitors.

13. (Average) Students' responses should indicate the blacks' mistrust of whites (Hurston's grandmother's comment about lynching); their desire to impress them (presenting the children in school in the best possible way); their dependence on them (the schoolteacher's job may have been in jeopardy if his students were not presentable), and any other appropriate response. The white's attitudes toward the blacks must be mostly inferred: they were curious about and amused by the black school; they may have felt guilty and

therefore went to the trouble to reward Hurston for her obvious talent; their actions toward Hurston may have made them feel complacent, like "good Christians," because they had encouraged one gifted child.

14. (Average) Students should note that Hurston describes her reading likes and dislikes to reveal her character and personality. The fact that she admires strong characters suggests that she identifies with them and wants to be more like them. As for the weaker characters in the "other thin books," Zora did not admire them because they "had no meat on their bones."

15. (Challenging) Students should cite specific examples in discussing both how the critic's view is supported by the selection and how it is not. For example, they may say that Zora's descriptions of white people are generally positive enough to support the critic's view: she is curious about differences, but not critical; her view of the white women's hands arouses wonder, not distaste. In contrast, students might suggest that Zora implies criticism when she mentions white curiosity about a "Negro school." The fact that the ladies had Zora read from a magazine at the hotel implies that they had suspicions about her performance at school.

Oral Response

16. (Challenging) In their oral responses, students should cite specific passages from the autobiography that substantiate their presentations and expand on their earlier responses.

"Refugee in America," "Ardella," "The Negro Speaks of Rivers," and "Dream Variations"
by Langston Hughes

"The Tropics in New York"
by Claude McKay

Open-Book Test (p. 157)

Multiple Choice and Short Answer

1.a Only answer a contains a hint about the identity of the speaker. The pronoun "my" shows the first person speaker is the author himself.

2. Sample answer: The speaker may mean the woman is as beautiful and mysterious and black as a starless night, but her eyes are as bright an shining as a star.

3. Sample answer: Students should recognize that the speaker in "Ardella" feels admiration for Ardella because her eyes and her songs make her an interesting person. Without these two attributes, it seems that Ardella would be dull ("a night without stars" and "a sleep without dreams").

4. Sample answer: The student can cite any of the images in the poem, especially the historical references, to support this view.

5.c Explanation: Students should recognize that the speaker is proud, as shown by the repeated line, "My soul has grown deep like the rivers."

6. Sample answer: Students should see that the speaker thinks the day is a time to dance. The supporting lines are the first four lines of each stanza.

7. Sample answer: Students should see that the speaker in "Dream Variations" is dark, as stated in the following passages: "While night comes on gently, / Dark like me" and "Night coming tenderly / Black like me."

8.d Explanation: The fruit is "Set in the window, bringing memories" of his homeland, which makes him cry in the end.

9.b Explanation: The phrase "bringing memories" is a clue. Also lines 9–12 provide clues.

10. Sample answer: Students should define **dusky** as "dim; shadowy." Synonyms might include **swarthy, darkish, dark, clouded, gloomy, faint, blurred, murky,** and **indefinite.** Antonyms might include **brilliant, distinct, definite, clear, bright,** and **dazzling.** Students should use the word **dusky** in two sentences of their own.

Questions are classified in these categories:

Comprehension	2 (A), 6 (A)
Interpretation	4 (C), 8 (C)
Literary Analysis	1 (E), 7 (A), 9 (A)
Reading Strategy	3 (E), 5 (A)
Vocabulary	10 (A)

E=Easy, A=Average, C=Challenging

Extended Response

11. (Easy) Students should mention some specific ways in which the poem is effective in contributing to African American awareness and pride. For example, they might cite how the association with ancient rivers from the earliest times reminds African Americans of their roots. Students might also suggest that the use of the pronoun *I* enables African American readers to identify with the history of their people. The connection of the Nile and the pyramids, representing one of the world's greatest civilizations, provides to African Americans a source of pride.

12. (Average) Students should mention that the lines "If you had known what I knew / you would know why" suggest that the speaker has known a time when he did not have the freedom he enjoys today. Now that he is in America and can experience the meaning of "words like **Freedom"** and "words like **Liberty,"** he really appreciates them because of the contrast of his earlier life.

13. (Average) In their essays, students should compare and contrast the speakers in the three poems, telling whom the *I* represents and what effect the use of this pronoun has on the reader. For example, in "Refugee in America" students might decide that the speaker is the poet who has experienced a lack of liberty, although a reader who shared these experiences might see the *I* as representing the African American race. In "The Negro Speaks of Rivers," they might recognize that speaker as the whole African American race throughout time. The use of *I* invites the reader to become part of the narration and to identify with the race. In "The Tropics in New York," they might suggest that *I* is the poet, and any reader might identify with his feelings of homesickness.

14. (Easy) The speaker sees night as a positive time. He says it "comes on gently" and "tenderly." He has great love and affection for the night. He says the night is "dark like me" and "black like me."

15. (Challenging) Students should discuss words and images of darkness in "Ardella," "The Negro Speaks of Rivers," and "Dream Variations," using supporting details. For example, they might note that the word "dusky" connotes a physical trait Africans share with rivers and emphasizes the identification of the two. Students might point out that, in "Dream Variations," the African American speaker identifies with evening and night in their darkness, which are represented positively as cool, gentle, and tender. They might note that although the darkness of Ardella is a physical fact and is presented as something mysterious and closed, it is not the point of what she is. Students could suggest that Hughes uses such words and images in positive ways to make African Americans take pride in their "blackness."

Oral Response

16. In their oral responses, students should cite specific passages from the poem or poems that substantiate their presentations and expand on their earlier responses.

"From the Dark Tower"
by Countee Cullen

"A Black Man Talks of Reaping"
by Arna Bontemps

"Storm Ending"
by Jean Toomer

Open-Book Test (p. 160)

Multiple Choice and Short Answer

1. Sample answer: Students should recognize that the last line of "From the Dark Tower" suggests hope for a better future for blacks. Additional support can be found in the first line, among others: "We shall not always plant while others reap."

2. Sample answer: planting while others reap is a reference to the agricultural work of the slaves; the slaves also presumably made music ("with mellow flute") for the landowners; also, "countenances, abject and mute, That lesser men should always hold their brothers cheap" refers to the fact that the slaves were forced to look on silently while the landowners sold their families and held them (the slaves) in such low esteem.

3. Sample answer: The soft blackness of the night provides a welcome contrast to the harsh white light of the stars, and is beautiful for being black. Cullen is comparing the blackness of the night to his people; he finds them both to be beautiful.

4.c Explanation: Students should realize the poem compares the work of the black race to that of one man's annual planting and harvesting. They might mention that the reference to "seed enough to plant the land / in rows from Canada to Mexico" indicates that the one man symbolizes the entire race, since no one man could have planted that much.

5. Sample answer: Students should recognize that the speaker's sowing represents human effort, not merely in agriculture but in all fields of endeavor.

6. Sample answer: Students should realize that in "A Black Man Talks of Reaping," reaping represents being rewarded for one's efforts.

7. Sample answer: The students should indicate that the theme is the beauty of the storm as it comes to a climax in the heavens, and nourishes the earth below.

8. Sample answer: Some of the visual images students might mention are "Thunder blossoms", "Great, hollow, bell-like flowers," "Full-lipped flowers / Bitten by the sun," and "Dripping rain like golden honey."

9.d Explanation: Students should recognize that the other answer choices do not cover all the uses of the metaphors in Toomer's poem. Only choice d mentions the images that are suggested by metaphors: flowers ("blossoms," "flowers, "Full-lipped flowers"), bells ("bell-like" "clappers to strike our ears"), and people ("bleeding," "flying from the thunder").

10. Sample answer: The last line leaves the reader with a feeling of release, of being refreshed, as after a storm and rain, the earth smells sweet.

Questions are classified in these categories:

Comprehension	7 (E)
Interpretation	1 (A), 8 (A)
Literary Analysis	4 (C), 5 (A), 6 (A), 9 (C)
Reading Strategy	2 (A), 3 (C)
Vocabulary	10 (A)

E=Easy, A=Average, C=Challenging

Extended Response

11. (Easy) Students' essays should give a word or phrase describing the mood of the poem and cite details that show how it captures the mood of the poem. For example, students may choose the word "bitter" or a synonym, citing references to sowing much but reaping little and the detail of the speaker's children eating "bitter fruit."

12. (Average) Students might paraphrase the poem something like this: "I have planted crops all my life, always fearing that the weather or birds would destroy the crop. I have planted enough to cover the entire United States. But all I can show for my labor is a handful of food. Yet other people are gathering the results of my work. It is not surprising that my children are not really interested in working hard and therefore have become bitter." They might see the crops as symbols for any kind of work, and the handful of food as a symbol of insufficient reward for the work. They might see the theme of the poem as this: Because generations of black people were poorly rewarded for honest work, their descendants have given up on honest work.

13. (Average) Students may select any one of the poems as long as they explain how it uses metaphors. For example, students might choose "From the Dark Tower" or "A Black man Talks of Reaping," citing the comparison of African American life to planting without reaping, which reminds readers of the agricultural slavery of that life and evokes feelings of anger and despair. If they select "Storm Ending," they might mention that thunder is compared to bell-like flowers, which convey the noise and beauty of the storm and evoke a sense of awe.

14. (Average) Students should recognize that Cullen implies that the job situation during the 1920s was much more difficult for blacks than it was for whites, but that it will someday be changed.

Lines from the poem that support this view are as follows: "We shall not always plant while others reap," "And there are buds that cannot bloom at all," and "So in the dark we hide the heart that bleeds, / And wait, and tend our agonizing seeds."

15. (Challenging) Students may agree or disagree with the statement but should support their position with examples. For example, students agreeing that Toomer intended to write about the African American experience might assert the thunder represents the trials of African Americans and, like other writers of the Harlem Renaissance, he wanted to call attention to their lives. Students who disagree might reason that the images of the storm give no hint of any further meaning and that the poem was written to show that African American writers could produce literature equal in quality to that of white writers.

Oral Response

16. In their oral responses, students should cite specific passages from the poem that substantiate their presentations and expand on their earlier responses.

UNIT 6: PROSPERITY AND PROTEST (1946–PRESENT)

"The Life You Save May Be Your Own"

by Flannery O'Connor

Open-Book Test (p. 163)

Multiple Choice and Short Answers

1.d Explanation: He spots the car, and immediately asks about it.

2. Sample answer: Students' webs and descriptions should include traits such as his "fast talking" or manipulative nature; his physical disability and the manner in which he deals with it; his exaggerated concern for the younger Lucynell; his obsession with the car; and his world-weary approach to life.

3. Sample answer: Students should realize that Mr. Shiftlet is only telling partial truths, at best, throughout the story and he probably will not keep any promises he makes.

4. Sample answer: Mr. Shiftlet is trying to establish his authority and superiority; he partially succeeds, however, the old woman has her own agenda and to some extent ignores what Mr. Shiftlet wants.

5.c Explanation: The old woman is obsessed with marrying off her daughter and will say or do whatever is necessary to make this happen.

6. Sample answer: Her behavior is bizarre and she is fascinated to the point of obsession with minute details such as the movement of Mr. Shiftlet's Adam's apple as he speaks.

7.c Explanation: Everything he asks for focuses on the old woman providing money.

8. Sample answer: Students may say that Mr. Shiftlet assumes that the boy behind the counter will take Lucynell in or that he will make sure she gets back home.

9. Sample Answer: The mother's hunger for a son-in-law may blind her to the true nature of Mr. Shiftlet.

10. Sample Answer: Students may have predicted correctly or incorrectly, but they should explain their predictions. In the very first paragraph the author hints ironically about Mr. Shiftlet: "Although the old woman lived in this desolate spot with only her daughter and she had never seen Mr. Shiftlet before, she could tell, even from a distance, that he was a tramp and no one to be afraid of." And near the end of the story, Mr. Shiftlet begins to show his shifty behavior more clearly: "As they came out of the courthouse, Mr. Shiftlet began twisting his neck in his collar. He looked morose and bitter as if he had been insulted while someone held him."

Questions are classified in these categories:

Comprehension	1 (E), 7 (A)
Interpretation	8 (C)
Literary Analysis	2 (E), 5 (A), 6 (A)
Reading Strategy	3 (A), 9 (C), 10 (C)
Vocabulary	4 (A)

E=Easy, A=Average, C=Challenging

Extended Response

11. (Easy) The action between the characters would probably have been thrown off by normality; the story revolves around each character's grotesque traits and the interaction that results from them.

12. (Challenging) Students may note that his comment about mothers has been reflected in his treatment of the old woman.

13. (Average) Students' Venn diagrams should specify the individual obsessions of all three characters and note that all three are obsessed in some way; Mr. Shiftlet and the younger Lucynell are more easygoing about life, enjoying more of what there is; the old woman and Mr. Shiftlet are both very specific about what they want and how they intend to get it; both Lucynells are caught up in their lives at home. Students should recognize that grotesque characters' limits point out distinct ideas.

14. (Challenging) Students' writing may discuss the disembodied nature of the doctors' removal of the heart and explore the emotional connotations of not knowing anything about the heart even after physical examination.

15. (Average) Students' essays may explore the guilt that Mr. Shiftlet may be feeling; his limited concern about the boy running away; his feelings about his own mother; and his feelings about the old woman and the younger Lucynell and how he has left them.

Oral Response

16. In their oral responses, students should cite specific information from the story that substantiates their presentations and expands on their earlier responses.

"The First Seven Years"

by Bernard Malamud

Open-Book Test (p. 166)

Multiple Choice and Short Answers

1.b Explanation: The events of the story have focused on Feld's understanding of Sobel's motivation and at the end of the story, Feld finally understands what Sobel wants and is willing to give in to it; students should note that a and c are d are all accurate to some extent, but do not relate to Feld's epiphany.

2. Sample answer: Feld consistently wants what is best for his daughter and thinks her life should be "better" than his—to that end, he imposes his own ideas of what her life should be like on her; Miriam has developed an independence that allows her to tolerate Feld's actions and comments, but she pursues her own goals and wishes.

3. Sample answer: Their relationship is based on mutual respect and love and develops according to each character's individual personalities; their relationships with the other characters are resistant in various ways because they do not share as much.

4. Sample answer: Feld has decided that Max is the type of husband he wants for his daughter; Max is surprised and cautious, wanting to know more about Miriam and trying to ascertain Feld's motivation—he is not as interested as Feld would like for him to be.

5. Sample answer: Sobel is responsible and extremely good at his job; he is also willing to work for a low wage. Sobel does his job well because of his personal desire to be near Miriam; another assistant would be doing the job simply because of the money.

6.a Explanation: Feld has not taken into account either Max's or Miriam's interests and goals.

7. Sample answer: Students' charts should address the specifics of Feld's relationships and identify Feld's epiphanies about Miriam's independence; Sobel's love for Miriam; and Max's limited interest in Miriam.

8.c Explanation: *Discern* addresses the perception or understanding that is associated with the meaning of something.

9.c Explanation: Sobel wants to be near Miriam in order to share books and ideas with her and Feld knows from experience that other assistant's are not as reliable and trustworthy as Sobel is.

10. Sample answer: Feld realizes that Sobel loves his daughter very much—as much or more than he does himself—and would do anything for her and accepts the fact that he cannot change Sobel's and Miriam's feelings, nor force someone like Max to care about his daughter as much as he does.

Questions are classified in these categories:

Comprehension	2 (A), 4 (A)
Interpretation	5 (A), 6 (A), 9 (A)
Literary Analysis	1 (A), 7 (A), 10 (C)
Reading Strategy	3 (C)
Vocabulary	8 (E)

E=Easy, A=Average, C=Challenging

Extended Response

11. (Easy) Students' Venn diagrams should address the differences in Miriam's and Feld's attitudes toward college, reading books, marrying a man like Max, and so forth. They should recognize the similarities of a desire to be happy and live a fulfilling life. Their essays should include these similarities and differences and identify the conflict of whom Miriam should marry.

12. (Average) Students should recognize that the Feld's failure at matchmaking and the responses of Sobel and Miriam lead Feld to his epiphany.

13. (Challenging) Sobel has had a difficult life and cherishes his love for Miriam, wanting to share books and ideas with her and be near her; he is angry and disappointed that Feld is trying to prevent him from spending his life with Miriam.

14. (Average) Students should describe Miriam's independence and individuality that she maintains despite her father's interference.

15. (Average) Sobel and Feld resolve their differences about Miriam and about how her life should be led; ultimately the characters seem to have found a path to satisfaction in life, if not complete happiness.

Oral Response

16. In their oral responses, students should cite specific information from the story that substantiates their presentations and expands on their earlier responses.

"The Brown Chest"
by John Updike
Open-Book Test (p. 169)

Multiple Choice and Short Answers

1.d Explanation: There are elements of accuracy in all of the answers, but d describes the importance and role of the brown chest.

2. Sample answer: The atmosphere is slightly forbidding and overwhelming, yet it holds many symbols and ideas that strongly affect the main character in his childhood.

3.c Explanation: Parts of himself have entered into the chest and become part of the family history.

4.a Explanation: The main character is "overwhelmed by decisions," he occasionally has to flee the house to escape the oppression of the past, he faces many childhood memories, and packing is a struggle.

5. Sample answer: The atmosphere seems cluttered and confusing because there are so many things in the attic and they represent so many memories, ideas and feelings.

6. Sample answer: Similarities may include that the chest is "full" of family at the beginning and at the end of the story, the main character is aware of the details, but vague about specifics, and he respects the chest and what it represents; differences include his stronger appreciation of the chest at the end, his awareness that he has become part of the chest, and he is less intimidated by what the chest represents.

7.c Explanation: They are tired and want to get where they are going, so getting lost is completely undesirable.

8. Sample answer: Morna is willing to assimilate the furniture because she appreciates what it represents as she asks how the furniture was used in the past.

9. Sample answer: Morna knows that she needs to have the main character's permission to open the chest; acknowledges that the chest is an important part of his life; and the chest motivates a similar interest to what she has been showing in furniture.

10. Sample answer: Morna will probably never understand the specific significance of all the items in the chest, but will share the main character's respect and appreciation for what the individual items represent and the family history that the chest represents, as a whole.

Questions are classified in these categories:

Comprehension	1 (E), 4 (A)
Interpretation	3 (A), 10 (C)
Literary Analysis	2 (A), 5 (A), 6 (A)
Reading Strategy	9 (A)
Vocabulary	7 (A), 8 (C)

E=Easy, A=Average, C=Challenging

Extended Response

11. (Easy) Students' diagrams and essays should examine the varied and conflicting responses and emotions that the main character has toward the brown chest.

12. (Average) Students' essays should acknowledge that the brown chest symbolizes the narrator's family and, by extension, himself; they should cite details and quotations that indicate this importance.

13. (Challenging) Students should recognize that the specific contents in the brown chest are not as important as the overall significance of what it represents.

14. (Challenging) Gordon and his father are both aware of the importance of family; but neither seems to want to know about the details that make up the family; the main character grew up with the brown chest; Gordon will need Morna to help him more aware of the specifics of what the brown chest is about.

15. (Average) Students will probably say that Gordon and Morna will take the chest home and add to its contents, as the family's history extends.

Oral Response

16. In their oral responses, students should cite specific information from the story that substantiates their presentations and expands on their earlier responses.

"Hawthorne"
by Robert Lowell

"Gold Glade"
by Robert Penn Warren

"The Light Comes Brighter"
and "The Adamant"
by Theodore Roethke

"Traveling Through the Dark"
by William Stafford

Open-Book Test (p. 172)

Multiple Choice and Short Answers

1.b Explanation: Hawthorne finds inspiration in common things; Lowell's word choices indicate the inspiration that can be found in these things.

2.d　Explanation: Sneaky and stealthy support the idea of "something you are not supposed to see," which is not the case with the other answers.

3.　Sample answer: Students' answers should reflect Warren's inviting and colorful description of the glade.

4.　Sample answer: Students should note Warren's style of strong imagery. Sights include the color images and words and phrases such as high as treetop, geometric, and circular; sounds include no fox bark, woodpecker coding, jay calling, and silence; smell and taste images are limited, but students may note the implication of wet and damp smells and tastes; physical sensations include wandering, solid in soil, and setting foot.

5.c　Explanation: The stronger sun is melting snow and ice, trees and plants are becoming green (wearing and April look), and birds begin singing.

6.　Sample answer: A possible paraphrase of the stanza might be: trees will leaf out and the new growth will be recognized and appreciated by people.

7.　Sample answer: The subject of the poem is truth and the theme is that it is strong and unshakable.

8.　Sample answer: The core of truth cannot be tampered with; the poet wants to emphasize the strength of truth.

9.　Sample answer: The speaker comes across a dead deer in the road and removes it. During the process he discovers the deer is carrying a fawn and experiences mixed emotions about the task.

10.a　Explanation: The poem is written as if the speaker were relating the incident to a friend—explaining what happened and offering thoughts and feelings about the experience.

Questions are classified in these categories:

Comprehension	5 (E)
Interpretation	3 (A), 7 (A), 8 (C)
Literary Analysis	1 (A), 4 (A), 10 (C)
Reading Strategy	6 (A), 9 (A)
Vocabulary	2 (E)

E=Easy, A=Average, C=Challenging

Extended Response

11.　(Easy) Students' charts should show changing seasons, new growth, and descriptive for "The Light Comes Brighter"; truth, unshakable nature of truth, and brief imagery for "The Adamant." Essays should address the conciseness of "The Adamant," and the growing ideas of "The Light Comes Brighter."

12.　(Average) Students' essays should explore the specific style and diction of the poems about which they are writing.

13.　(Challenging) Students should recognize that in each poem, the poets touch on a growing self-awareness.

14.　(Average) Students' opinions will vary—depending on which poem they select, they should note the grim, stark nature of "Hawthorne," the rich imagery of "Gold Glade," the growing ideas of "The Light Comes Brighter," the concise "truth" of "The Adamant," or the poignancy of "Traveling Through the Dark."

15.　(Challenging) Students' essays should consider the individual conciseness or description of each title in relation to the subjects, themes, style, and diction of the poem it titles.

Oral Response

16.　In their oral responses, students should cite specific information from the poems that substantiates their presentations and expands on their earlier responses.

"Average Waves in Unprotected Waters"
by Anne Tyler
Open-Book Test (p. 175)
Multiple Choice and Short Answers

1.d　Explanation: Arnold is mentally challenged and caring for him has become too much for Bet.

2.　Sample answer: A change in the characters' lives is foreshadowed.

3.　Sample answer: Students should identify current events as preparations to leave, saying good-bye to Mrs. Puckett, the train trip, the taxi ride, the interaction with the nurse at the hospital, and the incident at the train station; the main flashback is Bet's memories and students may cite shorter flashbacks such as the reference to the red duffel coat.

4.b.　Explanation: Arnold's feelings about the coat from his past reveal aspects of Bet's and Arnold's character traits, but are not part of the current sequence of events.

5.　Sample answer: Mrs. Puckett cares about Arnold and is sorry that she can no longer take care of him—her tears, words, and the peanut butter cookies reveal her feelings.

6.　Sample answer: Bet's memories of gaining independence may be repeated or improved to some extent when she no longer must care for Arnold.

7.c　Explanation: Process of elimination should exclude all answers but "malign." The lady acts insulted when the conductor says she hasn't paid.

8. Sample answer: Bet is anxious and wants to be able to leave the hospital quickly, indicating that she is unhappy and worried about leaving Arnold there; she will probably be sad.

9.b Explanation: The description of her tears and desire to get away from the hospital show that she is grief-stricken about leaving Arnold.

10. Sample answer: Bet discovers that she cannot leave right away and is initially upset; the Mayor's speech offers a diversion to her.

Questions are classified in these categories:

Comprehension	1 (A), 9 (E)
Interpretation	5 (A), 10 (A)
Literary Analysis	2 (A), 6 (C), 8 (A)
Reading Strategy	3 (A), 4 (E)
Vocabulary	7 (A)

E=Easy, A=Average, C=Challenging

Extended Response

11. (Easy) Students should fill the organizer in with Bet's earlier life; preparations to leave; the train trip; the taxi ride; the interaction with the nurse at the hospital; and the incident at the train station. Students may recognize that the point of the story would have been harder to get to, had the author started with a description of Bet's earlier life.

12. (Average) Students' essays should indicate that the flashbacks help fill out the portrayal of the characters.

13. (Challenging) Students should describe the last section of the story and recognize that it indicates Bet's turmoil over leaving Arnold at the hospital, yet her transition to a new life has begun.

14. (Challenging) Students may say that the apparent and more subtle foreshadowing offers readers insights while preventing them from being overwhelmed by the emotional impact of the story's events. Example of fine shadowing: "he was getting to be too much for her."

15. (Average) Students may suggest that Bet moves, perhaps back to Salt Spray; they may also speculate that remarries and has other children; some may say that she moves to Parkinsville to be near Arnold.

Oral Response

16. In their oral responses, students should cite specific information from the story that substantiates their presentations and expands on their earlier responses.

from *The Names*
by N. Scott Momaday

"Mint Snowball"
by Naomi Shihab Nye

"Suspended"
by Joy Harjo

Open-Book Test (p. 178)

Multiple Choice and Short Answers

1.a Explanation: All of the answers are accurate, but he is exploring his Kiowa heritage in the essay.

2. Sample answer: He is looking forward to his journey and feels good about it—students may cite details such as Momaday's comments that "it was appropriate" and "let there be wonderful things."

3. Sample answer: Momaday meets up with a friend and exchanges horses for a day; sees animals and settlements; gets injured; races his horse; learns a new feat with his horse, and finally sells his horse.

4.c Explanation: All of the answers are synonyms for the word, *supple*; however in the context of describing the horse, flexible is correct.

5.a Explanation: Nye describes the impressions and sensations of an old-fashioned soda fountain with strong images that appeal to the pleasures of the senses.

6. Sample answer: Students' webs and summaries should include tastes, smells, visual impressions, and specialness of the Mint Snowball, as well as her disappointment that the recipe was lost, the elusiveness of recreating the Mint Snowball at a later time, and her strong memories of the feelings the Mint Snowball represents.

7. Sample answer: Nye's grandfather sold the recipe and it was never used. She feels that an important part of her life was lost and cannot be retrieved or recreated.

8.c Explanation: "I became acutely aware of the line the jazz trumpeter was playing." "The music made a startling bridge between familiar and strange lands."

9. Sample answer: She discovers that art and creativity are a means of communicating everyday experiences to the rest of the world.

10. Sample answer: Momaday's and Nye's anecdotes are part of their essays; Harjo's comprises her essay.

Questions are classified in these categories:

Comprehension	3 (A), 7 (A)
Interpretation	2 (A), 6 (A), 9 (C)
Literary Analysis	1 (A), 8 (A), 10 (C)
Reading Strategy	5 (E)
Vocabulary	4 (E)

E=Easy, A=Average, C=Challenging

Extended Response

11. (Easy) Students should describe an anecdote from the essay they choose and explain how it connects the essayist's personal experience to a larger meaning in life.

12. (Average) Students may choose to describe any of Momaday's anecdotes, such as receiving his horse, leaving on his journey, traveling with his friend or racing his horse; with the anecdotes they describe, students should relate Momaday's experiences with his descriptions of his Kiowa heritage.

13. (Challenging) Students' organizers and essays should address the specific anecdotes that the essayists use and relate them to their understanding of a larger truth in life than their own individual existences.

14. (Average) Students should recount everyday experiences that opened up connections to a larger meaning in their lives.

15. (Challenging) Students may explore symbols of everyday life that represent aspects of life in general.

Oral Response

16. In their oral responses, students should cite specific information from the essays that substantiates their presentations and expands on their earlier responses.

"Everyday Use"

by Alice Walker

Open-Book Test (p. 181)

Multiple Choice and Short Answers

1.b Explanation: The story includes conflicts between rural and city life, poor and rich, educated and uneducated, African American cultures and African cultures.

2. Sample answer: Dee wants some of the family's "everyday" items to display in her own home.

3. Sample answer: Contrasts include the difference in their outlook on what is everyday; and Dee's confidence and looks, education, worldliness, outgoing personality, as compared to Maggie's shyness and simple life.

4.b Explanation: Maggie is very self-conscious about her scars and probably suffers from memories of the tragedy that caused them.

5. Sample answer: Dee has taken an interest in her African cultural roots.

6.a Explanation: The narrator and Maggie accept and appreciate the everyday nature of their lives, so they do not feel that they are being kept down.

7. Sample answer: Maggie would use the quilts in an everyday manner. To Maggie they are something that she can and has created, and they are useful items; to Dee they are something she does not have that represents her culture.

8.c Explanation: The narrator has promised them to Maggie and realizes that Dee's interest in them is not as important as Maggie's relationship to what they mean.

9. Sample answer: Students may write sentences such as the following: The narrator is forthright and proud of her daughters even though she doesn't always understand them. Dee is selfish because she is searching for her identity. Maggie is shy, but has a strong sense of herself. The characters have individual personalities that are reflected in their behavior.

10. Sample answer: The quilts are a symbol of all parts of Maggie's and the narrator's lives which are "everyday."

Questions are classified in these categories:

Comprehension	7 (A)
Interpretation	1 (E), 8 (A), 10 (C)
Literary Analysis	2 (A), 4(A), 5 (C)
Reading Strategy	3 (A), 9 (C)
Vocabulary	6 (A)

E=Easy, A=Average, C=Challenging

Extended Response

11. (Average) Students should recognize that Dee has a global cultural sense of what the quilts mean and feels that they should not be worn out by everyday use.

12. (Easy) Students' organizers and writing should show that Dee was interested in getting away from the everyday life when she was growing up and now that she has developed a more worldly lifestyle, she wants to recapture some of the everyday aspects of her childhood.

13. (Challenging) Students' essays should explore the strong influence of "everyday" items in both Dee's and the narrator's lives, but acknowledge the change in Dee's perspective that has come from her wanting to get away from the everyday and then discovering that she still wants to have that part of her life intact.

14. (Challenging) Students will probably feel that Dee's family have not oppressed her because she so strongly wanted to get away and be a different kind of person.

15. (Challenging) Students should recognize that the narrator loves her daughter very much, but is sometimes frustrated because she does not understand and/or appreciate her behavior.

Oral Response

16. In their oral responses, students should cite specific information from the story that substantiates their presentations and expands on their earlier responses.

from *The Woman Warrior*

by Maxine Hong Kingston

Open-Book Test (p. 184)

Multiple Choice and Short Answers

1.d Explanation: The essay is a third-person account of an event that the writer was not a witness to, but instead heard about.

2. Sample answer: Brave Orchid has not seen her sister for thirty years and is worried about her long trip and about her coming through Customs because of Brave Orchid's experience when she came to the United States.

3. Sample answer: Students' diagrams and summaries should indicate that Brave Orchid keeps many of her Chinese customs, disapproves of many of her children's American ways, worries a lot, and does what she feels is right or necessary, she has a strong personality, and cares a great deal about her family.

4. Sample answer: The ghosts refer to Americans and the narrator's ancestors.

5. Sample answer: The narrator's children have grown up in the United States and have more American ways than their cousin who spent most of her life in China.

6.a Explanation: Moon Orchid's voice cannot be heard through the glass wall.

7. Sample answer: For Brave Orchid there is significance in being reunited with a sister who has lived a separate life from her for so long; for the niece, there is significance in reuniting with her mother, who is probably the most important person in her life.

8.b Explanation: "Here everything was new plastic, a ghost trick to lure immigrants into feeling safe . . . the Alien Office could send them right back." "Luggage conveyors fooled immigrants into thinking the going was going to be easy."

9. Sample answer: They are very happy to see each other; they cannot believe how each other has changed and continually comment on the changes.

10.b Explanation: Most memoirs recount historically or personally significant events in which the writer was an eyewitness or a participant.

Questions are classified in these categories:
Comprehension   2 (E), 9 (E)
Interpretation   3 (E), 5 (A), 8 (A)
Literary Analysis   1 (A), 7 (A), 10 (A)
Reading Strategy   4 (A)
Vocabulary   6 (E)
E=Easy, A=Average, C=Challenging

Extended Response

11. (Easy) Students' charts and summaries may include: Brave Orchid awoke when Moon Orchid's plane took off in Hong Kong; she went to the airport nine hours early with her children and niece; she concentrates on the airplane staying up; and she worries about her sister getting through Customs. Students should indicate which of her behaviors are cultural and which are universal.

12. (Average) Brave Orchid's children respect their mother's wishes by coming to the airport, but do not sit with her and eat with her like her niece does; they are more interested in watching TV and eating American food.

13. (Challenging) Students should recognize that Brave Orchid is aware of American culture and probably display more examples of it than she realizes, but she scorns her children's interest in American culture and does not worry about not doing things in an American way even when she is in public.

14. (Average) Students may note that background about Hong Kong allows readers to understand the difficulties of living in China for political reasons; background about Ellis Island explains why Brave Orchid is concerned about Moon Orchid coming through Customs; and background about palanquins reveals more of Brave Orchid's Chinese beliefs.

15. (Challenging) Students should realize that the civil unrest in Vietnam during the 1960s spawned immigration to the United States in a similar manner to the fall of China to Hong Kong in the 1940s.

Oral Response

16. In their oral responses, students should cite specific information from the memoir that substantiates their presentations and expands on their earlier responses.

"Antojos"
by Julia Alvarez

Open-Book Test (p. 187)

Multiple Choice and Short Answers

1.c Explanation: Yolanda's quest for **antojos** is a main reason for traveling.

2. Sample answer: **Antojos** are something that a person craves, such as sweets.

3.d Explanation: The rest of the story has been leading to this point. Yolanda believes her life is actually in danger and the rising tension reaches its climax.

4. Sample answer: Students should note that guavas represent something that is unique to her homeland; they are sweet; Yolanda can't get them easily; she obviously remembers picking them; they are her craving.

5. Sample answer: Student's may agree or disagree, but they should support their view. Agree: When Yolanda realizes that the men will not harm her, the tension is broken, and the situation is resolved. Disagree: The real tension is not with the actual men, but with Yolanda, herself. This doesn't get resolved immediately.

6.d Explanation: It is getting dark and there is no one around that she knows, so Yolanda thinks the men may mistake her for someone who is an enemy and try to hurt her—her aunts have warned of the dangers of her traveling alone because she might encounter strangers in this manner.

7. Sample answer: The man does not think Yolanda can understand the meaning of his words and wants to help her find the road.

8. Sample answer: She feels that it will be safer if they think she is an American because it means she is not part of their country's disagreements. It makes her feel safe enough to allow the men to help her.

9. Sample answer: Yolanda's awareness of the Palmolive woman—an American sight—frames the intensity of her encounter with the men and her finding her **antojos.**

10.a Explanation: She has had the opportunity to interact directly with the people of her country.

Questions are classified in these categories:

Comprehension	1 (E), 6 (A)
Interpretation	4 (A), 8 (C), 10 (A)
Literary Analysis	3 (E), 5 (A), 9 (C)
Reading Strategy	2 (A)
Vocabulary	7 (A)

E=Easy, A=Average, C=Challenging

Extended Response

11. (Easy) Students should realize that Yolanda has wanted to see her country up close and on her trip she has accomplished that and will take her experiences back with her.

12. (Average) Yolanda's aunts are protective of her and spoil her which she enjoys but also chafes under; the boys think she is exotic because she is an American, has a car, and wants to go with them to pick guavas while Yolanda enjoys their company and appreciates that they know where to find guavas; the men simply think she is an American woman in need of help while Yolanda is terrified of them and then appreciates their help. Students' essays should portray Yolanda as independent and interested in her cultural roots.

13. (Challenging) Students' essays should clarify that the flashback scene has prepared readers to understand Yolanda's fear and the potential danger when she encounters the men.

14. (Average) Students should recognize that **antojos** are the main reason that Yolanda takes her trip and discovers the people of her country (which leads her to understand her heritage better).

15. (Challenging) Students may realize that the Dominicans do not feel that she should pay them for their help, Jose is excited about earning money for helping her and disappointed when he has been unable to get help.

Oral Response

16. In their oral responses, students should cite specific information from the story that substantiates their presentations and expands on their earlier responses.

"Freeway 280"
by Lorna Dee Cervantes

"Who Burns for the Perfection of Paper"
by Martín Espada

"Hunger in New York City"
by Simon Ortiz

"Most Satisfied by Snow"
by Diana Chang

"What For"
by Garrett Hongo

Open-Book Test (p. 190)

Multiple Choice and Short Answers

1. Sample answer: The setting is a barrio beside a freeway in California; rigid lanes describes the freeway and the Spanish words describe the barrio.

2.c Explanation: The poet's voice reflects her Mexican heritage.

3. Sample answer: The speaker uses legal pads in his profession now when he made the pads 10 years ago. He still appreciates the work and pain of making the pads as he uses them in his current work.

4.d Explanation: The poet's voice is candid and sincere, and gets to the point.

5. Sample answer: The beginning of the poem describes the pain and difficulty of hunger for self and home; the middle explains how it affects a person; the end describes how it is fed. The poem describes a person becoming self-aware.

6. Sample answer: The hunger is for a place to feel at home.

7. Sample answer: The poem contrasts the empty spaces of fog with the substance of snow, representing missing and coming to know the substance of one's self.

8.c Explanation: *Pervade* means to be all around, as it is used in the poem.

9.a Explanation: "I wanted to take away the pain . . .", ". . . give him back his hearing," "let him play. . . ."

10. Sample answer: " . . . a few Hawaiian words could call up the rain . . . ," " . . . with a sharp Japanese *kiai*," "grained as koa wood." Many of the poem's images indicate the poet's Japanese and Hawaiian heritage.

Questions are classified in these categories:

Comprehension	1 (A)
Interpretation	3 (A), 6 (C), 9 (A)
Literary Analysis	2 (A), 4 (E), 7 (C), 10 (A)
Reading Strategy	5 (A)
Vocabulary	8 (E)

E=Easy, A=Average, C=Challenging

Extended Response

11. (Easy) Students' essays should adequately summarize the poems they select.

12. (Average) Depending on the poems they choose, students' essays should address the Mexican culture of Cervantes, the city culture of Espada, the Native American culture of Ortiz, the Chinese culture of Chang, or the Japanese and Hawaiian culture of Hongo.

13. (Challenging) Students should note the Mexican voice of Cervantes, the city voice of Espada, the Native American voice of Ortiz, the Chinese voice of Chang, and the Japanese and Hawaiian voice of Hongo, recognizing that each poet is expressing a message about finding one's self.

14. (Challenging) Students' essays should explore the concept of self-awareness in relation to the poets and themes of the poems they choose.

15. (Challenging) Students should address how the poets' voices are evidenced in the words of the titles of their poems.

Oral Response

16. In their oral responses, students should cite specific information from the poems that substantiates their presentations and expands on their earlier responses.

from *The Mortgaged Heart*
by Carson McCullers

"Onomatopoeia"
by William Safire

"Coyote v. Acme"
by Ian Frazier

Open-Book Test (p. 193)

Multiple Choice and Short Answers

1.d Explanation: In the first paragraph McCullers states, "It has been said that loneliness is the great American malady" and ends with ". . .—the answer waits in each separate heart—the answer of our own identify and the way by which we can master loneliness and feel that at last we belong."

2.b Explanation: She analyzes the subject of loneliness by considering many different aspects of it.

3. Sample answer: After establishing a separate identity, people have difficulty reconnecting with others.

4. Sample answer: He gives the etymology of the word; he defines the word; he offers examples of onomatopoeia; he explains how it is used; and offers examples of how and why onomatopoeic words develop.

5. Sample answer: *Yakking* sounds like people's voices when they are talking continuously; *pooh-pooh* is a sound that people make when they are expressing scorn; *murmur* is a pleasant sound associated with slow-moving water or soft gentle voices.

6. Sample answer: Students' main points and summaries should include an explanation of what onomatopoeia is; how it originated; its history; and why it will continue to be used.

7.a. Explanation: Students may cite any of the arguments in the essay that support the complaint against Acme.

8. Sample answer: The essay uses irony and sarcasm to ridicule litigation. The "case" itself is a sarcastic comment; students may also cite individual examples of ironic or sarcastic arguments in the essay.

9.c Explanation: *Precipitate*, as an adjective, means very sudden; unexpected or abrupt so a *precipitate* sound would be startling.

10. Sample answer: Coyote was a victim of products that were not designed for safety and not properly labeled: Exhibit A proves Coyote bought the products; B proves he suffered injury; C proves the catalog offers a products that would be of use in Coyote's profession; D proves the type of damage caused by the products.

Questions are classified in these categories:

Comprehension   1 (E)
Interpretation   3 (A), 6 (C), 7 (A)
Literary Analysis   2 (A), 4 (E), 8 (A)
Reading Strategy   5 (A), 10 (C)
Vocabulary   9 (E)

E=Easy, A=Average, C=Challenging

Extended Response

11. (Easy) Students should identify McCullers's main points as the existence of loneliness in America; and the development of loneliness due to establishing one's individuality and then not reestablishing contact with others; most students will find the essay effective; others may think that it is a somewhat abstract concept.

12. (Average) Most students will find Frazier's line of reasoning to be most effective because, despite its humor and sarcasm, it follows a clear line of logic.

13. (Challenging) Students' essays should address the similarities and differences among McCullers's analytical essay, Safire's expository essay, and Frazier's satirical essay; the essayists thoroughly cover their topics and have chosen styles and approaches that fit their topics.

14. (Challenging) Students' essays will probably focus on the similarities in the confrontations between the characters in the cartoon and the parties of the lawsuit.

15. (Challenging) Students may suggest that an expository or analytical essay could address the same issue, but either of these types of essays would probably appeal to a different audience.

Oral Response

16. In their oral responses, students should cite specific information from the essays that substantiates their presentations and expands on their earlier responses.

"Straw Into Gold: The Metamorphosis of the Everyday"
by Sandra Cisneros

"For the Love of Books"
by Rita Dove

"Mother Tongue"
by Amy Tan

Open-Book Test (p. 196)

Multiple Choice and Short Answers

1.b Explanation: She is given the ingredients for corn tortillas, but doesn't know how to use them to make the tortillas—she is only familiar with flour tortillas.

2. Sample answer: Cisneros thinks that she can do anything she is asked, if she tries.

3. Sample answer: Students may suggest Cisneros's Mexican heritage, poverty, poor performance in school, or frequent moves while growing up. She became a writer because of her background.

4. Sample answer: Dove not only loves to read books, but also enjoys holding them, smelling them, and turning their pages.

5.c Explanation: She realizes that is possible to write down a poem or story on one's own and then communicate it to others.

6. Sample answer: She probably knew that Dove needed to meet a real author in order to understand that she, herself, could become a writer.

7.c Explanation: All of the answers might provide the basis for a hypothesis, but empirical evidence is derived from observation or experiment.

8. Sample answer: Students' charts and explanations should include standard English, with its grammatical and syntactical aspects, that she uses when speaking and writing professionally and the "broken" or "limited" English which she uses with her mother and sometimes with her husband.

9.d Explanation: The "Mother Tongue" that her mother uses allows her to read anything and she can communicate easily with her daughter and take advantage of her daughter's understanding of her English if she needs to have her communication translated so others understand it.

10. Sample answer: Communication is more about intent than specific words and word usage.

Comprehension   1 (E), 4 (E), 8 (A)
Interpretation   3 (C), 6 (C)
Literary Analysis   2 (A), 5 (A), 9 (A)
Reading Strategy   10 (C)
Vocabulary   7 (A)

E=Easy, A=Average, C=Challenging

Extended Response

Guidelines for student response:

11. (Easy) Students' writing should address the specific experiences and messages of the essays that they choose.

12. (Average) Students' should recognize and understand Dove's message that ideas begin with people and writing allows them to share their ideas with the world.

13. (Challenging) Students' organizers and essays should address the different ideas that the three essayists present about the power of writing and communicating thoughts and ideas to others.

14. (Challenging) Students should recognize that all three titles are extensions of the ideas that the essayists present in their writings.

15. (Average) Students' essays will probably address slang and jargon that they use, standard English that they use for most of their school experiences, and possibly formal English that they may use with relatives or in work situations.

Oral Response

16. In their oral responses, students should cite specific information from the essays that substantiates their presentations and expands on their earlier responses.

"The Rockpile"

by James Baldwin

Open-Book Test (p. 199)

Multiple Choice and Short Answers

1. Sample answer: The setting is Harlem in the 1930s; most of the story takes place in an apartment building that faces a busy street.

2.b Explanation: The boys at the rockpile play recklessly and there is "a confusion of dust and screams and upended, flying feet."

3. Sample answer: Students charts should include information such as the following: John is supposed to be the man of the family when Gabriel is not home; he is quiet, shy, timid; he is afraid of the rockpile and the boys who play there; he is Elizabeth's favorite child; Gabriel and he are somewhat estranged. Roy is the "bad boy" of the family; he is outgoing and a bit reckless; he wants very much to play at the rockpile and feels abused because he is not

allowed; Elizabeth tolerates his behavior; he is Gabriel's favorite child. The boys are both caring and sensitive to their parents and each other, but Roy's gregarious personality sets him apart from John's quiet personality and causes significant differences in their behavior.

4. Sample answer: The boys see passers-by—all different kinds of people, most of them "sinners." The setting is full of diverse people.

5.a Explanation: It is in good taste to shake hands when greeting people.

6. Sample answer: Roy's is bored and restless so when his friend urges him to go to the rockpile, he can't resist the urge to play there; he tells John "I'll be back in five minutes" in order to return before his father gets home, and knows that he is sneaking out behind his mother's back while she is visiting with a friend: "She won't even know I'm gone, less you run and tell her."

7. Sample answer: The confrontation takes place in the living room of their apartment after Gabriel has gotten home from work. They are free to fight and argue and Elizabeth cares for the baby while she is discussing the situation with Gabriel.

8.a Explanation: Gabriel says "It sure ain't your fault that he ain't dead," accuses her of being negligent about caring for Roy, and threatens to beat John; Elizabeth replies that "He [Roy] got a head like his father, it got to be broken before it'll bow," tells Gabriel that if he can't make Roy behave, John can't.

9.c Explanation: Elizabeth blames Gabriel for spoiling Roy; Gabriel looks at Elizabeth with malevolence, longing for her perdition.

10. Sample answer: Elizabeth and Gabriel seem to have finished venting their anger; Elizabeth goes about her business of caring for the children and Gabriel realizes that he cannot hate the mother of his children.

Questions are classified in these categories:

Comprehension   2 (E), 6 (A)
Interpretation   3 (A), 9 (A), 10 (C)
Literary Analysis   1 (A), 4 (A), 7 (C)
Reading Strategy   8 (A)
Vocabulary   5 (E)

E=Easy, A=Average, C=Challenging

Extended Response

11. (Easy) Students cause and effect patterns and summaries should follow the story's sequence of events including: the boys are forbidden to go to the rockpile, causing Roy to sneak out to so that he gets hurt, causing his parents to know that the rockpile is dangerous.

12. (Average) Students' essays may suggest that the incident will blow over and be forgotten or that Roy and John will have stricter rules and be watched more carefully.

13. (Challenging) Students should recognize that a child getting hurt is often cause for tension because parents are scared and tense about the child's safety; however, there seems to be some deep-seated anger in the family.

14. (Average) Students' essays should address the fact that the rockpile was a somewhat unusual attraction in a neighborhood that did not have other diversions, so the setting clearly provides the circumstances for the specific events that occur in the story.

15. (Challenging) Students may suggest that the rockpile symbolizes what is forbidden; it may also symbolize danger or the enticements of what is outside; Baldwin probably had an encounter with a rockpile or some place equally dangerous as a child; students should suggest things that have similar symbolism in their own lives.

Oral Response

16. In their oral responses, students should cite specific information from the story that substantiates their presentations and expands on their earlier responses.

from *Hiroshima*

by John Hersey

"Losses" and "The Death of the Ball Turret Gunner"

by Randall Jarrell

Open-Book Test (p. 202)

Multiple Choice and Short Answers

1.d Explanation: people are leaving the city; taking their belongings to safety; and they are tired and worn out.

2. Sample answer: The distance shows how extensive the explosion's destruction was—reaching more than two miles as it killed people and crushed buildings.

3. Sample answer: Students graphic organizers should include information such as Hersey's specific details, the ordinary day-to-day activities of the people, flashbacks, the varied places that the people were, the air raid warnings, and so forth; they can draw inferences that the bomb destroyed the lives of many ordinary people in a senseless manner; the theme is that the horrors of war reach everywhere.

4. Sample answer: To Americans at home, the bomb in Hiroshima was somewhat removed; Hersey, however, spent time in Japan and saw the destruction up close, knowing how it had ruined many lives.

5.b Explanation: He chose to write about Hiroshima on his own.

6.a Explanation: The lines take on a casual air about dying; the repetition suggests the routine nature of death during wartime.

7. Sample answer: The pilots did as they were told and from their planes did not see the people who were dying because of the bombs they were told to drop.

8. Sample answer: The poem illustrates the pilot's impersonal responsibility of dropping bombs that destroy cities and kill people; points out the high casualty rate and makes the point that the pilots can't seem to understand the sense of what they are doing.

9.b Explanation: The last line states "When I died."

10. Sample answer: He dies a cruel, violent, and senseless death.

Questions are classified in these categories:
Comprehension   1 (A)
Interpretation   2 (E), 6 (A), 7 (C), 9 (A)
Literary Analysis   4 (C), 8 (E), 10 (C)
Reading Strategy   3 (A)
Vocabulary   5 (E)
E=Easy, A=Average, C=Challenging

Extended Response

11. (Easy) Students should recognize the theme of the poems as the violent, impersonal, and senseless qualities of war; the two poems offer two different perspectives—one that is detached and observant and one that is a victim.

12. (Average) Students' organizers and essays should address the details and horrific effects of war on ordinary people that the selections offer.

13. (Challenging) Students should recognize that the selections portray the death and destruction that happens to individuals rather than the statistics and assumption that soldiers die for a cause.

14. (Average) Students will note that the details and routine that Hersey writes about give an immediacy and personal outlook that a general description would have missed.

15. (Challenging) Students may point out that ball turret gunners were specific to World War II, but realize that each war has its own specific horror and potential impact on individuals; they may cite details from a recent war or one such as the Civil War in their essays.

Oral Response

16. In their oral responses, students should cite specific information from the selections that substantiates their presentations and expands on their earlier responses.

"Mirror"

by Sylvia Plath

"In a Classroom"

by Adrienne Rich

"The Explorer"

by Gwendolyn Brooks

"Frederick Douglass"
and **"Runagate Runagate"**

by Robert Hayden

Open-Book Test (p. 205)

Multiple Choice and Short Answers

1.b Explanation: The woman in the poem sees more than just her image—she witnesses her aging, "searching my reaches for what she really is." (line 11)

2.a Explanation: *Meditate* refers to pondering or the internal process of thinking about something in depth.

3. Sample answer: The students in the poem are intent on delving into poetry.

4. Sample answer: He is interested in finding meaning in the poetry, as well as in his life.

5.c Explanation: Brooks probably knows very well what it is to search for a quiet place when you are living in a crowded space.

6. Sample answer: He wants to find "a still spot in the noise"; after searching he finds that "there were no quiet rooms."

7. Sample answer: Students' diagrams should include the images that Douglass represents that compare freedom to basic needs; the elusiveness of it in relation to politics; the persecution that prevents it; and the beauty of it. They should recognize that the theme is that the dream of freedom is a "beautiful, needful thing."

8. Sample answer: Hayden was writing about the freedom of enslaved African Americans in his poem, but was addressing the need for freedom from the conditions that he saw African Americans still enduring during the twentieth century.

9.b Explanation: Emerson and Thoreau were not specifically known for writing about the freedom and independence of African Americans, but they wrote about the need for freedom and independence that every person has.

10. Sample answer: The printing of lines 8 and 33 conveys the feeling of running; the other indentations set off, or emphasize, certain ideas in the poem.

Questions are classified in these categories:

Comprehension	1 (E), 6 (A)
Interpretation	4 (A), 9 (C), 10 (C)
Literary Analysis	3 (A), 5 (A), 8 (C)
Reading Strategy	7 (A)
Vocabulary	2 (E)

E=Easy, A=Average, C=Challenging

Extended Response

11. (Average) Students should use the biographical information provided on page 1048, information they can obtain from other sources, or knowledge that they have to make connections about the theme of the poem they choose to write about.

12. (Challenging) Students' essays should address the concerns and worry about aging in society to the poem's details and theme.

13. (Easy) Students should cite historical information about abolitionists and the Underground Railroad and then connect the information to the poems' details to recognize the theme of freedom for enslaved African Americans.

14. (Average) The speaker is agitated and looking to escape the noise that surrounds him; students should recognize this and find clues in Brooks's word choice such as scrambled, throbbing, and the scream of nervous affairs.

15. (Average) Students should use information regarding Hayden's life and the message of "Runagate Runagate" to conclude that Hayden is searching for freedom for African Americans in the present, as well as noting the struggle for freedom in the past.

Oral Response

16. In their oral responses, students should cite specific information from the poems that substantiates their presentations and expands on their earlier responses.

"For My Children"

by Colleen McElroy

"Bidwell Ghost"

by Louise Erdrich

Open-Book Test (p. 208)

Multiple Choice and Short Answers

1.c Explanation: The reference to Bilad as-Sudan places her heritage in the northern area of Africa.

2. Sample answer: The phrasing takes on a melodic effect; the images produce a single, unified effect of describing the speaker's heritage.

3. Sample answer: My past is a slender dancer reflected briefly like a leopard in fingers of fire. / The future of Dahomey is a house of 16 doors, the totem of the Burundi counts 17 warriors—in reverse generations. / While I cling to one stray Seminole. There are three sentences in the stanza.

4. Sample answer: Heritage is something handed down from one's ancestors, or something from the past; the speaker feels that her heritage is important because much of it comes from a different land and a different culture—she wants her children to appreciate their ancestors and where they have come from.

5. Sample answer: She sees physical features that come from their African heritage, reminding her of what life might have been like in those places, but she also recognizes that their lives in St. Louis are also part of who they are.

6.b Explanation: The poem describes the wandering of this tragic creature, whose home burnt down 20 years ago.

7. Sample answer: Students' graphic organizers and summaries should note her unkempt, strange behavior and relate it to the tragedy she suffered.

8.c Explanation: The third stanza explains that the apples trees were charred, but not killed—like the woman who was traumatized, but not killed.

9.b Explanation: The poem does not tell the story of the tragedy, instead it creates the effect of the results of the tragedy.

10. Sample answer: The mood is haunting and tragic; the single, unified effect of lyric poem provides images without telling a story so the mood is created and recreated throughout the poem.

Questions are classified in these categories:
Comprehension   1 (A), 6 (A), 8 (A)
Interpretation   5 (C), 7 (E)
Literary Analysis   2 (A), 9 (A), 10 (C)
Reading Strategy   3 (E)
Vocabulary   4 (A)
E=Easy, A=Average, C=Challenging

Extended Response

11. (Average) Students recognize that knowing one's heritage strengthens one's sense of self; they may note the oral tradition as a source for learning about one's heritage; by sharing heritage, it is passed on to others; their essays should cite the specific cultures that are part of the poem.

12. (Challenging) Students should recognize that both poems have strong lyric qualities, but may note that the vague nature of "Bidwell Ghost" fits its topic and message just as the more specific details about African cultures in "For My Children" suits its topic of heritage.

13. (Easy) Students' organizers and writing should address the lyric effects of the poem that they choose to write about.

14. (Challenging) Students should recognize that final stanzas of both poems give them closure; however, "For My Children" looks to the future while "Bidwell Ghost" refers to the past.

15. (Challenging) Students will note similes such as "limbs as smooth and long as the neck of a bud vase" ("For My Children") and metaphors such as "the orchard bowed low and complained" ("Bidwell Ghost") and "skin of honey and beauty of ebony" ("For My Children"); they suggest that figurative language helps create the melodic quality of a lyric poem and contributes to the images.

Oral Response

16. In their oral responses, students should cite specific information from the poems that substantiates their presentations and expands on their earlier responses.

"The Writer in the Family"
by E.L. Doctorow
Open-Book Test (p. 211)
Multiple Choice and Short Answers

1.c Explanation: Most of the story's events and conversations, and many of the narrator's thoughts, relate to the death of his father.

2. Sample answer: She is very old, and not even knowing that he was ill, they think the shock might kill her. The grandmother wants to know why she no longer hears from her son and the narrator's letter-writing is requested; a fair amount of lying is required to maintain her ignorance of her son's death.

3. Sample answer: He is to write the letters as though they were written by his father.

4. Sample answer: Students' charts should note the early reflection on his father in relation to the first letter he writes; the more practical tone of events relating to getting on with life in the middle of the story, corresponding to the routine that is being established with the letters; and the final events that precipitate the narrator's decision to write one final letter telling his grandmother the truth. Throughout the story, the narrator's outlook on his family and circumstances shifts and changes, so he is a dynamic character.

5.b Explanation: The mother and Aunt Frances seem to have the same thoughts and discussions—they each blame each other for the father's failure in business—with some, but little, variation, so they are static.

6.c Explanation: The remarks are insulting and not necessarily true.

7. Sample answer: The brother is a dynamic character—by bringing his girlfriend home for dinner, his behavior is changing and his attitude toward his place in the family is changing.

8.c Explanation: He is surprised that he did not know something so important about his father and never made the connection to his father's interest in the things related to the sea.

9. Sample answer: The narrator's dreams about his father still being alive relate to the fact that the letters he is writing to his grandmother basically keep his father alive in his mind.

10. Sample answer: Most students will say that the narrator's actions are defensible because he and his immediate family are moving on from his father's death and he is not responsible for his aunts' decisions. The letter he writes is not completely honest but at least communicates the truth to his grandmother.

Questions are classified in these categories:

Comprehension	1 (E), 2 (A), 8 (A)
Interpretation	3 (A), 9 (C)
Literary Analysis	4 (A), 5 (A), 7 (C)
Reading Strategy	10 (A)
Vocabulary	6 (A)

E=Easy, A=Average, C=Challenging

Extended Response

11. (Easy) Students' essays should address Aunt Frances's request to keep his grandmother happy and they will probably note that it is a burden and unfair because of the toll it takes on him by preventing him from letting go of his father.

12. (Average) Students should recognize the financial and emotional adjustments the family is having to make due to the loss of the father; the aunts' decision and demands are upsetting and they continue to encounter challenges as a result of the father no longer being with them.

13. (Challenging) Students' charts and essays should address both scenarios—if he continues to write the letters he will probably continue to dream about his father and experience the anxiety that writing the letters causes; by putting an end to the letters he probably will develop a new lifestyle in which his father remains important, but does not seem "larger than life." Students will probably evaluate the narrator's decision to stop writing the letters as a wise move.

14. (Challenging) Students should note the patterns are established among the family members; they should cite specific examples such as the repetitive comments from his aunts.

15. (Average) Students may note that the narrator's reference to scattering his father's ashes in the ocean confirms that he knew his father and being honest with his grandmother is probably

what his father would have preferred that he do, thus affirming his decision to stop writing the letters.

Oral Response

16. In their oral responses, students should cite specific information from the story that substantiates their presentations and expands on their earlier responses.

"Camouflaging the Chimera"
by Yusef Komunyakaa

"Ambush" from *The Things They Carried*
by Tim O'Brien

Open-Book Test (p. 214)

Multiple Choice and Short Answers

1.b Explanation: The last stanza refers to "ready to spring the L-shaped ambush."

2. Sample answer: Students should summarize the camouflage preparations described in the stanzas.

3. Sample answer: The first-person perspective allows readers to feel the tension of waiting, without moving, while time passes.

4.b Explanation: The soldiers are a group of entities that is preparing to attack like a monster.

5. Sample answer: The jungle is not a refuge because it presents and symbolizes danger for them, not safety or protection from danger.

6.c Explanation: The story is written from a personal perspective; students may cite the author's personal thoughts that are revealed and the feelings that he expresses about what happens.

7. Sample answer: The narrator had a sense of disbelief about what happened and felt that he shouldn't have thrown the grenade because there was no real danger; Kiowa assesses it as a "good kill"; years later the narrator still cannot see it as something that should have happened and still fantasizes about it not having happened.

8.c Explanation: "I was terrified. There were no thoughts about killing."

9. Sample answer: He has not resolved his feelings and his fantasy about what it would have been like for the young man to walk on past.

10. Sample answer: As an adult who threw a grenade that killed a man, he does not understand the killing himself—he wants her to understand his mixed feelings about the experience and feels that she needs to be mature to understand the situation that brought about the killing.

Questions are classified in these categories:

Comprehension	1 (E)
Interpretation	4 (A), 7 (C), 8 (A), 10 (C)
Literary Analysis	3 (A), 6 (A), 9 (A)
Reading Strategy	2 (A)
Vocabulary	5 (A)

E=Easy, A=Average, C=Challenging

Extended Response

11. (Easy) Students' essays should include examples of specifics from the selection they choose, revealing the personal nature of the experience that is described—this allows readers to feel as though they are experiencing what the writer is describing.

12. (Average) Students' Venn diagrams and essays should note that both selections portray the grisly and appalling aspects of war, but "Camouflaging the Chimera" focuses on the danger, while "Ambush" addresses the personal damage that the war inflicted.

13. (Challenging) Students should address the context of the Vietnam War in their essays, the fact that many people did not believe in sending Americans to die, and the personal trauma that resulted for many of the soldiers who went there—the selections represent two individual experiences with the type of horror that was part of being in Vietnam during the war.

14. (Challenging) Students' essays should reflect an understanding of the outlet for emotions that Komunyakaa found in the poems he wrote about his experiences in Vietnam.

15. (Average) Students should recognize that the terms "camouflage" and "ambush" represent two concepts of what much of the Vietnam War was about—instilling fear and distrust for anyone and everything; in addition, the use of the image of the chimera points out the monstrousness of what was happening there.

Oral Response

16. In their oral responses, students should cite specific information from the selections that substantiates their presentations and expands on their earlier responses.

The Crucible, Act I

by Arthur Miller

Open-Book Test (p. 217)

Multiple Choice and Short Answers

1. c Explanation: Her father is completely distraught; Abigail is concerned but thinks she may be pretending; Tituba is afraid she will die.

2. Sample answer: They know that the girls have been doing things that the community will think is witchcraft.

3. Sample answer: The girls were dancing while Tituba sang and cast spells.

4. Sample answer: Thomas Putnam is a man that has suffered many ills—some imagined, some real and it has made him mean and vindictive; John Proctor is a steady man who has his faults, but is basically decent—he does not suffer fools gladly.

5.b Explanation: Others will want to find fault in him so that they may bring him down.

6.d Explanation: The dialogues between Abigail and Parris and between Abigail and Proctor reveal the relationship.

7. Sample answer: Hale is educated as a minister and has unique knowledge of the Devil's ways—in which he believes implicitly, he believes that proof of the Devil and the Devil's presence in people is definitive, he is proud that he is a specialist in the ways of the Devil and is self-confident, if not smug, about his knowledge.

8. Sample answer: Abigail becomes defensive and starts bending the truth because she is concerned about what may happen to her; she tries to get Betty to stop pretending.

9.b Explanation: When Abigail sees Tituba she says, "She made me do it! She made Betty do it!

10. Sample answer: At first Tituba tries to honestly deny the accusations, then she gives into what they want from her and falls back on her Caribbean beliefs about the Devil.

Questions are classified in these categories:

Comprehension	1 (E), 6 (E), 10 (C)
Interpretation	2 (A), 8 (A)
Literary Analysis	4 (C), 7 (C), 9 (A)
Reading Strategy	3 (A)
Vocabulary	5 (A)

E=Easy, A=Average, C=Challenging

Extended Response

11. (Average) Students should find the pieces of the story and note the girls' forbidden dancing, casting spells, strange brews, nakedness, and generally unacceptable behavior for the times and culture. Abigail and Parris are key characters in the controversy.

12. (Challenging) Students should recognize the impact of the Puritan religious beliefs, the hard lives that the people led, the unmanageable qualities of a "mob mentality," the tenuous positions of young girls who are ostracized, and so forth.

13. (Average) Students will probably recognize that the early accusations of witchcraft are only the beginning and that the situation is bound to blow up and become a serious situation; they may note Abigail's selfishness and seeming unconcern for what happens to anyone else.

14. (Easy) Students' webs and essays should indicate Abigail's strong influence over the other girls; her careless attitude toward what will happen to Tituba when she blames her, her animosity toward Elizabeth Proctor and her obsession with John Proctor; and her rebellious, manipulative manner with Parris.

15. (Average) Students should recognize that the girls' activities in the woods are completely unacceptable in the eyes of the Puritan community and that the girls' fascination with what they were doing and their fears about what will happen to them are complicating things in a religious society—Abigail and Parris, despite their original concerns about the accusations of witchcraft, are key to the spread of the witch hunt.

Oral Response

16. In their oral responses, students should cite specific information from the play that substantiates their presentations and expands on their earlier responses.

The Crucible, Act II
by Arthur Miller
Open-Book Test (p. 220)
Multiple Choice and Short Answers

1.b Explanation: They are courteous and considerate with one another, but tension is evident; eventually a strong dispute between them becomes apparent.

2. Sample answer: She has been to the witch trials; Proctor does not believe in witches, nor does he have any patience for the accusations and trials that are taking place.

3. Sample answer: They discover that members of the community including their friends, and even Elizabeth, are being accused or implicated, and some are being sentenced to hanging; thirty-nine have been arrested; Goody Osborn will hang; Sarah Good confessed to save herself; Elizabeth has been "somewhat mentioned."

4.c Explanation: The Puritans live by the Commandments which, among other things, indicate how they should treat one another, and include adultery, which is a sensitive topic with the Proctors.

5. Sample answer: Tricking someone would be low or contemptible.

6. Sample answer: Hale's mission is to determine whether there are witches in Salem; he sees potential signs when he first arrives, but begins to suspect the children's accusations to not be entirely true and astutely observes the mass hysteria that is growing in the community.

7.a Explanation: The Gospel is the portion of the Bible that is the record of the teachings of Jesus that include loving one's neighbors.

8.c Explanation: He knows that Abigail wants revenge on Elizabeth because he has spurned the girl after having an affair with her.

9.b Explanation: If they confess to being a witch, they will not be hanged.

10. Sample answer: The Bible teaches not to do many of the things that the people of Salem are doing even though they think they are being religious by searching out the work of the Devil.

Questions are classified in these categories:

Comprehension	2 (A), 3 (A)
Interpretation	6 (C), 8 (C), 9 (A)
Literary Analysis	4 (A), 7 (A), 10 (C)
Reading Strategy	1 (A)
Vocabulary	5 (E)

E=Easy, A=Average, C=Challenging

Extended Response

11. (Easy) Students' essays should address Proctor's disbelief at what is happening, trying to stop the men from taking her, belief in her innocence, anger at what Abigail has done, and confusion over the state of things in Salem.

12. (Average) Students should recognize that the poppet is incriminating evidence against Elizabeth; a means for Abigail to doom Elizabeth; an innocent gesture on Mary's part; and another example of the "Devil's work" to the court.

13. (Challenging) In the first act, Mary Warren is simply one of the girls who is going along with Abigail; by the second act, she has the means to stop the witch hunt and is being pressured by John Proctor to do so, but she is a weak character.

14. (Challenging) Students should realize that, although Abigail does not appear in the act, her influence is strongly felt in what is happening, being discussed and the arrests that are being made; they may comment on the power that Abigail is enjoying and exploiting.

15. (Average) Students' essays should reflect the general chaos and unhappiness of the community and realize that things may still get worse; they should recognize Abigail as being the catalyst, but the collusion of the other girls and the court's nearsighted treatment of the situation is heightening the impact of the girls' pretense.

Oral Response

16. In their oral responses, students should cite specific information from the play that substantiates their presentations and expands on their earlier responses.

The Crucible, Act III
by Arthur Miller
Open-Book Test (p. 223)
Multiple Choice and Short Answers

1.d Explanation: There is no point in questioning the accused; their guilt is assumed and the only point of the questioning is to get them to confess.

2. Sample answer: Thomas Putnam, Abigail Williams and Danforth are all for the witch hunt—Putnam and Abigail for personal reasons, Danforth because he feels it his duty; John Proctor and Giles Corey are against it—they do not believe in what is happening; at the beginning of the act, Mary Warren has been convinced to be against it by telling the truth, and Reverend Hale is still vacillating about it.

3. Sample answer: Hale feels that there should be proof and is finding that what is considered proof are actually only accusations and what he is realizing is pretense on the part of the girls.

4. Sample answer: Parris feels that he has as much power as the court, and continually interferes with the proceedings and anyone's attempts to explain the truth.

5. Sample answer: The reference to the dragon is irony because it is so ludicrous, but as much the truth and provable as what he is hearing.

6.c An unhappy employee is most apt to argue with his boss.

7.b Explanation: *Anonymity* is the condition of being unknown or unacknowledged, most often for safety reasons.

8. Sample answer: Elizabeth, for once in her life, lies because she thinks she is protecting Proctor's good name.

9. Sample answer: Mary shifts and goes back to the girls' pretense, saying that she has seen the Devil, but she loves God, possibly because she feels isolated and pressured, possibly because she may fear that she will hang; her capitulation reinforces the pretense and dooms the Proctors.

10. Sample answer: Hale has become convinced that the witch hunt is unfounded and the consequences are serious; Proctor points out the irony of the evil that is really taking place.

Questions are classified in these categories:

Comprehension	4 (A), 9 (A)
Interpretation	3 (A), 10 (C)
Literary Analysis	1 (A), 5 (E), 8 (C)
Reading Strategy	2 (E)
Vocabulary	6 (A), 7 (E)

E=Easy, A=Average, C=Challenging

Extended Response

11. (Easy) Students should recognize that Abigail is a leader while Mary is a follower, John Proctor and Danforth are leaders; Hale and Parris, though they are in leadership positions are actually followers.

12. (Average) Students should understand that Hale is coming to conclusions that affect his behavior based on observation and thinking while Mary is being coerced about whose lead she will follow.

13. (Challenging) Some students may think that Abigail has the most influence; others may think that Danforth has the most influence; their essays should be supported with details from the play.

14. (Average) Students will probably say that Hathorne and Danforth are doing their jobs, but may note that they are encouraging a great deal of the hysteria because they accept the girls' pretense and do not question the situation appropriately.

15. (Challenging) Students may address Abigail's growing sense of power and continued hopes to remove Elizabeth from her path in getting to John Proctor; they may realize that Abigail had no idea what was going to happen, but doesn't seem concerned that people are going to die because of her self-absorbed actions.

Oral Response

16. In their oral responses, students should cite specific information from the play that substantiates their presentations and expands on their earlier responses.

The Crucible, Act IV
by Arthur Miller
Open-Book Test (p. 226)
Multiple Choice and Short Answers

1.b Explanation: Students may note that while they are constantly searching for signs of the Devil, the people are treating each other in an evil way.

2. Sample answer: He believes they have left on a ship for Barbados. Abigail may realize that she will not succeed in getting John Proctor back and she may eventually be found out for what she has done; or that she is tired of the charade and wants to escape the life she has been living in Salem.

3. Sample answer: The person would awkwardly struggle to say the words or phrase their thoughts.

4.a	Explanation: He has been told and understands that someone needs to influence those that have been sentenced to hang; he thinks Proctor is influential with the others and that his pregnant wife may be able to convince him to confess.

5.d	Explanation: He is ready to accept the personal consequences of making a confession in order to live and be with his family, however he is not willing to sacrifice his name and what it means to him.

6.	Sample answer: The conversation that John and Elizabeth have brings John's feelings and ideas about his wife and the situation to a head; the conversation he had with Abigail has caused her vindictive behavior toward him and his wife and has brought on tragedy for many others; he cannot carry out what Danforth wants him to do in order to live; his efforts to get Mary to tell the truth have failed; he has been instrumental in convincing Hale that the situation is not what it seems; his actions typically have backed up his words.

7.b	Explanation: She has softened in her strict judgments of people including her husband John. Her final comment in the play reveal this softening.

8.	Sample answer: The trial process itself is a severe test and the situation is a severe test of the beliefs and understanding, and trust of the people of Salem.

9.	Sample answer: Students may feel that the theme relates to infectious fear and suspicion that has driven the action in the play; they may also see the lack of trust and understanding as a message, or the narrow-mindedness that does not allow for the truth to come out.

10.	Sample answer: Students should recognize the influence of Miller's personal experience with McCarthyism in his message in the play.

Questions are classified in these categories:

Comprehension	2 (A), 4 (A)
Interpretation	1 (A), 5 (A), 7 (A)
Literary Analysis	6 (A), 8 (C), 9 (A)
Reading Strategy	10 (A)
Vocabulary	3 (E)

E=Easy, A=Average, C=Challenging

Extended Response

11.	(Easy) Students' charts and summaries should include the following: Act I—accusations of witchcraft arise as the girls try to cover up their disobedience; Act II—the accusations become widespread and complicated because of the girls' pretense; Act III—the truth is further buried by more accusations and complications; Act IV—the strength and willingness of the accused to stick to their beliefs is tested and proved.

12.	(Average) Students' essays should explore the fact that Abigail has been an instigator and when the tide turns in the last act, she is no longer there to perpetuate the situation; students may realize that if she had stayed, she might have kept up the pretense for a while longer, but undoubtedly the hysteria would have died out at some point.

13.	(Challenging) Students should realize that Elizabeth's comment is the true comment on the goodness that everyone is trying to defend throughout the play.

14.	(Challenging) Some students may think that the lessons have been learned and that witch hunts may no longer be likely because of the strong historical examples of Salem and McCarthyism; others may feel that the potential for mass hysteria will always be inherent in societies.

15.	(Average) Students essays' should reflect an understanding of how the community has been like a boiling pot that has melted away and distilled the beliefs and lives of the people; they should also recognize the severe test of wills that has occurred; their opinions about what Miller intended but will probably tend toward the implication of both meanings; their opinions should be substantiated.

Oral Response

16.	In their oral responses, students should cite specific information from the play that substantiates their presentations and expands on their earlier responses.